KEY ACCOUNTING PRINCIPLES WORKBOOK

Volume One, Fourth Edition

Lead Author
Neville Joffe

Contributors and Reviewers

Bharat Aggarwal, BBA, MBA, CMA
Sheridan College

Jason Armstrong, CPA, CGA
Fanshawe College

Maria Belanger, CPA, CA
Algonquin College

Ben Carnovale, BBA, MASc
Confederation College

Annette deWeerd, CMA, CGA, MBA
Northern Alberta Institute of Technology

Dave Hummel, CPA, CA
Conestoga College

Laurette Korman, MBA, CMA
Kwantlen Polytechnic University

Chris Leduc, CPA, CA
Cambrian College

Kayla Levesque, CPA, CA
Cambrian College

Sarah Magdalinski, CA, MPACC, BCOMM
Northern Alberta Institute of Technology

Rachel McCorriston, CPA, CMA, MBA
Fanshawe College

Penny Parker, MBA, CPA, CGA
Fanshawe College

Susan Rogers, CPA, CMA
Sheridan College

Ruby So, B. Comm, CA, CGA
Northern Alberta Institute of Technology

Textbook ISBN: 978-1-926751-27-6
Workbook ISBN: 978-1-926751-28-3

Key Accounting Principles Workbook, Volume 1, Fourth Edition
Author: Neville Joffe
Publisher: AME Learning Inc.
Content Contributors and Developmental Editors:
        Kobboon Chotruangprasert/Graeme Gomes/Kyle Kroetsch
Production Editors: Joshua Peters/Melody Yousefian
Copy Editor: Nicola Balfour
Indexer: Elizabeth Walker
Typesetter: Paragon Prepress Inc.
Vice President and Publishing Manager: Linda Zhang
Cover Design: Sasha Moroz/Bram Wigzell
Online Course Design & Production: AME Multimedia Team

1 2 3 MCRL 17 16 15

This workbook is written to provide accurate information on the covered topics. It is not meant to take the place of professional advice.

For more information contact:

AME Learning Inc.
410-1220 Sheppard Avenue East
Toronto, ON, Canada M2K 2S5
Phone: 416.479.0200
Toll-free: 1.888.401.3881
E-mail: info@amelearning.com
Visit our website at: www.amelearning.com

Table of Contents

Chapter 1

FINANCIAL STATEMENTS: PERSONAL ACCOUNTING

LEARNING OUTCOMES

❶ Describe the purpose of accounting

❷ Describe the balance sheet and the income statement

❸ Define an accounting period

❹ Explain how the accounting equation works

❺ Explain accrual-based accounting

❻ Explain how to account for debt and assets

❼ Explain how to account for prepaid expenses

❽ Distinguish between capital and revenue

❾ Demonstrate how double entries are recorded in T-accounts

AMEENGAGE™ *Access **ameengage.com** for integrated resources including tutorials, practice exercises, the digital textbook and more.*

Assessment Questions

AS-1 (❶)

Define accounting and describe the purpose of accounting.

_____

_____

_____

AS-2 (❷)

What is net worth?

_____

_____

AS-3 (❷)

In simple terms, what are assets and liabilities?

_____

_____

AS-4 (❷)

What are revenues and expenses?

_____

_____

_____

_____

AS-5 (❷)

Explain the role of the balance sheet.

_____

_____

_____

_____

AS-6 (❷)

Explain the role of the income statement.

_____

_____

_____

AS-7 (❸)

What are some advantages of using monthly accounting periods in your personal balance sheet?

_____

_____

_____

AS-8 (④)

What is the accounting equation?

_____

_____

AS-9 (⑧)

What is the equation for calculating ending net worth for a period?

_____

_____

AS-10 (②)

Define surplus and deficit.

_____

_____

_____

AS-11 (④)

What is a T-account?

_____

_____

_____

AS-12 (⑤)

Explain accrual-based accounting.

_____

_____

_____

AS-13 (❺)

Briefly describe the cash-based method of accounting.

_____

_____

AS-14 (❻)

True or False: When you borrow money, you have more cash but your net worth decreases.

_____

AS-15 (❻)

True or False: When you pay off a loan, your cash decreases and your net worth increases.

_____

_____

AS-16 (❻)

True or False: Buying an asset has no impact on net worth.

_____

AS-17 (❼)

What is a prepaid expense?

_____

_____

AS-18 (❼)

When an expense is initially prepaid, which accounts increase or decrease?

_____

_____

AS-19 (❼)

When does an expense need to be recorded under accrual-based accounting? What are the three possible timings the payment can be made for an expense?

_____

_____

_____

_____

_____

AS-20 (❽)

What is capital?

_____

_____

Application Questions Group A

AP-1A (❷)

April Rose had the following financial data for the year ended December 31, 2016

Cash	$6,000
Jewellery	10,000
Automobile	18,000
House	256,000
Bank Loan	45,000
Credit Card	5,000
Mortgage	140,000

Required

a) Calculate April Rose's total assets.

_____

_____

_____

_____

b) Calculate April Rose's total liabilities.

_____

_____

_____

AP-2A (❷ ❹)

Consider the following information for Julius Troy

Cash	$12,000	12,000
Jewellery	18,000	18,000
Automobile	22,000	22,000
House	161,000	161,000
Credit Card	5,000	213,000
Bank Loan	10,000	15,000
Mortgage	125,000	10,000
		125,000
		140,000

Required

a) Calculate Julius Troy's total assets.

213,000

b) Calculate Julius Troy's total liabilities.

140,000

c) Calculate Julius Troy's net worth.

73

AP-3A (❻)

Darryl purchased a new laptop on January 1, 2016 worth $2,000. He paid the entire amount using cash. He also purchased a new cell phone worth $300 on account. How will these transactions affect Darryl's net worth?

AP-4A (❷ ❺ ❽ ❾)

The following information was taken from the personal records of Juliet Lahm on April 30, 2016

Cash	$3,000
Jewellery	2,000
House	190,000
Mortgage	80,000
Net Worth	115,000

Transactions for the month of May 2016

1. Earned monthly salary of $5,050.

2. Paid $1,200 cash for utilities.

3. Purchased an automobile worth $10,000 on account.

4. Paid $600 cash for food expenses.

5. Paid $400 cash for gas.

Required

a) Complete the Cash T-account to determine the ending balance of cash.

INCREASE		DECREASE
+	**CASH**	−
Opening Bal.		

b) Complete the personal income statement to determine the surplus or deficit for the period.

Personal Income Statement For the Month Ended May 31, 2016		

c) What is Juliet Lahm's net worth on May 31?

_____

_____

_____

AP-5A (❷ ❹)

A person has the following information with regard to his own balance sheet, but the liability section is missing.

Cash	$35,000
Automobile	58,000
House	100,000
Net Worth	55,000

Required

Determine the total amount of liabilities.

_____

_____

_____

_____

AP-6A (❹)

Calculate the missing amounts in the following table.

	Scenario 1	Scenario 2
Total Assets	$123,000	148,000
Total Liabilities		$34,000
Net Worth	$94,000	$114,000

AP-7A (❹)

As of December 31, 2015, Maria Green had total assets of $40,000, and total liabilities of $15,000. As of December 31, 2016, Maria's total assets and liabilities increased to $50,000 and $30,000, respectively. How has Maria's net worth changed since the end of 2015?

_____

_____

_____

_____

AP-8A (❷ ❹ ❾)

The following information pertains to Ken White's personal financial transactions

<table>
<tr><td colspan="2">Opening Balances as at January 1, 2016</td></tr>
<tr><td>Cash</td><td>$9,000</td></tr>
<tr><td>Contents of Home</td><td>6,000</td></tr>
<tr><td>Automobile</td><td>29,000</td></tr>
<tr><td>House</td><td>156,000</td></tr>
<tr><td>Unpaid Accounts</td><td>5,500</td></tr>
<tr><td>Bank Loan</td><td>60,000</td></tr>
<tr><td>Net Worth</td><td>134,500</td></tr>
</table>

Transactions for the month of January 2016

1. Paid maintenance expense for the month of January with $120 cash.
2. Purchased new furniture worth $2,500 with cash.
3. Paid credit card liability of $5,500 (Unpaid Accounts) in full.
4. Paid telephone, electricity and water bill for January with $1,200 cash.
5. Purchased $2,000 of groceries and goods for personal consumption with cash.
6. Deposited $4,040 salary earned during the month.

Required

a) Using the information provided, record the opening balances in the T-accounts.
b) Record the transactions for the month of January in the T-accounts.

PERSONAL BALANCE SHEET
As at January 31, 2016

ASSETS

INCREASE	DECREASE
+ **CASH** -	
Opening	

INCREASE	DECREASE
+ **CONTENTS OF HOME** -	
Opening	

INCREASE	DECREASE
+ **AUTOMOBILE** -	
Opening	

INCREASE	DECREASE
+ **HOUSE** -	
Opening	

LIABILITIES

DECREASE	INCREASE
- **UNPAID ACCOUNTS** +	
	Opening

DECREASE	INCREASE
- **BANK LOAN** +	
	Opening

NET WORTH

DECREASE	INCREASE
- **NET WORTH** +	
	Opening

TOTAL ASSETS _____

TOTAL LIABILITES _____ } _____

NET WORTH _____

PERSONAL INCOME STATEMENT
For the Month Ended Jan. 31, 2016

DECREASE	INCREASE
- **REVENUE** +	

LESS EXPENSES

INCREASE	DECREASE
+ **ENTERTAINMENT EXPENSE** -	

INCREASE	DECREASE
+ **FOOD EXPENSE** -	

INCREASE	DECREASE
+ **INTEREST EXPENSE** -	

INCREASE	DECREASE
+ **MAINTENANCE EXPENSE** -	

INCREASE	DECREASE
+ **UTILITIES EXPENSE** -	

TOTAL REVENUE _____

LESS TOTAL EXPENSES _____

SURPLUS (DEFICIT) _____

AP-9A (❷ ❹ ❾)

Alan Marshall is preparing his balance sheet and income statement for the month ended April 30, 2016. Use the following information to help him prepare his financial statements.

Opening Balances as at April 1, 2016	
Cash	$5,000
Contents of Home	1,000
Automobile	4,000
House	280,000
Unpaid Accounts	10,000
Auto Loan	30,000
Net Worth	250,000

Transactions for the month of April

1. Purchased new furniture worth $2,000 for home using credit card.
2. Paid credit card bill with $3,000 cash.
3. Paid utility bills of $800 for the month of April using credit card.
4. Purchased groceries and food for $2,500 using cash.
5. Made a principal payment of $1,250 for the auto loan.
6. Paid April's rent of $1,500 with cash.
7. Deposited $4,050 salary earned during the month.

Required

a) Using the information provided, record the opening balances in the T-accounts.

b) Record the transactions for the month of April in the T-accounts.

PERSONAL BALANCE SHEET
As at April 30, 2016

ASSETS		LIABILITIES	

ASSETS

INCREASE	DECREASE
+ CASH -	

Opening

INCREASE	DECREASE
+ CONTENTS OF HOME -	

Opening

INCREASE	DECREASE
+ AUTOMOBILE -	

Opening

INCREASE	DECREASE
+ HOUSE -	

Opening

LIABILITIES

DECREASE	INCREASE
- UNPAID ACCOUNTS +	

Opening

DECREASE	INCREASE
- AUTO LOAN +	

Opening

NET WORTH

DECREASE	INCREASE
- NET WORTH +	

Opening

TOTAL ASSETS   _____

TOTAL LIABILITES   _____   } _____

NET WORTH   _____

PERSONAL INCOME STATEMENT
For the Month Ended April 30, 2016

DECREASE	INCREASE
- REVENUE +	

LESS EXPENSES

INCREASE	DECREASE
+ ENTERTAINMENT EXPENSE -	

INCREASE	DECREASE
+ FOOD EXPENSE -	

INCREASE	DECREASE
+ INTEREST EXPENSE -	

INCREASE	DECREASE
+ MAINTENANCE EXPENSE -	

INCREASE	DECREASE
+ RENT EXPENSE -	

INCREASE	DECREASE
+ UTILITIES EXPENSE -	

TOTAL REVENUE   _____

LESS TOTAL EXPENSES   _____

SURPLUS (DEFICIT)   _____

AP-10A (❷ ❸)

John Black is a senior administrator at a market research firm, and recently received a salary increase from $3,500 per month to $4,000 per month. He feels richer and would like to know the increase in his net worth. However, he has never prepared a personal balance sheet or an income statement that would help him understand his net worth. John gathered the following information to help him understand his financial position.

	September 30, 2016	October 31, 2016	November 30, 2016
Cash	$1,000	$2,150	$4,050
House	120,000	120,000	120,000
Bank Loan	400	350	300
Salary	3,500	3,500	4,000
Entertainment Expense	200	500	400
Food Expense	1,500	1,200	1,100
Insurance Expense	150	150	150
Utilities Expense	200	400	300
Miscellaneous Expense	175	50	100

Required

Prepare John Black's income statement for the three months.

John Black Personal Income Statement For the Month Ending				
	September 30, 2016	October 31, 2016	November 30, 2016	Total
Salary	3,500			3,500
Entertainment	200			2,225
Food	1,500			1,275
Insuranse	150			
miscellaneous	175			
utilites	200			

AP-11A (❸ ❽)

Jeff Winger is working at a law firm. His salary recently increased and he would like to keep track of his net worth. Jeff has gathered the following information to help you track his net worth. Assume the opening net worth for June 30 is $0.

	June 30, 2016	July 31, 2016	August 31, 2016
Cash	$2,500	$4,100	$6,300
Automobile	13,000	13,000	13,000
Credit Card Bills	1,000	800	500
Automobile Loan	12,000	11,500	11,000
Salary	4,300	4,900	4,900
Food Expense	290	500	100
Entertainment Expense	210	800	500
Rent Expense	1,300	1,300	1,300

Complete the table below.

	June 30, 2016	July 31, 2016	August 31, 2016
Opening Net Worth			
Surplus (Deficit)			
Closing Net Worth			

Analysis

After looking at the table you prepared for Jeff, he notices that his cash has not increased by as much as his net worth has. Why is this the case?

_____

_____

_____

_____

AP-12A (❷ ❹)

Using the opening balances provided in the balance sheets below, enter the updated amounts for each transaction in the blank balance sheets labelled Answers.

1. Borrowed $4,000 from the bank.

Opening Balances

Assets		Liabilities	
Cash	$5,000	Unpaid Accounts	$3,000
Investment	8,000	Bank Loan	0
Contents of Home	6,000	Automobile Loan	5,000
Automobile	20,000	Student Loan	6,000
House	280,000	Mortgage	250,000
		Total Liabilities	264,000
		Net Worth	55,000
Total Assets	$319,000	**Total Liabilities + Net Worth**	$319,000

Answers

2. Purchased $3,000 of investments in cash.

Opening Balances

Assets		Liabilities	
Cash	$7,000	Unpaid Accounts	$3,000
Investment	8,000	Bank Loan	0
Contents of Home	6,000	Automobile Loan	5,000
Automobile	20,000	Student Loan	6,000
House	180,000	Mortgage	150,000
		Total Liabilities	164,000
		Net Worth	57,000
Total Assets	$221,000	**Total Liabilities + Net Worth**	$221,000

Answers

3. Paid $1,000 to reduce an outstanding automobile loan (principal portion).

Opening Balances

Assets		Liabilities	
Cash	$3,000	Unpaid Accounts	$3,000
Contents of Home	6,000	Bank Loan	0
Automobile	20,000	Automobile Loan	5,000
House	180,000	Student Loan	6,000
		Mortgage	150,000
		Total Liabilities	164,000
		Net Worth	45,000
Total Assets	$209,000	**Total Liabilities + Net Worth**	$209,000

Answers

4. Bought a motorcycle for $6,000. Paid a $1,000 deposit with cash and borrowed $5,000 from the bank.

Opening Balances

Assets		Liabilities	
Cash	$2,000	Unpaid Accounts	$3,000
Contents of Home	4,000	Bank Loan	1,000
Motorcycle	0	Student Loan	11,000
Automobile	20,000	Mortgage	150,000
House	180,000	**Total Liabilities**	165,000
		Net Worth	41,000
Total Assets	$206,000	**Total Liabilities + Net Worth**	$206,000

Answers

AP-13A (⑧)

John Hollister collected the following amounts in cash for the month of February 2016

Salary paid by employer	$2,400
Winnings at the casino	$270
Gifts	$295
Performance bonus paid by employer	$450

Required

Calculate John's total revenue and total capital items for February 2016.

_____

_____

_____

AP-14A (④)

Indicate whether the terms of the accounting equation will increase, decrease or stay the same for each transaction by placing a "+" or "−" in the appropriate space. If an item is not changed by the transaction, leave the space blank. The first transaction has been completed for you.

Transaction	Assets	= Liabilities	+ Net Worth
Deposited salary earned.	+		+
1. Purchased a new TV on credit.			
2. Received a cash gift.			
3. Purchased fuel for car on credit.			
4. Made a loan payment including interest.			
5. Received cash from a student loan.			
6. Received a paycheque.			

AP-15A (❷ ❺ ❾)

The following information is available from Anna Edison's financial records

Opening Balances as at June 1, 2016	
Cash	$18,000
Furniture	3,100
Valuables & Electronics	3,200
House	255,000
Student Loans	39,000
Family Loan	2,000
Mortgage	100,000
Net Worth	138,300

The following transactions took place during the month of June

1. $350 was taken from the bank account for a car lease payment.
2. Paid $1,000 cash against the student loans. Includes $140 of interest.
3. Won a tablet worth $800 as a raffle prize.
4. Made a mortgage payment of $2,000 with cash. Includes $400 interest.
5. $4,800 salary earned was directly deposited to the bank account.
6. Family member accepted jewellery of $2,000 in repayment of the loan.

a) Record the transactions in the T-accounts.

PERSONAL BALANCE SHEET
As at June 30, 2016

ASSETS		LIABILITIES	

Increase	Decrease
+	CASH	-

Opening

Increase	Decrease
+	FURNITURE	-

Opening

Increase	Decrease
+ VALUABLES & ELECTRONICS -

Opening

Increase	Decrease
+	HOUSE	-

Opening

Decrease	Increase
-	STUDENT LOANS	+

Opening

Decrease	Increase
-	FAMILY LOAN	+

Opening

Decrease	Increase
-	MORTGAGE	+

Opening

Decrease	Increase
-	NET WORTH	+

Opening

Total Assets _____

Total Liabilites _____

Net Worth _____ } _____

INCOME STATEMENT
For the Month Ended June 30, 2016

REVENUE	

Decrease	Increase
-	+

LESS EXPENSES

Increase	Decrease
+	AUTOMOBILE EXPENSE	-

Increase	Decrease
+	ENTERTAINMENT EXPENSE	-

Increase	Decrease
+	GROCERIES EXPENSE	-

Increase	Decrease
+	INTEREST EXPENSE	-

Increase	Decrease
+	TRAVEL EXPENSE	-

Total Revenue _____

Less Total Expenses _____

Surplus (Deficit) _____

b) Complete the income statement and balance sheet.

Income Statement For the Month Ended June 30, 2016		

Personal Balance Sheet As at June 30, 2016			

AP-16A (❹ ❾)

Indicate whether assets, liabilities or net worth will increase or decrease and by how much, based on each transaction. The first one has been done for you. Always ensure the accounting equation is balanced.

Provide an explanation only if net worth is affected.

	Assets	= Liabilities	+ Net Worth	Explanation
1. Purchased a new television for $700 on credit.	+700	+700		
2. Received $2,000 salary.				
3. Paid $1,200 cash for one year of insurance.				
4. Purchased a new $500 gaming console with cash.				
5. Paid for groceries with $80 cash.				
6. Paid $400 toward the car loan.				
7. Paid $30 interest on the car loan.				
8. Paid $600 toward unpaid bills.				
9. Used one month of insurance.				

AP-17A (❹ ❼ ❾)

Indicate whether the account balances will increase or decrease and by how much, based on each transaction. The first one has been done for you. Always ensure the accounting equation is balanced.

	Assets =	Liabilities +	Net Worth	Explanation
1. Purchased a new television for $700 on credit.	+ 700	+ 700		
2. Purchased $100 worth of gas on credit.				
3. Made a $850 car loan payment.				
4. Purchased a chandelier for $200 cash.				
5. Prepaid three months of rent with $3,300 cash.				
6. Received a cash gift of $500.				
7. Used up one of three months of prepaid rent.				
8. Paid interest of $50, in cash, on the car loan.				
9. Received a phone bill for $110.				

Analysis

The net worth account is only updated at the end of an accounting period. Revenue and expense accounts, and the net worth account, track changes in net worth during the period. For each transaction that affects net worth, determine whether a revenue, expense, or net worth is used to track the change.

_____

_____

_____

_____

AP-18A (❷ ❹ ❼)

On December 1, 2016, Shervin decided to track his finances. On this date, his assets and liabilities were

Cash	$14,000
Prepaid Rent	3,000
Prepaid Insurance	300
House	160,000
Contents of Home	19,000
Automobile	30,000
Student Loan	10,000
Unpaid Accounts	17,000
Bank Loan	25,000
Mortgage	120,000

Required

a) What is the value of his total assets?

_____

_____

_____

_____

b) What is the value of his total liabilities?

_____

_____

_____

c) What is Shervin's net worth on December 1, 2016?

_____

_____

d) During the month of December, Shervin recognized $150 of prepaid expenses as an actual expense on the income statement. Calculate the change in his cash account and net worth.

Transaction	Cash	Net Worth
Effect		

AP-19A (❹ ❻)

Nick Miller wrote down his personal accounting information but some of it was destroyed.

Bicycle	$700
Automobile	3,000
Cash	800
Furniture	?
Net Worth	3,350
Overdue Rent	?
Television	500
Total Assets	6,100
Unpaid Bills	2,300

Required

a) How much is Nick's furniture worth?

_____

_____

_____

b) How much rent does Nick owe?

_____

_____

_____

_____

Analysis

Nick has worked 80 hours at his job as a bartender and earned $1,900 but will not get paid for another two weeks. According to accrual-based accounting has Nick's net worth increased? Why or why not?

_____

_____

_____

AP-20A (④)

State how the following transactions would affect net worth (increase, decrease, no change)

Transaction	Effect on Net Worth
Borrow cash.	
Pay entertainment expense with cash.	
Pay food expense with cash.	
Buy assets with cash.	
Charge home repairs expense on credit card.	
Pay insurance expense with cash.	
Pay loan principal with cash.	
Purchase assets on account.	
Receive salary.	
Pay rent expense with cash.	

AP-21A (❷ ❺)

Using the following chart, indicate whether there would be an increase, decrease or no change to cash and net worth for the transactions provided. The first transaction has been completed for you.

	Transaction	Cash			Net Worth		
		Increase	Decrease	No Change	Increase	Decrease	No Change
1	Deposit salary earned:	X			X		
2	Pay cash for food.						
3	Purchase a new car.						
4	Pay rent expense in advance.						
5	Reduce student loan principal.						
6	Buy a new computer with cash.						
7	Obtain a bank loan.						
8	Pay entertainment expenses.						
9	Record cash earned from a part-time job.						

AP-22A (❽)

Joana Harwin collected the following amounts in cash for the month of March 2016

Full-time employment income	$1,200
Income from part-time babysitting job	$220
Rental income	$525

Required

Calculate Joana's total revenue and total capital items for March 2016.

_____

_____

_____

Application Questions Group B

AP-1B (❷)

Dana Shukrun was reviewing her records on December 31, 2016. Below is a list of items and their value.

Cash	$7,900
Computer	700
Automobile	19,100
House	255,000
Mortgage	150,000
Credit Card	4,600
Bank Loan	37,700

Required

a) Calculate Dana Shukrun's total assets.

_____

_____

b) Calculate Dana Shukrun's total liabilities.

_____

_____

AP-2B (❷ ❹)

John Bonham was performing a year-end review of his finances and came up with this list:

Cash	$13,200
Furniture	1,900
Automobile	21,900
House	210,000
Credit Card	4,600
Student Loan	11,400
Mortgage	100,000

Required

a) Calculate John Bonham's total assets.

b) Calculate John Bonham's total liabilities.

c) Calculate John Bonham's net worth.

AP-3B (❷ ❹)

Consider the following information

Cash	$6,000
Automobile	50,000
Prepaid Insurance	3,000
Bank Loan	10,000
Unpaid Credit Card Bills	2,000
Net Worth	?

How much is the net worth?

AP-4B (❷ ❹ ❺ ❾)

Christine Sutherland compiled the following information on May 31, 2016

Cash	$2,100
Jewellery	3,000
House	186,200
Mortgage	171,800
Net Worth	19,500

Transactions for the month of June 2016

1. Received $4,100 cash for her monthly salary.
2. Paid $590 cash for maintenance on her car.
3. Paid cash for telephone, water and electricity for $540.
4. Purchased an automobile worth $10,600 on credit.
5. Received $30 interest earned on bank deposits.
6. Paid $320 for food with cash.

Required

a) What is the ending balance of cash?

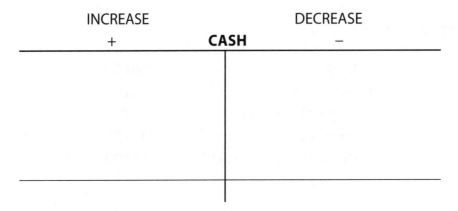

b) What is the surplus or deficit for the accounting period?

_____

_____

c) What is Christine Sutherland's net worth on June 30?

_____

_____

AP-5B (❷ ❸ ❺)

Arthur's financial records show that his assets and net worth as of May 1, 2016 are

Cash	$6,000
Computer	4,000
Contents of Home	17,500
Automobile	20,000
House	137,500
Student Loan	?
Net Worth	113,000

Required

a) Arthur wants to find out how much he owes. Determine his total liabilities.

_____

_____

_____

_____

_____

_____

b) During the month of May, Arthur paid $2,000 for two months of rent in advance ($1,000 per month). Calculate the change in Arthur's cash account and personal net worth.

Transaction	Cash	Net Worth
Effect		

AP-6B (❹)

Calculate the missing amounts in the following table.

	Scenario 1	Scenario 2
Total Assets	$125,900	
Total Liabilities		$33,200
Net Worth	$92,700	$117,100

AP-7B (❶ ❸)

As of December 31, 2015, Deena Balsdon had total assets of $42,800 and total liabilities of $16,700. As of December 31, 2016, Deena's total assets and liabilities increased to $48,900 and $26,100, respectively. Fill out the following table of account balances. How has Deena's net worth changed since 2015?

	As at December 31, 2015	As at December 31, 2016
Net Worth		

_____

_____

AP-8B (❷ ❹ ❾)

Alan Marshall is preparing his balance sheet and income statement for the month ended July 31, 2016. Use the following information to help him prepare his financial statements.

Opening Balances as at July 1, 2016

Cash	$4,400
Contents of Home	2,800
Automobile	4,800
House	287,900
Unpaid Accounts	8,500
Mortgage	239,300
Net Worth	52,100

Transactions for the month of July

1. Purchased a $1,600 high definition television using the credit card.
2. Paid a telephone bill of $640 for the month of July using the credit card.
3. Paid credit card bill with cash for $3,300.
4. Purchased $1,010 of groceries and food using cash.
5. Paid July's utilities for $1,100 with cash.
6. Made a principal payment of $1,100 for the mortgage.
7. Deposited $4,700 salary earned during the month.
8. Earned $60 interest on savings account.

Required

a) Using the information provided, record the opening balances in the T-accounts.

b) Record the transactions for the month of July in the T-accounts.

PERSONAL BALANCE SHEET
As at July 31, 2016

ASSETS		LIABILITIES	

CASH

Increase	Decrease
+	-

Opening

CONTENTS OF HOME

Increase	Decrease
+	-

Opening

AUTOMOBILE

Increase	Decrease
+	-

Opening

HOUSE

Increase	Decrease
+	-

Opening

UNPAID ACCOUNTS

Decrease	Increase
-	+

Opening

MORTGAGE

Decrease	Increase
-	+

Opening

NET WORTH

NET WORTH

Decrease	Increase
-	+

Opening

Total Assets

Total Liabilites _____ } _____

Net Worth

PERSONAL INCOME STATEMENT
For the Month Ended July 31, 2016

REVENUE	

Decrease	Increase
-	+

LESS EXPENSES

+ CLOTHING EXPENSE -

Increase	Decrease

+ FOOD EXPENSE -

Increase	Decrease

+ TELEPHONE EXPENSE -

Increase	Decrease

+ UTILITIES EXPENSE -

Increase	Decrease

Total Revenue

Less Total Expenses

Surplus (Deficit)

AP-9B (❷ ❹ ❺ ❾)

The following information is available from Tory Barnes' financial records

	Opening Balances as at February 1, 2016
Cash	$34,000
Prepaid Insurance	3,500
Automobile	45,000
Boat	81,000
Unpaid Accounts	21,000
Automobile Loan	25,000
Net Worth	117,500

The following transactions took place during the month of February

1. Purchased fuel for the boat with $85 cash.
2. Earned $1,250 wages and deposited in bank account.
3. Purchased $420 of groceries on a credit card.
4. Won $200 cash from a lottery.
5. Paid $3,600 cash for credit card bills due.
6. Paid $360 interest on credit card bill with cash.
7. Booked a flight on credit for $900.
8. Recognized one month of car insurance used up for $350.

Record the transactions in the T-accounts.

PERSONAL BALANCE SHEET
As at February 29, 2016

ASSETS		LIABILITIES	

Increase	Decrease	Decrease	Increase
+ CASH -		- UNPAID ACCOUNTS +	
Opening			Opening

Increase	Decrease	Decrease	Increase
+ PREPAID INSURANCE -		- AUTOMOBILE LOAN +	
Opening			Opening

Increase	Decrease
+ AUTOMOBILE -	
Opening	

NET WORTH	

Increase	Decrease	Decrease	Increase
+ BOAT -		- NET WORTH +	
Opening			Opening

Total Assets

Total Liabilites

Net Worth

INCOME STATEMENT
For the Month Ended February 29, 2016

REVENUE	

Decrease	Increase
-	+

LESS EXPENSES

Increase	Decrease
+ ENTERTAINMENT EXPENSE -	

Increase	Decrease
+ FOOD EXPENSE -	

Increase	Decrease
+ FUEL EXPENSE -	

Increase	Decrease
+ INSURANCE EXPENSE -	

Increase	Decrease
+ INTEREST EXPENSE -	

Increase	Decrease
+ TRAVEL EXPENSE -	

Total Revenue

Less Total Expenses

Surplus (Deficit)

Analysis

Tory will be cancelling her auto insurance with no cancellation fee incurred. Which accounts will be affected by the insurance cancellation? How will the balances change?

_____

_____

AP-10B (❷ ❸)

Ethan is a famous songwriter and composer. His income is based solely on royalties that he receives regularly. Ethan opted to use three months as his accounting period.

The following information pertains to income earned and expenses incurred from January 1, 2016 to March 31, 2016

	January	February	March
Royalty Income	$12,000	$13,000	$10,000
Interest Expense	60	60	60
Food Expense	2,000	2,100	1,900
Maintenance Expense	350	500	180
Clothing Expense	900	1,500	0
Utilities Expense	300	500	0
Rent Expense	1,500	1,500	1,500
Miscellaneous Expense	15	50	5

Required

a) Prepare a personal income statement for each of the three months.

Ethan Personal Income Statement For the Period Ended March 31, 2016				
	January	February	March	Total

b) What amount should be added to Ethan's net worth on March 31, 2016?

_____

_____

_____

AP-11B (❷ ❸)

Archie always prepares an income statement and balance sheet each month, but he has fallen behind. Assume the opening net worth for October 31, 2016 is $6,770. Luckily, he has kept track of his account balances as shown below

	October 31, 2016	November 30, 2016
Cash	$2,500	$6,900
Entertainment Expense	500	250
Food Expense	280	270
Gasoline Expense	140	130
Prepaid Rent	4,200	2,800
Rent Expense	1,400	1,400
Salary	5,050	5,050
Unpaid Accounts	700	700
Automobile	3,500	3,500

Complete the table below.

	October 31, 2016	November 30, 2016
Opening Net Worth		
Surplus (Deficit)		
Closing Net Worth		

Analysis

Archie noticed that his net worth did not increase as much as his cash did during November. Why is this the case?

_____

_____

_____

_____

AP-12B (❷ ❹)

Using the opening balances provided in the balance sheets below, enter the updated amounts for each transaction in the blank balance sheets labelled Answers.

1. Applied for and received a student loan of $5,700.

Opening Balances

Assets		Liabilities	
Cash	$5,600	Unpaid Accounts	$2,500
Investment	8,400	Bank Loan	900
Contents of Home	6,200	Automobile Loan	4,800
Automobile	22,300	Student Loan	5,500
House	287,900	Mortgage	241,500
		Total Liabilities	255,200
		Net Worth	75,200
Total Assets	$330,400	**Total Liabilities + Net Worth**	$330,400

Answers

2. Purchased some furniture and Jewellery for $5,000 cash.

Opening Balances

Assets		Liabilities	
Cash	$8,200	Unpaid Accounts	$2,400
Investment	7,200	Bank Loan	200
Contents of Home	6,100	Automobile Loan	4,400
Automobile	22,900	Student Loan	6,200
House	272,300	Mortgage	242,200
		Total Liabilities	255,400
		Net Worth	61,300
Total Assets	$316,700	**Total Liabilities + Net Worth**	$316,700

Answers

3. Paid a portion of the principal of the automobile loan for $1,200.

Opening Balances

Assets		Liabilities	
Cash	$4,500	Unpaid Accounts	$2,200
Contents of Home	5,500	Bank Loan	600
Automobile	19,000	Automobile Loan	4,200
House	290,000	Student Loan	6,800
		Mortgage	242,800
		Total Liabilities	256,600
		Net Worth	62,400
Total Assets	$319,000	**Total Liabilities + Net Worth**	$319,000

Answers

4. Bought a motorcycle for $7,100—paid a $1,400 deposit with cash and borrowed $5,700 from the bank.

Opening Balances

Assets		Liabilities	
Cash	$5,000	Unpaid Accounts	$2,000
Contents of Home	6,700	Bank Loan	1,000
Motorcycle	0	Student Loan	11,000
Automobile	17,000	Mortgage	242,000
House	283,300	**Total Liabilities**	256,000
		Net Worth	56,000
Total Assets	$312,000	**Total Liabilities + Net Worth**	$312,000

Answers

AP-13B (❽)

Stacey Green received the following amounts in cash for the month of November 2016

Salary	$2,100
Gifts	$240
Winnings at the casino	$170
Performance bonus paid by employer	$460

Calculate Stacey's total revenue and total capital items for November 2016.

AP-14B (❹)

Indicate whether the terms of the accounting equation will increase, decrease or stay the same for each transaction by placing a "+" or "−" in the appropriate space. If an item is not changed by the transaction, leave the space blank. The first transaction has been completed for you.

Transaction	Assets	= Liabilities	+ Net Worth
Deposited salary earned.	+		+
1. Purchased a new bicycle on credit.			
2. Purchased groceries on credit.			
3. Borrowed money from the bank.			
4. Purchased a ring for $200 cash.			
5. Received a cash gift.			
6. Made a loan payment with interest.			

AP-15B (❷ ❹ ❾)

The following information is available from Drew Bernard's financial records

Opening Balances as at September 1, 2016

Cash	$1,500
Automobile	9,400
Boat	18,000
Instruments	7,600
House	415,000
Student Loans	67,000
Unpaid Accounts	8,500
Mortgage	250,000
Net Worth	126,000

The following transactions took place during the month of September

1. Purchased a piano worth $900 using cash.
2. Put $720 food expenses on a credit card.
3. Purchased a $800 guitar on credit.
4. Received cash inheritance of $45,000.
5. Paid off unpaid accounts with $9,570 cash.
6. Received $50 interest on the bank account.

Record the transactions in the T-accounts.

| PERSONAL BALANCE SHEET |
| As at September 30, 2016 |

ASSETS

CASH
Increase (+) | Decrease (-)
Opening

AUTOMOBILE
Increase (+) | Decrease (-)
Opening

BOAT
Increase (+) | Decrease (-)
Opening

INSTRUMENTS
Increase (+) | Decrease (-)
Opening

HOUSE
Increase (+) | Decrease (-)
Opening

LIABILITIES

STUDENT LOANS
Decrease (-) | Increase (+)
Opening

UNPAID ACCOUNTS
Decrease (-) | Increase (+)
Opening

MORTGAGE
Decrease (-) | Increase (+)
Opening

NET WORTH
Decrease (-) | Increase (+)
Opening

Total Assets _____
Total Liabilites _____
Net Worth _____
} _____

| INCOME STATEMENT |
| For the Month Ended September 30, 2016 |

REVENUE
Decrease (-) | Increase (+)

LESS EXPENSES

ENTERTAINMENT EXPENSE
Increase (+) | Decrease (-)

GROCERIES EXPENSE
Increase (+) | Decrease (-)

INTEREST EXPENSE
Increase (+) | Decrease (-)

MAINTENANCE EXPENSE
Increase (+) | Decrease (-)

Total Revenue _____
Less Total Expenses _____
Surplus (Deficit) _____

AP-16B (❹ ❾)

Indicate whether assets, liabilities or net worth will increase or decrease and by how much, based on each transaction. The first one has been done for you. Always ensure the accounting equation is balanced.

Provide an explanation only if net worth is affected.

	Assets	= Liabilities	+ Net Worth	Explanation
1. Purchased a new television for $700 on credit.	+700	+700		
2. Won $700 in a lottery.				
3. Deposited a $2,800 salary earned.				
4. Purchased furniture for $400 in cash.				
5. Transferred $500 of a checking account to savings.				
6. Paid $150 for concert tickets with a credit card.				
7. Paid $200 cash for utilities.				
8. Paid $1,500 toward the mortgage.				
9. Paid $1,100 toward unpaid bills.				

AP-17B (❹ ❾)

The following information is available from Lily's financial record

Opening Balances as at November 1, 2016

Cash	$18,000
Furniture	3,100
Valuables & Electronics	3,200
House	255,000
Student Loans	39,000
Mortgage	100,000
Family Loan	2,000
Net Worth	138,300

Indicate whether the account balances will increase or decrease and by how much, based on each transaction. Always ensure the accounting equation is balanced.

	Assets =	Liabilities +	Net Worth	Explanation
1. Purchased $1,600 of new furniture for the bedroom with cash.				
2. Won a tablet worth $800 as a raffle prize.				
3. $350 was taken from the bank account for a car lease payment.				
4. Family member accepted $2,000 worth of Jewellery in repayment of the loan.				
5. Made a $2,000 mortgage payment with cash. Includes $400 of interest.				
6. Paid $1,000 towards the student loans with cash. Includes $140 of interest.				
7. Salary earned of $4,800 was directly deposited to the bank account.				

Analysis

The net worth account is only updated at the end of an accounting period. Revenue and expense accounts, and the net worth account track changes in net worth during the period. For each transaction that affects net worth, determine whether a revenue, expense, or net worth is used to track the change.

_____

_____

_____

_____

_____

AP-18B (❷)

Consider the following financial information of Pete Griphin

Automobile	$66,000
Boat	55,000
Automobile Loan	50,000
Cash	14,500
Coin Collection	1,200
Cottage	84,000
House and Property	510,000
Prepaid House Insurance	8,500
Mortgage Principal	450,000
Trailer	4,000

Required

a)   Calculate Pete's total assets.

_____

_____

_____

_____

_____

_____

b)   Calculate Pete's total liabilities.

_____

_____

_____

c)   Calculate Pete's net worth.

_____

_____

_____

Analysis

Pete makes payments against his liabilities and updates all of his account balances at the end of each month. Which account balances will change at the end of the month? Which will increase and which will decrease?

_____

_____

_____

_____

AP-19B (❹ ❺ ❻)

Jess Day stored her personal accounting information in the computer but some of it was deleted by accident.

Appliances	$1,100
Cell Phone	500
Family Loan	?
Jewellery	800
Net Worth	4,500
Unpaid Bills	350
Automobile	5,000

Required

a) What are Jess' total assets?

_____

_____

b) What is the amount of Jess' family loan?

_____

_____

_____

_____

Analysis

Jess works as a teacher. She has agreed to work as a substitute during one day next week for extra wages. According to accrual-based accounting, has Jess' net worth increased? Why or why not?

_____

_____

_____

AP-20B (❹ ❺ ❼)

Dex had the following transactions during the month of May

1. Purchased a new laptop for $1,200 cash.
2. Put $1,600 of car repairs on his credit card.
3. Spent $80 on a steak dinner with his sister and paid with his credit card.
4. Prepaid his son's nanny $850 cash for future services.
5. Received salary of $5,500.

How have these transactions affected Dex's net worth?

_____

_____

_____

_____

Analysis

Has Dex's cash changed the same amount as his net worth? Why or why not?

_____

_____

_____

_____

_____

AP-21B (❷ ❺ ❾)

On June 1, 2016, Joey had $3,100 in cash (including his bank account). The following transactions took place for the month of June

1. Returned a newly purchased cell phone to the store for $150 cash.
2. Purchased a new laptop for $1,200 cash.
3. Went to a concert—ticket price was $90 paid by cash.
4. Received wages of $3,200 for the month.
5. Spent $300 cash on food for the month.
6. Received monthly utility bills of $310, due July 21.
7. Received interest on a savings account of $35.

Required

a) What is the balance of cash on June 30?

INCREASE		DECREASE
+	**CASH**	−

b) Prepare a personal income statement for Joey for June.

Personal Income Statement		
For the Month Ended June 30, 2016		
Revenue		
Expenses		
Surplus (Deficit)		

Analysis

Joey purchased his car using 0% financing. This means there is no interest on the loan. What is the effect on net worth after each car payment? Would the effect be any different if the loan had interest? Explain.

_____

_____

_____

_____

AP-22B (❹)

Rita has total assets of $35,000 and total liabilities of $20,000. She owns a few pieces of gold Jewellery that were originally purchased for $1,000 total. She recently purchased some additional Jewellery for $3,000 cash. Which account balances will change from this transaction and by how much? Use the accounting equation to check your answer.

_____

_____

_____

_____

_____

_____

_____

Analysis

Rita wants to increase her net worth so she decided to purchase a new automobile by getting a bank loan. Has her net worth changed as expected? Explain.

_____

_____

_____

AP-23B (❷ ❹ ❺)

Jed Mosley had the following financial data for the year ended December 31, 2016

Automobile	$6,500
Chequing Account	1,100
Credit Card Bill	2,100
Electronics	1,000
Furniture	2,000
Hydro Bill	120
Phone Bill	150
Savings Account	10,000

Required

a) Calculate Jed's total assets.

_____

_____

_____

_____

_____

b) Calculate Jed's total liabilities.

_____

_____

_____

_____

Analysis

Jed realized he has a rent payment coming up on January 1, 2017 that will cover January's rent. Should this be included in December's financial data? Explain.

_____

_____

_____

_____

_____

Case Study

CS–1 (❷ ❹ ❺ ❻ ❼ ❽ ❾)

After taking the first part of this financial accounting course, you excitedly tell a friend what you have learned. You tell him about assets, liabilities and net worth and how they increase and decrease in value with every financial transaction. Your friend decides to start getting organized and apply accounting principles to his personal finances. He compiles everything that he thinks is important and calculates his net worth. He then asks you to look over what he had done to make sure it is correct. His list of important financial items is listed below, along with his version of the T-account records.

1. He had $950 in his bank account at the beginning of the month.
2. He had a $1,200 balance on his credit card at the beginning of the month.
3. He estimates that he had about $3,000 worth of "stuff" in his apartment at the beginning of the month (TV, sound system, computer and furniture).
4. Deposited his salary of $1,500.
5. Paid in advance for three months of rent with $1,350 cash.
6. Paid $600 to pay off a portion of the credit card bill.
7. Purchased a new video game system for $350 with his credit card.
8. Bought $120 worth of food with cash.
9. Got hired at a second job. He will start next month and will earn $800 per month.
10. Spent $250 cash on movies, stage plays and Dave and Buster's.
11. Lived in his apartment for one of the three months he already paid for (see #5)

+	CASH		-		
1.	$950		5.	$1,350	
4.	1,500		6.	600	
			8.	120	
			10.	250	
Total	**$130**				

-	UNPAID ACCOUNTS		+	
6.	$600		2.	$1,200
			7.	350
			Total	**$950**

-	NET WORTH		+	
5.	$1,350		3.	$3,000
8.	120		4.	1,500
10.	250		7.	350
			9.	800
			Total	**$3,930**

Required

a) What are some immediate problems that you see with what your friend has prepared?

_____

_____

_____

_____

b) With all the problems you see, your friend asks you to show him what the correct records should look like. Use the templates at the end of this problem to record the transactions.

_____

After showing your friend the corrected version, he asks a number of questions.

c) Why did you use all of these accounts when I only used three (Cash, Unpaid Accounts and Net Worth)?

_____

_____

_____

_____

_____

d) Why is the $3,000 worth of "stuff" not considered net worth?

_____

_____

_____

_____

_____

_____

e) I was having trouble figuring out how to record my second job which I start next month. They are going to be paying me $800 a month! I figured it will increase my net worth, but I didn't know where else to put it. I knew it couldn't be cash, because they haven't paid me yet. What did you do with it and why?

_____

_____

_____

_____

f) What did you do with my rent? Shouldn't the entire $1,350 decrease my net worth? And what would happen if I did it my way?

_____

_____

_____

_____

_____

_____

_____

_____

_____

_____

g) I forgot to tell you that the $600 credit card payment included $30 of interest. I didn't think it mattered since the total payment amount is the same. This won't change anything, right?

_____

_____

_____

h) You may have noticed that I am running low on cash. Any suggestions on how I can raise more cash?

_____

_____

_____

_____

_____

_____

i) This is very useful and I would like to do this more often. I can do it this weekend, then two weeks from now once I finish my exams, then probably not for another month after that. I'm going on a well-deserved vacation after my exams, so I won't be around to look after it. Do you think this will work out well?

_____

_____

_____

_____

_____

PERSONAL BALANCE SHEET

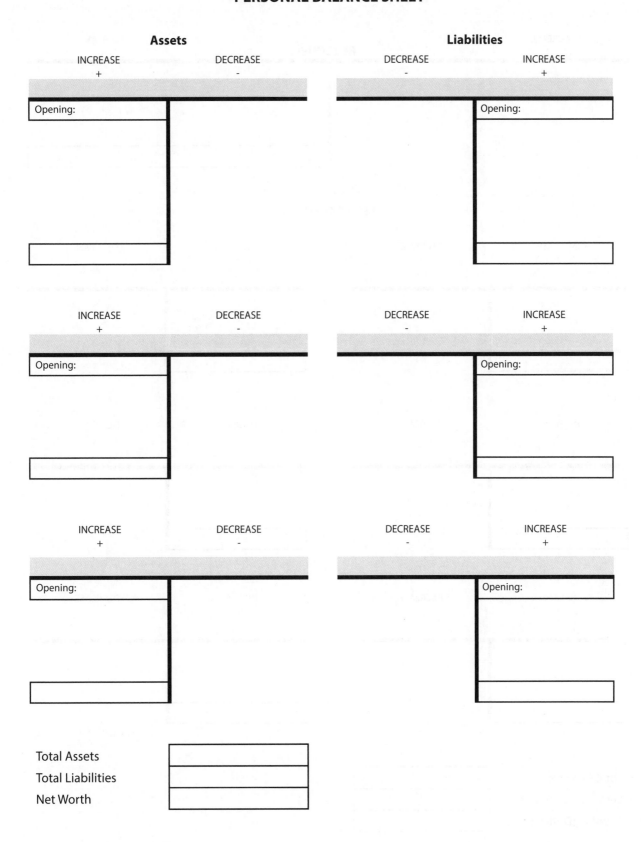

Assets

INCREASE +	DECREASE -
Opening:	

INCREASE +	DECREASE -
Opening:	

INCREASE +	DECREASE -
Opening:	

Liabilities

DECREASE -	INCREASE +
	Opening:

DECREASE -	INCREASE +
	Opening:

DECREASE -	INCREASE +
	Opening:

Total Assets	
Total Liabilities	
Net Worth	

PERSONAL INCOME STATEMENT

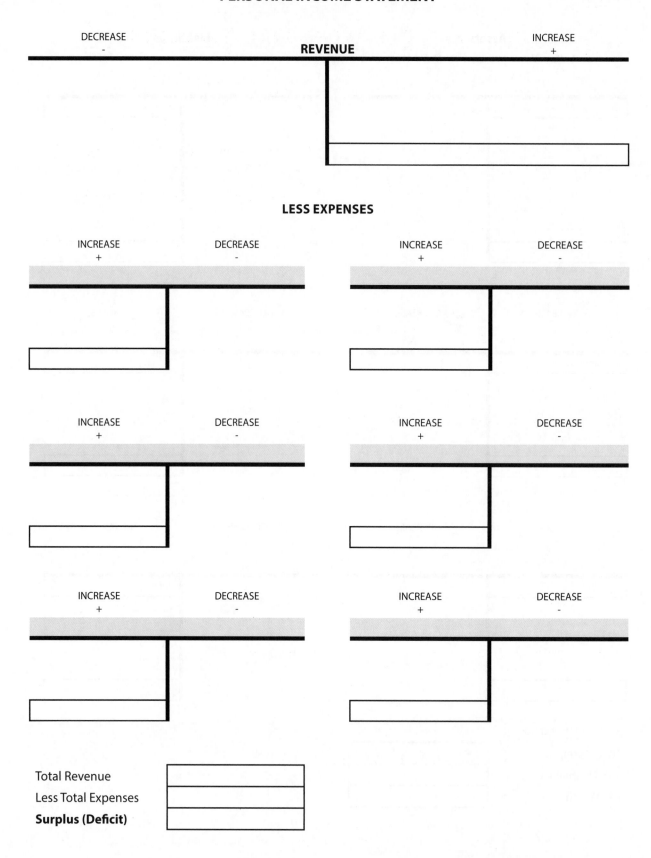

Total Revenue	
Less Total Expenses	
Surplus (Deficit)	

Chapter 2

LINKING PERSONAL ACCOUNTING TO BUSINESS ACCOUNTING

LEARNING OUTCOMES

❶ List the differences between personal accounts and business accounts

❷ Describe the sequence of assets and liabilities as they appear on the balance sheet

❸ Define equity and calculate the balance of the capital account

❹ Describe the three main types of businesses

❺ Record revenue based on the concept of accruals

❻ Record expenses based on the concept of accruals

❼ Record business transactions in T-accounts

AMEENGAGE™ Access **ameengage.com** for integrated resources including tutorials, practice exercises, the digital textbook and more.

Assessment Questions

AS-1 (❶)

Net worth in personal accounting is similar to which item in accounting for businesses?

_____

_____

AS-2 (❷)

In what order are the assets of a business listed? Explain.

_____

_____

_____

AS-3 (❷)

In what order are the liabilities of a business listed? Explain.

_____

_____

_____

AS-4 (❸)

What is equity?

_____

_____

_____

AS-5 (❸)

What is the formula for calculating the ending owner's equity balance?

_____

_____

AS-6 (❸)

Describe owner's contributions and owner's drawings and explain how they affect the balance sheet.

_____

_____

_____

AS-7 (❹)

List the three main types of businesses.

_____

_____

AS-8 (❹)

Describe what a service business does. Provide two examples of service businesses.

_____

_____

_____

AS-9 (④)

Describe what a merchandising business does. Provide an example of a merchandising business.

_____

_____

_____

AS-10 (④)

Describe what a manufacturing business does. Provide two examples of a manufacturing business.

_____

_____

_____

AS-11 (⑥)

Give three examples of expenses that businesses commonly prepay.

_____

_____

_____

AS-12 (⑥)

Describe the three different times cash can be paid to a supplier related to an expense.

_____

_____

_____

AS-13 (❻)

What does it mean to *incur* an expense?

_____

_____

_____

AS-14 (❻)

What is the entry to record an expense if a company pays *when* the expense is incurred?

_____

_____

AS-15 (❻)

What is the entry to record an expense if a company pays *after* the expense is incurred?

_____

_____

AS-16 (❻)

What is the entry if a company pays *before* the expense is incurred?

_____

_____

AS-17 (❺)

What does it mean to *recognize* revenue?

_____

_____

_____

AS-18 (⑤)

Describe the three different times cash can be received from a customer related to earning revenue.

_____

_____

_____

AS-19 (⑤)

What is the entry to record revenue if a customer pays *when* the service is delivered?

_____

_____

AS-20 (⑤)

What is the entry to record revenue if a customer pays *after* the service is delivered?

_____

_____

AS-21 (⑤)

What is the entry if a customer pays *before* the service is delivered?

_____

_____

AS-22 (⑤)

What type of account is unearned revenue?

_____

_____

Application Questions Group A

AP-1A (❸ ❺ ❻)

For each transaction, indicate whether the total assets (A), liabilities (L) or owner's equity (OE) increased (+), decreased (−) or did not change (o) by placing the symbol in the appropriate column.

		A	L	OE
1.	Paid salaries for current month.			
2.	Purchased equipment on credit.			
3.	Purchased furniture using cash.			
4.	Additional investment into the business.			
5.	Received payment for services to be provided next month.			
6.	Made partial payment for equipment purchased on credit.			
7.	Billed customers for services performed.			
8.	Withdrew cash for personal use.			
9.	Received payment from customers already billed.			
10.	Received bills for utilities to be paid next month.			

AP-2A (❸ ❺ ❻)

The given transactions were completed by Juliet's Delivery Services during May 2016. Indicate the effects of each transaction by placing the appropriate letter in the space provided.

A   Increase in asset, decrease in another asset
B   Increase in asset, increase in liability
C   Increase in asset, increase in owner's equity
D   Decrease in asset, decrease in liability
E   Decrease in asset, decrease in owner's equity

_____ Received cash for providing delivery services.
_____ Paid amount owing that was outstanding to a creditor.
_____ Invested additional cash in the business.
_____ Paid advertising expense with cash.
_____ Billed customers for delivery services on account.
_____ Purchased office furniture on account.
_____ Paid rent for the month.
_____ Received cash from customers on account.
_____ Received cash in advance for services to be provided in the next month.
_____ Owner withdrew cash for personal use.

AP-3A (❷)

Organize the following asset and liability accounts in the order they are likely to appear in a balance sheet.

Assets	Liabilities
Accounts Receivable	Bank Loan
Cash	Accounts Payable
Equipment	Unearned Revenue
Prepaid Expenses	

_____

_____

_____

_____

AP-4A (❺ ❻)

Simpson Moving had the following transactions during the month. Indicate whether assets, liabilities or owner's equity will increase or decrease and by how much, based on each transaction. Provide an explanation only if equity is affected. The first entry has been done for you. Always ensure the accounting equation is balanced.

	Assets	= Liabilities	+ Owner's Equity	Explanation
1. Paid $200 cash for maintenance expense.	-200		-200	Paid for maintenance expense
2. The owner invested $4,000 cash in the business.	+ 4000			owner investment
3. Paid $2,400 cash for one year insurance.	- 2400 + 2400			
4. Received a telephone bill for $150, which will be paid later.		+ 150	+ 150	Recieved Phone bill
5. Purchased equipment worth $1,000 on account.	+ 1000	+ 1000		
6. Provided services and collected $4,200 cash.	+ 4200		4 200	Provided Services
7. Paid $500 towards the bank loan.	- 500	- 500		
8. Paid $50 interest related to the bank loan.	- 50		- 50	Paid for interest expense
9. Paid $700 of accounts payable.	- 700	- 700		

Debit entry first
Credit entry second

AP-5A (❺ ❻ ❼)

Dry Cleanest offers extensive dry cleaning services. Amy York started this company one year ago. The opening balances of the accounts on August 1, 2016 are shown below.

Cash	$980
Accounts Receivable	620
Prepaid Expenses	300
Machinery	3,800
Accounts Payable	1,020
Bank Loan	0
York, Capital	4,680

Required

a) Indicate whether assets, liabilities or owner's equity will increase or decrease and by how much, based on each transaction during August. Provide an explanation only if equity is affected. The first one has been done for you. Always ensure the accounting equation is balanced.

b) Record the transactions in the T-accounts.

	Assets	= Liabilities	+ Owner's Equity	Explanation
1. Borrowed $10,000 from the bank.	+10,000	+10,000		
2. Purchased machinery for $7,300 cash.				
3. Billed clients $2,950 for completed services. Due in 30 days.				
4. Paid $130 cash for regular maintenance on the machine.				
5. Collected $1,300 from clients who owed money.				
6. Paid 4 months' rent of $3,000 in advance.				
7. Recorded $1,600 of cash sales for the month.				
8. Paid $700 owed to a supplier.				

Dry Cleanest
Balance Sheet
As at August 31, 2016

ASSETS		LIABILITIES	

ASSETS

CASH

INCREASE	DECREASE
+	-

Opening

ACCOUNTS RECEIVABLE

INCREASE	DECREASE
+	-

Opening

PREPAID EXPENSES

INCREASE	DECREASE
+	-

Opening

MACHINERY

INCREASE	DECREASE
+	-

Opening

LIABILITIES

ACCOUNTS PAYABLE

DECREASE	INCREASE
-	+

Opening

BANK LOAN

DECREASE	INCREASE
-	+

Opening

OWNER'S EQUITY

YORK, CAPITAL

DECREASE	INCREASE
-	+

Opening

YORK, DRAWINGS

INCREASE	DECREASE
+	-

TOTAL ASSETS

TOTAL LIABILITES

OWNER'S EQUITY

Dry Cleanest
Income Statement
For the Month Ended August 31, 2016

REVENUE

SERVICE REVENUE

DECREASE	INCREASE
-	+

LESS EXPENSES

INSURANCE EXPENSE

INCREASE	DECREASE
+	-

MAINTENANCE EXPENSE

INCREASE	DECREASE
+	-

SALARIES EXPENSE

INCREASE	DECREASE
+	-

UTILITIES EXPENSE

INCREASE	DECREASE
+	-

TOTAL REVENUE

LESS TOTAL EXPENSES

NET INCOME (LOSS)

Chapter 2 Linking Personal Accounting to Business Accounting

Analysis

The owner of Dry Cleanest wants to withdraw cash from the business, but she does not want the net income to fall below $4,000. What is the maximum amount of cash she can withdraw in order to keep net income from falling below $4,000? Explain.

_____

_____

_____

_____

_____

AP-6A (❷ ❸)

Alex Limbo is the owner of Double Duplicator. The following is a list of Double Duplicator's accounts and balances as at March 31, 2016.

Cash	$4,700	Asset - 4700
Limbo, Capital	2,000	Equity 2300
Accounts Payable	5,000	Liability - 15,000
Unearned Revenue	2,000	Liability - 25,000
Prepaid Insurance	2,300	Assest - 37,000
Bank Loan	10,000	liability - 5000
Automobile Loan	18,000	liability - 2000
Prepaid Rent	5,000	asset - 10000
Equipment	25,000	asset - 18000 / 35,000

You owe more (note next to Accounts Payable)

Required

Prepare a balance sheet using the above information.

if ? doesnt balance in listings could be drawing

Double Duplicators Balance Sheet As at March 31, 2016			
Assets		Liabilitys	
Cash	$4,700	Accounts Payable	5,000
Prepaid insurance	2,300	Bank loan	10,000
Prepaid Rent	5,000	Automobile Loan	18000
Equipment	25,000	unearned Revenue	2,000
		Total Liabilities	35000
		Owner's Equity	
		Limbo capital	2000
Total Assets	37,000	Total liabilites and owner equity	37,000

look at accounts Recivebl if no end cash

AP-7A (❸ ❺ ❻ ❼)

Jessica Holmes recently started her own shoe repair business. Transactions for the first month of operations (June 2016) are as follows.

1. Jessica invested $10,000 cash in the business.
2. Paid two months of rent for $1,000 in advance.
3. Purchased store equipment worth $3,000 with cash.
4. Incurred business registration expenses, paid with $600 cash.
5. Paid travel expenses with $1,100 cash.
6. Received $2,300 cash from customers for shoe repair services performed during the month.
7. Provided shoe repair services worth $1,200 on account.
8. Paid $1,300 salary to an assistant.
9. Borrowed $3,000 cash from the bank.
10. Received $800 in bills for electricity, water and telephone, to be paid next month.
11. Jessica withdrew $500 cash for personal purposes.
12. Received $200 owing from a customer for service provided earlier this month.

Required

Record the above transactions on the T-account worksheet.

Holmes Shoe Repair
Balance Sheet
As at June 30, 2016

ASSETS		
INCREASE	DECREASE	
+	CASH	-

1. 10000	2. 1000
6. 2300	3. 3000
9. 3000	4. 600
12. 200	5. 1100
	8. 1300
	11. 500

INCREASE	DECREASE
+ ACCOUNTS RECEIVABLE -	
2. 1000	
1000	

INCREASE	DECREASE
+ PREPAID RENT -	
1000	

INCREASE	DECREASE
+	
EQUIPMENT	
3. 3000	3000
3000	

LIABILITIES		
DECREASE	INCREASE	
-	ACCOUNTS PAYABLE	+

800	10. 800

DECREASE	INCREASE
- BANK LOAN +	
	3000

OWNER'S EQUITY	
DECREASE	INCREASE
- HOLMES, CAPITAL +	

INCREASE	DECREASE
+ HOLMES, DRAWINGS -	

Holmes Shoe Repair
Income Statement
For the Month Ended June 30, 2016

REVENUE		
DECREASE	INCREASE	
-	SERVICE REVENUE	+

LESS EXPENSES

INCREASE	DECREASE
+ REGISTRATION AND LICENSES EXPENSE -	

INCREASE	DECREASE
+ RENT EXPENSE -	

INCREASE	DECREASE
+ SALARIES EXPENSE -	

INCREASE	DECREASE
+ TELEPHONE & UTILITIES EXPENSE -	

INCREASE	DECREASE
+ TRAVEL EXPENSE -	
1,100	

TOTAL ASSETS   13 000

TOTAL LIABILITES   3800   } 13000

OWNER'S EQUITY   9200

0 + 10,000 - 300 - 500 + 9,200

TOTAL REVENUE   ____

LESS TOTAL EXPENSES   ____

NET INCOME (LOSS)   ____

AP-8A (❸ ❺ ❻ ❼)

Sheila Abney opened a dormitory locator business called Dormitory Locators near a college campus. During the first month of operations, June 2016, Sheila had the following transactions.

1. Invested $10,000 of personal funds to start the business.
2. Incurred travel expenses for $650, which will be paid later.
3. Paid $700 cash for maintenance expense.
4. Received $5,000 cash for services provided to clients.
5. Paid $650 for the on account purchase in transaction 2.
6. Paid three months of office rent costing $1,500 in advance.
7. Incurred $300 of utilities expense, which will be paid next month.
8. Received $1,000 cash from a customer for services to be provided in two months.
9. Provided $1,200 in services for a customer who will pay later.
10. Recognized one month of office rent that was previously prepaid.
11. Sheila withdrew $1,000 cash for personal use.
12. Purchased second-hand car worth $10,000 for business use with cash.
13. Received $700 from the customer owing for the service provided earlier this month.

Required

Prepare a T-account worksheet.

Dormitory Locators
Balance Sheet
As at June 30, 2016

ASSETS		LIABILITIES	
INCREASE	DECREASE	DECREASE	INCREASE
+	-	-	+

Opening

Opening

INCREASE DECREASE
+   -

Opening

DECREASE INCREASE
-    +

Opening

INCREASE DECREASE
+   -

Opening

DECREASE INCREASE
-    +

Opening

INCREASE DECREASE
+   -

Opening

OWNER'S EQUITY

DECREASE INCREASE
-    +

Opening

INCREASE DECREASE
+   -

Dormitory Locators
Income Statement
For the Month Ended June 30, 2016

REVENUE	
DECREASE	INCREASE
-	+

LESS EXPENSES

INCREASE DECREASE
+   -

INCREASE DECREASE
+   -

INCREASE DECREASE
+   -

INCREASE DECREASE
+   -

INCREASE DECREASE
+   -

INCREASE DECREASE
+   -

TOTAL ASSETS _____
TOTAL LIABILITES _____ } _____
OWNER'S EQUITY _____

TOTAL REVENUE _____
LESS TOTAL EXPENSES _____
NET INCOME (LOSS) _____

AP-9A (❸ ❺ ❻ ❼)

Jeff Roberts Communications is a public relations firm. On April 30, 2016, the firm had the following ending balances:

Cash	$20,000
Prepaid Rent	10,000
Equipment	25,000
Accounts Payable	8,000
Roberts, Capital	47,000

During the month of May, the company completed the following transactions

1. Purchased $800 of office equipment on account.
2. Paid $6,000 to reduce amount owing to a supplier.
3. Received $5,000 cash from customers for services rendered.
4. Paid utilities bill for May with $700 cash.
5. Purchased a computer worth $1,500 on account.
6. Received a bill for $1,000 to be paid in July for advertisements placed in a national newspaper during the month of May to promote Jeff Roberts Communications.
7. Paid May's salaries with $1,900 cash.
8. Withdrew $3,000 cash for personal use.
9. Recognized $2,000 rent for May (which was previously prepaid).
10. Received $4,000 cash in advance for a contract to be completed in three months.

Required

Prepare the T-account worksheet.

Note: the ending balance for the month of April is the opening balance for the month of May.

Roberts Communications
Balance Sheet
As at May 31, 2016

ASSETS	
INCREASE	DECREASE
+	-
Opening	

INCREASE	DECREASE
+	-
Opening	

INCREASE	DECREASE
+	-
Opening	

LIABILITIES	
DECREASE	INCREASE
-	+
	Opening

DECREASE	INCREASE
-	+
	Opening

DECREASE	INCREASE
-	+
	Opening

OWNER'S EQUITY	
DECREASE	INCREASE
-	+
	Opening

INCREASE	DECREASE
+	-

TOTAL ASSETS _____

TOTAL LIABILITES _____ } _____

OWNER'S EQUITY _____

Roberts Communications
Income Statement
For the Month Ended May 31, 2016

REVENUE	
DECREASE	INCREASE
-	+

LESS EXPENSES

INCREASE	DECREASE
+	-

INCREASE	DECREASE
+	-

INCREASE	DECREASE
+	-

INCREASE	DECREASE
+	-

INCREASE	DECREASE

TOTAL REVENUE _____

LESS TOTAL EXPENSES _____

NET INCOME (LOSS) _____

AP-10A (❸ ❺ ❻ ❼)

On December 1, 2016, Sheila Ann established City Laundry. During the first month, the following transactions occurred

1. Sheila Ann deposited $15,000 into City Laundry's bank account.
2. Bought tables and chairs worth $1,000 with cash.
3. Received and paid utilities bill for $1,200 in cash.
4. Purchased washers and dryers worth $4,000; paying $2,000 cash with the remainder due in 30 days.
5. Purchased two additional dryers worth $1,100 from Marky Distributors, on account.
6. Received $4,000 cash for laundry services provided for the first half of the month.
7. Paid $900 cash for a one-year insurance policy.
8. Paid $1,000 cash for current month's rent.
9. Paid the amount owing to Marky Distributors.
10. Provided $3,500 of laundry services during the second half of the month for customers who will pay at a later date.
11. Paid employee salaries of $1,400.
12. Sheila withdrew $2,000 cash for personal use.
13. Recorded first month's insurance expense of $75.
14. Collected $3,000 cash from customers as payment on their account.
15. Received $2,000 cash in advance for services to be provided next year.

Required

Prepare the T-account worksheet.

City Laundry
Balance Sheet
As at December 31, 2016

ASSETS	
INCREASE	DECREASE
+	-

Opening

INCREASE	DECREASE
+	-

Opening

INCREASE	DECREASE
+	-

Opening

INCREASE	DECREASE
+	-

Opening

LIABILITIES	
DECREASE	INCREASE
-	+

Opening

DECREASE	INCREASE
-	+

Opening

OWNER'S EQUITY	
DECREASE	INCREASE
-	+

Opening

INCREASE	DECREASE
+	-

TOTAL ASSETS _____

TOTAL LIABILITES _____

OWNER'S EQUITY _____ } _____

City Laundry
Income Statement
For the Month Ended December 31, 2016

REVENUE	
DECREASE	INCREASE
-	+

LESS EXPENSES

INCREASE	DECREASE
+	-

INCREASE	DECREASE
+	-

INCREASE	DECREASE
+	-

INCREASE	DECREASE
+	-

INCREASE	DECREASE

INCREASE	DECREASE

TOTAL REVENUE _____

LESS TOTAL EXPENSES _____

NET INCOME (LOSS) _____

AP-11A (❸ ❺ ❻ ❼)

On April 1, 2016, Aaron Ragan established a business to manage rental properties. He had the following transactions during its first month of operations

1. Owner invested $20,000 cash into the business from his personal savings. This amount was deposited into the business Cash account.
2. Purchased $1,000 office equipment on account.
3. Received $5,000 cash for managing rental properties for a client.
4. Purchased furniture worth $350 on account.
5. Paid utilities bill of $400 for the month in cash.
6. Used a bank loan to purchase office furniture for $5,000.
7. Paid $500 cash to reduce the amount of bank loan principal.
8. Paid rent for the month with $1,800 cash.
9. Paid office staff salaries with $1,500 cash.
10. Withdrew $1,000 cash for personal use.
11. Provided $2,000 of services for a customer on account.

Required

Prepare the T-account worksheet.

Ragan Properties
Balance Sheet
As at April 30, 2016

ASSETS

INCREASE	DECREASE
+	-

Opening

INCREASE	DECREASE
+	-

Opening

INCREASE	DECREASE
+	-

Opening

LIABILITIES

DECREASE	INCREASE
-	+

Opening

DECREASE	INCREASE
-	+

Opening

OWNER'S EQUITY

DECREASE	INCREASE
-	+

Opening

INCREASE	DECREASE
+	-

TOTAL ASSETS _____

TOTAL LIABILITES _____

OWNER'S EQUITY _____   } _____

Ragan Properties
Income Statement
For the Month Ended April 30, 2016

REVENUE

DECREASE	INCREASE
-	+

LESS EXPENSES

INCREASE	DECREASE
+	-

INCREASE	DECREASE
+	-

INCREASE	DECREASE
+	-

INCREASE	DECREASE

INCREASE	DECREASE

INCREASE	DECREASE

TOTAL REVENUE _____

LESS TOTAL EXPENSES _____

NET INCOME (LOSS) _____

AP-12A (❸ ❺ ❻ ❼)

Edward James decided to start his own rent-a-car business after graduation, and recorded these transactions during the first month of operations (January 2016)

1. Edward invested $20,000 cash in the business.
2. Borrowed $20,000 from the bank.
3. Paid $35,000 cash for a new car to be used in the business.
4. Paid the principal of the bank loan with $2,000 cash.
5. Paid for $800 of maintenance expense with cash.
6. Paid monthly salaries for personnel with $1,000 cash.
7. Paid miscellaneous expenses with $300 cash.
8. Received $8,000 service revenue in cash for the month.
9. Received $600 of utilities bill for the month, payable next month.
10. Paid monthly interest on the bank loan with $200 cash.
11. Paid $1,500 of insurance for the next five months in advance.
12. Edward withdrew $1,000 cash for personal use.
13. Received $3,000 cash from customers for services to be provided next month.

Required

Prepare the T-account worksheet, income statement, statement of owner's equity, and balance sheet.

James' Rent-A-Car
Balance Sheet
As at January 31, 2016

ASSETS

INCREASE	DECREASE
+	CASH	-

INCREASE	DECREASE
+ PREPAID INSURANCE -	

INCREASE	DECREASE
+ AUTOMOBILE -	

LIABILITIES

DECREASE	INCREASE
- ACCOUNTS PAYABLE +	

DECREASE	INCREASE
- UNEARNED REVENUE +	

DECREASE	INCREASE
- BANK LOAN +	

OWNER'S EQUITY

DECREASE	INCREASE
- JAMES, CAPITAL +	

INCREASE	DECREASE
+ JAMES, DRAWINGS -	

TOTAL ASSETS _____

TOTAL LIABILITES _____ } _____

OWNER'S EQUITY _____

James' Rent-A-Car
Income Statement
For the Month Ended January 31, 2016

REVENUE

DECREASE	INCREASE
- SERVICE REVENUE +	

LESS EXPENSES

INCREASE	DECREASE
+ INTEREST EXPENSE -	

INCREASE	DECREASE
+ MAINTENANCE EXPENSE -	

INCREASE	DECREASE
+ MISCELLANEOUS EXPENSE -	

INCREASE	DECREASE
+ RENT EXPENSE -	

INCREASE	DECREASE
+ SALARIES EXPENSE -	

INCREASE	DECREASE
+ UTILITIES EXPENSE -	

TOTAL REVENUE _____

LESS TOTAL EXPENSES _____

NET INCOME (LOSS) _____

James' Rent-A-Car Income Statement For the Month Ended January 31, 2016		

James' Rent-A-Car Statement of Owner's Equity For the Month Ended January 31, 2016		

James' Rent-A-Car Balance Sheet As at January 31, 2016			

AP-13A (❸ ❺ ❻ ❼)

Jessica Cooper is the owner of Jessica's Computer Services. The balance sheet of Jessica's Computer Services on February 29, 2016 is shown below.

Jessica's Computer Services Balance Sheet As at February 29, 2016			
Assets		**Liabilities**	
Cash	$4,000	Accounts Payable	$3,000
Prepaid Insurance	3,000	Bank Loan	0
Furniture and Equipment	25,000		
		Total Liabilities	3,000
		Owner's Equity	
		Cooper, Capital	29,000
Total Assets	$32,000	**Total Liabilities and Owner's Equity**	$32,000

During March, the business engaged in the following transactions

1. Borrowed $20,000 from bank.
2. Purchased computer equipment for $5,000 cash.
3. Performed services for a customer and received $4,000 cash.
4. Purchased furniture for $1,000 on credit.
5. Paid $1,500 to a supplier for the amount owed.
6. Paid the following expenses in cash: salaries $1,000; rent, $1,500; and interest, $200.
7. Received a $900 utilities bill, due next month.
8. Withdrew $3,500 cash for personal use.
9. Received $1,000 cash in advance for services to be completed next month.

Required

Prepare the T-account worksheet, income statement, statement of owner's equity, and balance sheet.

Note: the ending balance for the month of February is the opening balance for the month of March.

Jessica's Computer Services
Balance Sheet
As at March 31, 2016

Jessica's Computer Services
Income Statement
For the Month Ended March 31, 2016

ASSETS				LIABILITIES	

ASSETS

INCREASE	DECREASE
+	-

Opening

INCREASE	DECREASE
+	-

Opening

INCREASE	DECREASE
+	-

Opening

LIABILITIES

DECREASE	INCREASE
-	+

Opening

DECREASE	INCREASE
-	+

Opening

DECREASE	INCREASE
-	+

Opening

OWNER'S EQUITY

DECREASE	INCREASE
-	+

Opening

INCREASE	DECREASE
+	-

REVENUE

DECREASE	INCREASE
-	+

LESS EXPENSES

INCREASE	DECREASE
+	-

INCREASE	DECREASE
+	-

INCREASE	DECREASE
+	-

INCREASE	DECREASE
+	-

INCREASE	DECREASE
+	-

INCREASE	DECREASE
+	-

TOTAL ASSETS _____

TOTAL LIABILITES _____ } _____

OWNER'S EQUITY _____

TOTAL REVENUE _____

LESS TOTAL EXPENSES _____

NET INCOME (LOSS) _____

Jessica's Computer Services Income Statement For the Month Ended March 31, 2016		

Jessica's Computer Services Statement of Owner's Equity For the Month Ended March 31, 2016		

Jessica's Computer Services Balance Sheet As at March 31, 2016			

——————————— **Application Questions Group B** ———————————

AP-1B (❸ ❺ ❻)

For each of the given transactions, determine the effect on owner's equity by placing a checkmark in the space provided.

		Increase	Decrease	No Effect
		Effect on Owner's Equity		
1.	Invested money in the business.			
2.	Purchased equipment on account.			
3.	Paid one third of the amount owing for the purchase of equipment.			
4.	Received cash for the services rendered.			
5.	Paid salaries for the month.			
6.	Withdrew cash for personal use.			
7.	Paid monthly rent.			
8.	Additional investment by the owner.			
9.	Provided services for a customer who will pay in two months.			
10.	Acquired land using cash.			

AP-2B (❸ ❺ ❻)

For the following transactions, fill in the table on the right with the two accounts related to each transaction.

		Account 1	Account 2
1.	Invested cash in the business.		
2.	Purchased service vehicle for business use.		
3.	Collected cash for services provided this week.		
4.	Provided services this week on credit.		
5.	Paid operating expenses in cash.		
6.	Received a bill for operating expenses incurred this week.		
7.	Received a loan from the bank.		
8.	Collected cash from a customer for services provided previously.		
9.	Paid monthly salaries to employees with cash.		
10.	Incurred operating expenses this week, to be paid next month.		
11.	Paid cash for expenses incurred previously.		
12.	Received cash in advance for the service to be performed next month.		

AP-3B (❶ ❹)

Match each term with the appropriate description.

    A   Merchandising

    B   Service

    C   Manufacturing

    D   Accounts Receivable

    E   Cash

_____ A law firm is an example of this type of business.

_____ This account represents the amount owed to the business by its customers for services preformed earlier.

_____ This type of business buys goods to resell to customers.

_____ An automaker is an example of this type of business.

_____ This is the most liquid asset.

AP-4B (❺ ❻)

Focus In had the following transactions during the month. Indicate whether assets, liabilities or owner's equity will increase or decrease and by how much, based on each transaction. Provide an explanation only if equity is affected. Always ensure the accounting equation is balanced.

	Assets	= Liabilities	+ Owner's Equity	Explanation
1. The owner invested $10,000 into the business.	+10,000		+10,000	Owner investment
2. Paid $3,300 cash for three months rent.				
3. Borrowed $5,000 from the bank.				
4. Purchased furniture for $2,500 on account.				
5. Paid $700 cash for advertising.				
6. Provided services and received $2,300 cash.				
7. Paid $400 for the furniture purchased earlier.				
8. The owner withdrew $2,500 for personal use.				
9. Used up one month of rent.				

AP-5B (❺ ❻ ❼)

Nelson's Auto Repair is a new business that started operations on April 1, 2016.

Required

a) Indicate whether assets, liabilities or owner's equity will increase or decrease and by how much, based on each transaction during April. Provide an explanation only if equity is affected. The first one has been done for you. Always ensure the accounting equation is balanced.

b) Record the transactions in the T-accounts.

	Assets =	Liabilities +	Owner's Equity	Explanation
1. Sam invested $8,000 cash into the business.	+8,000		+8,000	Owner invested cash
2. Sam invested $2,500 of equipment into the business.				
3. Purchased tools and supplies for $6,030 on credit.				
4. Paid 12 months of insurance in advance at $250/month.				
5. Made cash sales of $4,420 during the month.				
6. Received a utility bill for $370 for the month.				
7. Paid wages to employees of $5,800.				
8. Sam withdrew $2,000 cash from the business.				
9. Recorded one month of insurance used up.				
10. Received $2,000 cash for services to be provided in two months.				

Nelson's Auto Repair
Balance Sheet
As at April 30, 2016

ASSETS		LIABILITIES	
INCREASE	DECREASE	DECREASE	INCREASE
+ **CASH** -		- **ACCOUNTS PAYABLE** +	

INCREASE	DECREASE
+ **PREPAID INSURANCE** -	

DECREASE	INCREASE
- **UNEARNED REVENUE** +	

DECREASE	INCREASE
- **BANK LOAN** +	

OWNER'S EQUITY

DECREASE	INCREASE
- **NELSON, CAPITAL** +	

INCREASE	DECREASE
+ **TOOLS AND SUPPLIES** -	

INCREASE	DECREASE
+ **NELSON, DRAWINGS** -	

INCREASE	DECREASE
+ **EQUIPMENT** -	

TOTAL ASSETS _____

TOTAL LIABILITES _____ }
_____

OWNER'S EQUITY _____

Nelson's Auto Repair
Income Statement
For the Month Ended April 30, 2016

REVENUE	
DECREASE	INCREASE
- **SERVICE REVENUE** +	

LESS EXPENSES

INCREASE	DECREASE
+ **INSURANCE EXPENSE** -	

INCREASE	DECREASE
+ **SALARIES EXPENSE** -	

INCREASE	DECREASE
+ **UTILITIES EXPENSE** -	

INCREASE	DECREASE

TOTAL REVENUE _____

LESS TOTAL EXPENSES _____

SURPLUS (DEFICIT) _____

c) Complete the income statement, statement of owner's equity, and balance sheet for Nelson's Auto Repair.

AP-6B (❷)

Maya's Music offers music lessons to the public for all age groups. Maya Matlin is trying to assess her business by analyzing her balance sheet. Here are the accounts and balances of Maya's Music on October 31, 2016

Accounts Payable	$1,250
Bank Loan	55,000
Building	120,000
Cash	8,150
Instruments	21,650
Prepaid Insurance	3,600
Supplies	280
Unearned Revenue	1,000

Required

Prepare the balance sheet for Maya's Music.

Analysis

Maya thinks her business must be doing great because her capital is so high. Is the balance sheet a useful tool to analyze performance? What other information would you need to be able to assess whether Maya's Music has been performing well or not? Explain.

_____

_____

_____

_____

_____

_____

_____

_____

AP-7B (❸ ❺ ❻ ❼)

Brenda Darby recently started her own consulting business, and completed these transactions during the first month of operations (May 2016)

1. Brenda invested $10,700 cash in the business.
2. Purchased store furniture for $4,000 cash.
3. Paid $1,100 cash for two months of insurance in advance.
4. Incurred business registration expenses, paid with $640 cash.
5. Paid travel expenses with $1,200 cash.
6. Received $2,300 cash from clients for consulting services provided during the month.
7. Borrowed $3,800 cash from the bank.
8. Paid salary to an assistant with $790 cash.
9. Received bills of $900 for May's electricity, water and telephone, to be paid next month.
10. Brenda withdrew $700 cash for personal purposes.
11. Received $1,000 cash for a consulting service to be completed next month.

Required

Record the above transactions in the T-account worksheet.

Brenda's Shoe Repair
Balance Sheet
As at May 31, 2016

ASSETS

INCREASE	DECREASE
+	CASH	-

INCREASE	DECREASE
+	PREPAID INSURANCE	-

INCREASE	DECREASE
+ FURNITURE -

LIABILITIES

DECREASE	INCREASE
-	ACCOUNTS PAYABLE	+

DECREASE	INCREASE
-	UNEARNED REVENUE	+

DECREASE	INCREASE
-	BANK LOAN	+

OWNER'S EQUITY

DECREASE	INCREASE
-	DARBY, CAPITAL	+

INCREASE	DECREASE
+	DARBY, DRAWINGS	-

TOTAL ASSETS _____

TOTAL LIABILITES _____ } _____

OWNER'S EQUITY _____

Brenda's Shoe Repair
Income Statement
For the Month Ended May 31, 2016

REVENUE

DECREASE	INCREASE
-	SERVICE REVENUE	+

LESS EXPENSES

INCREASE	DECREASE
+	REGISTRATION EXPENSE	-

INCREASE	DECREASE
+	SALARIES EXPENSE	-

INCREASE	DECREASE
+	TRAVEL EXPENSE	-

INCREASE	DECREASE
+	UTILITIES EXPENSE	-

TOTAL REVENUE _____

LESS TOTAL EXPENSES _____

NET INCOME (LOSS) _____

AP-8B (❸ ❺ ❻ ❼)

Deep Drains is a plumbing company that started operations in February 2015. The company is fully owned by Emma Reno. Consider the following opening balances as of February 1, 2016.

Cash	$13,200
Prepaid Rent	5,700
Prepaid Insurance	4,000
Property, Plant & Equipment	38,200
Accounts Payable	3,300
Bank Loan	11,300
Reno, Capital	46,500

The following transactions were completed during the month of February

1. Purchased plane tickets for business travel with $1,140 cash.
2. Paid $3,300 cash to reduce the balance of accounts payable.
3. Purchased equipment worth $3,400 with a bank loan.
4. The owner invested $6,700 additional cash in the company.
5. Paid $850 cash for registration expenses.
6. Received a bill for $590 for utilities used during the month. The bill was immediately paid with cash.
7. Earned revenue and received $10,000 cash.
8. Recognized prepaid rent as an expense for $1,110.
9. Paid interest for the month of February with $50 cash.
10. Paid monthly salaries with for $4,100 cash.
11. The owner withdrew $2,500 cash from the business to pay for personal expenses.
12. Received $2,000 cash in advance for services to be rendered in three months.

Required

a) Using the information provided, record the opening balances in the T-accounts.

b) Record the transactions for the month of February in the T-accounts.

Deep Drains
Balance Sheet
As at February 29, 2016

ASSETS

INCREASE	DECREASE
+ CASH	-
Opening	

INCREASE	DECREASE
+ PREPAID RENT	-
Opening	

INCREASE	DECREASE
+ PREPAID INSURANCE	-
Opening	

INCREASE	DECREASE
+ EQUIPMENT	-
Opening	

LIABILITIES

DECREASE	INCREASE
- ACCOUNTS PAYABLE	+
	Opening

DECREASE	INCREASE
- UNEARNED REVENUE	+
	Opening

DECREASE	INCREASE
- BANK LOAN	+
	Opening

OWNER'S EQUITY

DECREASE	INCREASE
- RENO, CAPITAL	+
	Opening

INCREASE	DECREASE
+ RENO, DRAWINGS	-

Deep Drains
Income Statement
For the Month Ended February 29, 2016

REVENUE

DECREASE	INCREASE
- SERVICE REVENUE	+

LESS EXPENSES

INCREASE	DECREASE
+ INTEREST EXPENSE	-

INCREASE	DECREASE
+ REGISTRATION EXPENSE	-

INCREASE	DECREASE
+ RENT EXPENSE	-

INCREASE	DECREASE
+ SALARIES EXPENSE	-

INCREASE	DECREASE
+ TELEPHONE & UTILITIES EXPENSE	-

INCREASE	DECREASE
+ TRAVEL EXPENSE	-

TOTAL ASSETS _____

TOTAL LIABILITES _____ } _____

OWNER'S EQUITY _____

TOTAL REVENUE _____

LESS TOTAL EXPENSES _____

NET INCOME (LOSS) _____

AP-9B (❸ ❺ ❻ ❼)

Candace Harris Legal is a law firm. On July 31, 2016, the firm had the following ending balances

Cash	$18,500
Prepaid Insurance	9,200
Property, Plant & Equipment	22,300
Accounts Payable	8,100
Harris, Capital	41,900

During the month of August, the company completed the following transactions

1. Purchased $1,000 of office equipment on account.
2. Received $4,600 cash from customers for services rendered.
3. Paid $4,900 owing to a supplier.
4. Paid $570 utilities bill for August with cash.
5. Purchased a computer on account for $1,420.
6. Paid August's salaries with $3,600 cash.
7. Received a $1,150 bill to be paid in September for advertisements placed in a national newspaper during the month of August to promote Candace Harris Legal.
8. Performed services worth of $2,000 for customers on account.
9. Withdrew $3,200 cash for personal use.
10. Recognized $1,700 insurance for August (which was previously prepaid).
11. Received $1,500 cash for legal services to be done next month.
12. Collected all the balances owing from customers for services performed earlier.

Required

a) Using the information provided, record the opening balances in the T-accounts.
b) Record the transactions for the month of August in the T-accounts.

Candace Harris Legal
Balance Sheet
As at August 31, 2016

ASSETS		LIABILITIES	

CASH

INCREASE	DECREASE
+	-
Opening	

ACCOUNTS RECEIVABLE

INCREASE	DECREASE
+	-
Opening	

PREPAID INSURANCE

INCREASE	DECREASE
+	-
Opening	

EQUIPMENT

INCREASE	DECREASE
+	-
Opening	

ACCOUNTS PAYABLE

DECREASE	INCREASE
-	+
	Opening

UNEARNED REVENUE

DECREASE	INCREASE
-	+
	Opening

OWNER'S EQUITY

HARRIS, CAPITAL

DECREASE	INCREASE
-	+
	Opening

HARRIS, DRAWINGS

INCREASE	DECREASE
+	-

TOTAL ASSETS	
TOTAL LIABILITES	
OWNER'S EQUITY	

Candace Harris Legal
Income Statement
For the Month Ended August 31, 2016

REVENUE

SERVICE REVENUE

DECREASE	INCREASE
-	+

LESS EXPENSES

ADVERTISING EXPENSE

INCREASE	DECREASE
+	-

INSURANCE EXPENSE

INCREASE	DECREASE
+	-

SALARIES EXPENSE

INCREASE	DECREASE
+	-

UTILITIES EXPENSE

INCREASE	DECREASE
+	-

TOTAL REVENUE	
LESS TOTAL EXPENSES	
NET INCOME (LOSS)	

AP-10B (❸ ❺ ❻ ❼)

Christine Jacob is a financial planning consultant. During the month of February 2016, she completed the following transactions

1. Christine invested $8,000 cash in the business.
2. Paid $1,400 cash for February office rent.
3. Received $6,500 from a client for services rendered.
4. Paid $500 cash to Shell Super Service for gas purchases.
5. Paid $700 cash to Helpful Manpower Services for consulting services.
6. Purchased office equipment worth $900 on account.
7. Owner withdrew $2,500 cash for personal use.
8. Donated $800 cash to the National Red Cross.
9. Provided $2,000 worth of services for a client who paid on account.
10. Made partial payment of $500 on the equipment that was purchased on account.
11. Received $500 cash for services to be provided next month.
12. Collected $1,000 cash from a client who owed for services provided earlier in the month.

Required

Prepare the T-account worksheet.

Christine Jacob Financial Planning
Balance Sheet
As at February 29, 2016

ASSETS		LIABILITIES	
INCREASE	DECREASE	DECREASE	INCREASE
+	-	-	+

Opening

Opening

DECREASE	INCREASE
-	+

Opening

INCREASE	DECREASE
+	-

Opening

OWNER'S EQUITY

DECREASE	INCREASE
-	+

Opening

INCREASE	DECREASE
+	-

Opening

INCREASE	DECREASE
+	-

TOTAL ASSETS	_____
TOTAL LIABILITES	_____
OWNER'S EQUITY	_____

} _____

Christine Jacob Financial Planning
Income Statement
For the Month Ended February 29, 2016

REVENUE	
DECREASE	INCREASE
-	+

LESS EXPENSES

INCREASE	DECREASE
+	-

INCREASE	DECREASE
+	-

INCREASE	DECREASE
+	-

INCREASE	DECREASE
+	-

INCREASE	DECREASE
+	-

INCREASE	DECREASE

TOTAL REVENUE	_____
LESS TOTAL EXPENSES	_____
NET INCOME (LOSS)	_____

AP-11B (❸ ❺ ❻ ❼)

Troy Dale, an architect, opened his own business on March 1, 2016. During the month, he completed the following transactions related to his professional practice

1. Transferred $30,000 cash from personal bank account to the business account.
2. Provided services for $3,000 cash.
3. Purchased office and computer equipment worth $8,000 on account, which will be paid next month.
4. Paid $1,100 cash for meals and entertainment.
5. Paid insurance expense with $800 cash.
6. Performed services for clients for $4,000 on account.
7. Paid $600 cash for miscellaneous expenses.
8. Received utilities bill of $1,000, to be paid next month.
9. Paid $1,200 cash for office rent for the month of March.
10. Paid $1,000 salary to assistant.
11. Collected 50% of the balance owing from clients for services performed earlier this month.
12. Received $1,000 cash for services to be performed in three months.

Required

Prepare the T-account worksheet.

Dale Architect
Balance Sheet
As at March 31, 2016

ASSETS		LIABILITIES	
INCREASE	DECREASE	DECREASE	INCREASE
+	-	-	+

Opening

Opening

INCREASE	DECREASE	DECREASE	INCREASE
+	-	-	+

Opening

Opening

OWNER'S EQUITY

		DECREASE	INCREASE
		-	+

Opening

INCREASE	DECREASE
+	-

Opening

INCREASE	DECREASE
+	-

TOTAL ASSETS _____

TOTAL LIABILITES _____

OWNER'S EQUITY _____   } _____

Dale Architect
Income Statement
For the Month Ended March 31, 2016

REVENUE	
DECREASE	INCREASE
-	+

LESS EXPENSES

INCREASE	DECREASE
+	-

INCREASE	DECREASE
+	-

INCREASE	DECREASE
+	-

INCREASE	DECREASE
+	-

INCREASE	DECREASE
+	-

INCREASE	DECREASE
+	-

TOTAL REVENUE _____

LESS TOTAL EXPENSES _____

NET INCOME (LOSS) _____

AP-12B (❷ ❸ ❺ ❻ ❼)

Ella Kates founded Health-Plus Clinic as a medical clinic that started operations in January 2015. Consider the following opening balances as of January 1, 2016.

Cash	$15,000
Prepaid Rent	6,000
Prepaid Insurance	5,000
Equipment	30,000
Accounts Payable	3,000
Bank Loan	10,000
Kates, Capital	43,000

Transactions during the month of January

1. Purchased plane tickets with $1,500 cash. The plane tickets are to attend a business conference.
2. Paid $3,000 cash to reduce the balance of accounts payable.
3. The owner invested $5,000 additional cash in the company.
4. Purchased $4,000 worth of equipment with a bank loan.
5. Paid $1,000 cash for maintenance expenses.
6. Earned $15,000 revenue from patients on a cash basis.
7. Received a $900 bill for utilities used during the month. A cheque was issued to pay the bill immediately.
8. Recognized $2,000 of prepaid rent as an expense.
9. Paid $100 interest for the month with cash.
10. Paid $4,000 monthly salaries to all medical practitioners and clinic personnel.
11. Received $2,000 cash from one of its clients for services to be provided in March.
12. The owner withdrew $2,000 cash from the business to pay for personal expenses.

Required

Prepare the T-account worksheet, income statement, statement of owner's equity, and balance sheet.

Health-Plus Clinic
Balance Sheet
As at January 31, 2016

ASSETS	
INCREASE	DECREASE
+	-

Opening

INCREASE	DECREASE
+	-

Opening

INCREASE	DECREASE
+	-

Opening

INCREASE	DECREASE
+	-

Opening

LIABILITIES	
DECREASE	INCREASE
-	+

Opening

DECREASE	INCREASE
-	+

Opening

DECREASE	INCREASE
-	+

Opening

OWNER'S EQUITY	
DECREASE	INCREASE
-	+

Opening

INCREASE	DECREASE
+	-

TOTAL ASSETS _____

TOTAL LIABILITES _____ } _____

OWNER'S EQUITY _____

Health-Plus Clinic
Income Statement
For the Month Ended January 31, 2016

REVENUE	
DECREASE	INCREASE
-	+

LESS EXPENSES

INCREASE	DECREASE
+	-

INCREASE	DECREASE
+	-

INCREASE	DECREASE
+	-

INCREASE	DECREASE
+	-

INCREASE	DECREASE
+	-

INCREASE	DECREASE
+	-

TOTAL REVENUE _____

LESS TOTAL EXPENSES _____

NET INCOME (LOSS) _____

Health-Plus Clinic Income Statement For the Month Ended January 31, 2016		

Health-Plus Clinic Statement of Owner's Equity For the Month Ended January 31, 2016		

Health-Plus Clinic Balance Sheet As at January 31, 2016			

AP-13B (❷ ❸ ❺ ❻ ❼)

Helga Stiles operates a hairstyling company. The opening balances from Helga's Hairstyling's financial records on March 1, 2016 is shown below.

Cash	$18,000
Equipment	4,300
Supplies	1,200
Building	140,000
Accounts Payable	3,600
Bank Loan	100,000
Stiles, Capital	59,900

The following transactions took place during the month of March

1. $5,000 cash was taken from the bank account for a bank loan payment.
2. Paid down a portion of the accounts payable with $1,000 cash.
3. Recorded cash sales of $5,500.
4. Received a delivery of supplies for $2,000; invoice due in 30 days.
5. Received a bill of $650 for maintenance on equipment.
6. Paid salaries to employees with $1,500 cash.
7. Withdrew $2,000 cash from the business.
8. Provided services worth $2,000 for clients on account.
9. Received $1,500 cash in advance of service to be done next month.
10. Collected $1,000 of the amount owing from clients.

Required

a) Record the transactions in the T-accounts.

Helga's Hairstyling
Balance Sheet
As at March 31, 2016

ASSETS

INCREASE   DECREASE
+   CASH   -

Opening

INCREASE   DECREASE
- ACCOUNTS RECEIVABLE +

Opening

INCREASE   DECREASE
+   SUPPLIES   -

Opening

INCREASE   DECREASE
+   EQUIPMENT   -

Opening

INCREASE   DECREASE
+   BUILDING   -

Opening

LIABILITIES

DECREASE   INCREASE
-    ACCOUNTS PAYABLE   +

Opening

DECREASE   INCREASE
-    UNEARNED REVENUE   +

Opening

DECREASE   INCREASE
-        BANK LOAN   +

Opening

OWNER'S EQUITY

DECREASE   INCREASE
-      STILES, CAPITAL   +

Opening

INCREASE   DECREASE
+   STILES, DRAWINGS   -

Helga's Hairstyling
Income Statement
For the Month Ended March 31, 2016

REVENUE

DECREASE   INCREASE
-      SERVICE REVENUE   +

LESS EXPENSES

INCREASE   DECREASE
+   MAINTENANCE EXPENSE   -

INCREASE   DECREASE
+   SALARIES EXPENSE   -

INCREASE   DECREASE
+   TELEPHONE EXPENSE   -

INCREASE   DECREASE
+   UTILITIES EXPENSE   -

TOTAL ASSETS _____
TOTAL LIABILITES _____ } _____
OWNER'S EQUITY _____

TOTAL REVENUE _____
LESS TOTAL EXPENSES _____
NET INCOME (LOSS) _____

b) Complete the Income Statement and Balance Sheet for the end of March 2016.

AP-14B (❷)

Jake Martin operates a construction company as a sole proprietorship called Martin & Martin Construction. Jake is creating some financial records for the company for the end of April 2016 and has come up with the following account balances

Accounts Payable	$750
Accounts Receivable	350
Bank Loan	5,000
Cash	11,250
Storage Warehouse	36,200
Tools and Equipment	7,900
Vehicle	13,800

Required

Prepare the balance sheet for Martin and Martin Construction.

Case Study

CS-1 (❸ ❺ ❻ ❼)

Granyard Clockworks is a service company that repairs damaged watches and clocks. The company it is owned fully by John Granyard. John is fully liable for all activities of the business. In the most recent month (May 2016), Granyard Clockworks had the following transactions

1. John deposited $40,000 of additional cash into the business.
2. Borrowed $15,000 in cash from the bank.
3. Paid $3,500 cash for May's rent.
4. Paid $6,000 in salaries for May.
5. Performed services and earned $18,000 in cash.
6. Incurred telephone expenses of $500 (to be paid next month).
7. Performed services for a client for $3,000 on account.
8. Prepaid insurance for one year in the amount of $11,000.
9. Incurred maintenance expense of $1,000 (paid on account).
10. John withdrew $5,000 from the business for personal use.
11. Received $2,000 cash for repair services to be done in July.
12. Collected 80% of the $3,000 amount owing from a client for services performed earlier this month.

As at April 30, 2016, the ending account balances for Granyard Clockworks were

Cash	$50,000
Accounts Receivable	12,000
Prepaid Insurance	800
Equipment	40,000
Accounts Payable	2,000
Bank Loan	60,000
Granyard, Capital	40,800

Required

a) Complete the T-account worksheets for May 2016 (provided below).

Granyard Clockworks
Balance Sheet
As at May 31, 2016

Granyard Clockworks
Income Statement
For the Month Ended May 31, 2016

| ASSETS | | LIABILITIES | | REVENUE | |

ASSETS

INCREASE	DECREASE
+	CASH	-
Opening	

INCREASE	DECREASE
-	ACCOUNTS RECEIVABLE	+
Opening	

INCREASE	DECREASE
+	PREPAID INSURANCE	-
Opening	

INCREASE	DECREASE
+	EQUIPMENT	-
Opening	

LIABILITIES

DECREASE	INCREASE
-	ACCOUNTS PAYABLE	+
	Opening

DECREASE	INCREASE
-	UNEARNED REVENUE	+
	Opening

DECREASE	INCREASE
-	BANK LOAN	+
	Opening

OWNER'S EQUITY

DECREASE	INCREASE
-	GRANYARD, CAPITAL	+
	Opening

INCREASE	DECREASE
+	GRANYARD, DRAWINGS	-

REVENUE

DECREASE	INCREASE
-	REVENUE	+

LESS EXPENSES

INCREASE	DECREASE
+	MAINTENANCE EXPENSE	-

INCREASE	DECREASE
+	RENT EXPENSE	-

INCREASE	DECREASE
+	SALARIES EXPENSE	-

INCREASE	DECREASE
+	TELEPHONE EXPENSE	-

INCREASE	DECREASE

TOTAL ASSETS _____

TOTAL LIABILITES _____

OWNER'S EQUITY _____

TOTAL REVENUE _____

LESS TOTAL EXPENSES _____

NET INCOME (LOSS) _____

b) If John Granyard were to sell all of the assets of the business for cash on May 31, 2016 and use the cash to pay off the company's debts, what is the remaining amount? What does it represent?

_____

_____

_____

Chapter 3

THE ACCOUNTING FRAMEWORK

LEARNING OUTCOMES

❶ Describe the users of accounting information

❷ Describe the fields of accounting

❸ Compare the different forms of business organization

❹ Discuss the qualitative characteristics of financial information

❺ List and apply basic accounting assumptions and principles

❻ Illustrate the similarities and differences between ASPE and IFRS

❼ Explain the importance of ethics in accounting

AMEENGAGE *Access **ameengage.com** for integrated resources including tutorials, practice exercises, the digital textbook and more.*

───────── **Assessment Questions** ─────────

AS-1 (❶)

What is an internal user? What do internal users use financial information for?

_____

_____

_____

AS-2 (❶)

What is an external user? What do external users use financial information for?

_____

_____

_____

AS-3 (❷)

Briefly define financial accounting.

_____

_____

_____

AS-4 (❷)

Briefly define managerial accounting.

_____

_____

_____

AS-5 (❸)

What is a sole proprietorship? What is the title of a sole proprietorship's equity section?

_____

_____

AS-6 (❸)

Explain the concept of unlimited liability.

_____

_____

_____

AS-7 (❸)

What is a partnership?

_____

_____

AS-8 (❸)

What are the three types of partnerships that can be created?

_____

_____

_____

AS-9 (❸)

What is the difference between a general partnership and a limited partnership?

_____

_____

_____

_____

AS-10 (❸)

Describe a corporation.

_____

_____

_____

_____

AS-11 (❸)

What is a not-for-profit organization?

_____

_____

_____

AS-12 (❸)

Provide three examples of not-for-profit organizations.

_____

_____

AS-13 (❹ ❻)

Briefly define and explain GAAP. What are the two frameworks that have evolved from Canadian GAAP?

_____

_____

_____

_____

AS-14 (❹)

What are the four qualitative characteristics of effective and useful information?

_____

_____

AS-15 (❹)

Describe the characteristic of relevance.

_____

_____

_____

_____

AS-16 (❹)

Describe timeliness. Which characteristic is timeliness a component of?

_____

_____

_____

AS-17 (❹)

Describe the characteristic of reliability.

_____

_____

_____

_____

AS-18 (❹)

What is verifiability? Which characteristic is verifiability a component of?

_____

_____

_____

AS-19 (❹)

What is conservatism? Which characteristic is conservatism a component of?

_____

_____

_____

AS-20 (❹)

Describe the characteristic of understandability.

_____

_____

_____

AP-21 (④)

What is representational faithfulness? Which characteristic is representational faithfulness a component of?

_____

_____

_____

AP-22 (④)

What is neutrality? Neutrality is a component of which characteristic?

_____

_____

_____

AS-23 (④)

Describe the characteristic of comparability.

_____

_____

_____

AS-24 (④)

What is a trade-off? Provide an example of a commonly discussed trade-off of qualitative characteristics.

_____

_____

AS-25 (⑤)

Describe the business entity assumption.

_____

_____

AS-26 (5)

Describe the going concern assumption.

_____

_____

_____

AS-27 (5)

Describe the monetary unit assumption.

_____

_____

AS-28 (5)

Describe the principle of measurement.

_____

_____

_____

AS-29 (5)

Describe the time period concept.

_____

_____

_____

AS-30 (5)

Describe the principle of revenue recognition.

_____

_____

_____

_____

AS-31 (❺)

Describe the principle of expense recognition.

_____

_____

_____

AS-32 (❺)

Describe the principle of consistency.

_____

_____

AS-33 (❺)

Describe the principle of materiality.

_____

_____

_____

AS-34 (❺)

Describe the principle of disclosure.

_____

_____

_____

AS-35 (❻)

What is ASPE and which forms of organization can adhere to it?

_____

_____

_____

AS-36 (❻)

What is IFRS and which forms of organization can adhere to it?

_____

_____

_____

_____

AS-37 (❼)

List two ethical standards for accountants.

_____

_____

_____

_____

Application Questions Group A

AP-1A (❸)

Match each form of an organization with the appropriate description.

A	Sole proprietorship
B	Partnership
C	Corporation
D	Not-for-Profit Organization

_D_   This type of organization usually does not have an identifiable owner.   *improves society in some way*

_B_   There are two types: one that limits the liability of the owners and one that does not.   *owned two or more*

_A_   A business operated by a single owner.

_C_   This type of business often elects a board of directors.

AP-2A (❹ ❺)

Match each of the following basic ASPE and IFRS concepts and principles to the appropriate description in the table below.

- Business entity assumption
- Going concern assumption
- Monetary unit assumption
- Revenue recognition
- Measurement
- Conservatism

Term (fill in)	Description
Conservatism	The accountant should exercise the option that results in a lower balance of assets, lower net income or a higher balance of debt.
revenue Recognition	Sales must be recorded when ownership of a good transfers from the seller to the buyer.
going concern assumption	Assumes that a business will continue to operate into the foreseeable future.
monetary unit assumption	Financial reports should be expressed in a single currency.
Business entity assumption	Accounting for a business must be kept separate from the personal affairs of its owner or any other business.
measurment	Purchases must be recorded at their values on the date of purchase.

AP-3A (❹)

Hawkton Publishing Corporation is a publisher of math textbooks. The company is a large, well-known publicly traded corporation with thousands of shareholders. It produces financial statements on an annual basis. The most recent financial statements (for the year ended December 31, 2016) showed comparative balances for 2016 and 2015. The 2016 balances were derived using accrual-based accounting whereas the 2015 balances were derived using cash-based accounting.

Which characteristic(s) of information did Hawkton fail to represent? Explain.

_____

_____

_____

_____

_____

_____

_____

_____

AP-4A (❺)

Alton Floral is a new company that operates in the gardening industry. The owner of the company has decided not to hire an accountant but instead maintain the accounting records on his own. He has included his employees as assets on the balance sheet in the account "Human Resources." He has valued them at the present value of their future salaries on the balance sheet. Also, the financial statements are not supported by notes explaining some of the figures.

Which of the basic accounting principles and/or assumptions has Alton Floral violated? Explain.

_____

_____

_____

_____

AP-5A (❺)

Suppose that a company has changed its policy for depreciation from one year to the next. An employee in the accounting department addressed this change with the owner. The employee asked the owner why the accounting policy was changed and why the reasoning for the change was not disclosed in the financial statements. The owner replied, "IFRS gives you the option to use a different depreciation method from one year to the next. We also are not required to explain our choices." Is the owner correct in his reasoning? Explain.

_____

_____

_____

_____

_____

AP-6A (❺)

Heggy Company, a privately owned corporation, is producing cellphone accessories. It relies on ASPE to prepare its financial statements. The company is doing well and is planning to expand its product line. Assume you are a newly hired accountant for Heggy and you are reviewing the company's financial statements.

You realize that the company recently purchased machinery for $700,000 as part of its expansion strategy. After a long negotiation, Heggy's purchasing department was able to find the best deal which was well below the market value of $740,000. The machinery has been recorded in Heggy's books at $740,000.

Also, Heggy Company has paid $15,000 for the cost of the plant's insurance for the upcoming year and expensed the whole amount. Heggy believes that this expensing would be an effective cost-saving strategy in the long run as it will avoid the extra bookkeeping associated with updating the prepaid insurance account.

Has Heggy Company violated any of the basic concepts and principles of ASPE? Explain.

_____

_____

_____

_____

_____

_____

_____

_____

_____

AP-7A (❺)

Tasai Corporation is a Canadian manufacturer of wings for commercial aircrafts. Tasai is a large public company which is famous for the unique design of its wings. You are appointed as its audit manager.

As you go through the financial statements you notice, on the income statement, the company has set aside one line item under revenue which shows an amount of 800,000 in Brazilian currency (reals). In the notes related to this item, it is indicated that the company has completed a project in Brazil; and due to the large amount of foreign exchange loss, the company has decided to report the figure in reals. The accounting department thinks this practice is permitted under IFRS as long as it is clearly explained in the notes.

You also note this year's travel expense is significantly larger than last year's. As part of the audit procedures, you examine travel documents and invoices and realize that one of the owners included his personal travel expenses as part of his business-related travels. In addition, Tasai Corporation has changed one of its accounting policies and disclosed the nature, impact and reason of this change in the notes.

As the audit manager, discuss if any accounting assumptions or principles have been violated.

_____

_____

_____

_____

_____

_____

_____

_____

_____

_____

_____

AP-8A (❹ ❺)

Sood Supplies is in the business of selling electronic components to computer manufacturers. Sood Supplies' financial statements are issued on an annual basis for a large number of users such as investors and the bank. The financial reporting of the company is based on ASPE.

Prior to the issuance of the current year's financial statements, the head of engineering and the accounting manager had a discussion regarding the amount of warranty expense that should be recognized for the year. The head of engineering believes that only 2% of sales needs to be calculated as a provision for the warranty expense while the accounting manager believes that 6% of sales should be recorded as an expense. The accounting manager argues that the 6% is estimated based on historical trends of the company and the industry; however, the engineering department claims that its new method of quality assurance will reduce the future warranty expenses.The engineering department could not submit any documents to support the claim. Eventually, the accounting manager decides to trust the engineering department and uses the 2% calculation.

Do you believe any of the accounting principles or qualitative characteristics have been violated by Sood Supplies? Explain.

_____

_____

_____

_____

_____

_____

_____

_____

_____

_____

AP-9A (❹)

Identify the qualitative characteristic of financial information that has been violated in each of the following scenarios.

a) Thorn Company has reported several gains for the period, but has not provided any explanation or proof of how they occurred.

_____

b) Due to recent layoffs, Monte Carlo Ltd. was not able to complete and issue its 2015 financial statements and accompanying notes. The information was instead included with the 2016 financial report in the following year.

_____

c) To value inventory, Toland and Sons uses a different accounting policy from the rest of the companies in the same industry. There is no justification for the use of this accounting policy in the notes to the financial statements.

_____

d) Eris Laboratories used many uncommon medical terms and scientific language in the notes to the financial statements. This language was not explained anywhere else.

_____

e) A bank decided not to grant a loan to Mida Ltd. after a customer filed a substantial lawsuit. Mida Ltd. did not include any mention of the lawsuit in the financial statements or in the notes to the financial statements.

_____

AP-10A (❺)

Identify the accounting principle or concept that has been violated in each of the following scenarios.

a) Bill Co. purchased a two-year insurance policy and expensed the entire amount in period of purchase.

_Expense Recognition_____

b) Charlie Co. listed inventory at its market value of $31,000 on the balance sheet, even though it was purchased for $20,000.

_Measurment_____

c) Percy Co. did not include the details of its property, plant, and equipment, even though this information is relevant to the users.

_Disclousre_____

d) Fred Co. made a sale on the last day of the accounting period. The customer paid for the item in the following month, so this sale was included in the next period's financial statements.

e) George Co. has plans to restructure its operations next year and will sell off about half of the business. This information was not included in the notes to the financial statements because it does not affect the current financial information.

f) Ron Co. applied a certain accounting policy which allowed the company to report higher assets and net income. A different accounting policy was available which would have resulted in a lower balance of assets and net income.

g) Ginny Co. changed the accounting policy used to value property, plant, and equipment after using a different policy for 10 years. There was no justification for the change.

AP-11A (④ ⑤)

For each accounting principle or assumption, indicate which one of the four characteristics of information it is most related to.

Characteristic (fill in)	Basic Concept or Principle
	Monetary Unit Assumption
	Objectivity Principle
	Measurement
	Consistency
	Materiality
	Disclosure

AP-12A (❻)

Heath Trek Company has four different asset accounts: property, plant & equipment, accounts receivable, short-term investments and cash. Shown below is the average amount of time required to turn each asset into cash.

Asset	Cash Turnover Time (in days)
Property, plant & equipment	5,480
Accounts receivable	60
Short-term investments	120
Cash	N/A

Required

a) If Heath Trek's financial statements were prepared using ASPE, in which order will the assets be presented on the balance sheet?

CASh

Accounts Recievable

Short-term investments

Property, Plant & equipment

b) If Heath Trek's financial statements were prepared using IFRS instead, in which order will the assets be presented on the balance sheet?

Property, Plant & equipment

Short-term investments

Accounts Recievable

CASh

AP-13A (❼)

Joan is a senior accountant who recently agreed to give a professional review of the financial statements of Baker Consulting Inc. Joan is a personal friend of the president of this company and has an outstanding loan to the company. Baker Consulting Inc. is having cash flow issues which may force it to lay off some employees, but the owner has assured Joan that everything is under control and that the company is about to land several large sales contracts. He also explained that if the financial statements revealed any issues, the company would lose potential customers and suppliers. After some discussion, Joan decided to issue a positive opinion of the financial statements and not disclose any issues. Has Joan violated any ethical standards of accounting? Discuss.

Joan has violated neutrality. Since they are a friend of the president of the company. Conflict of intrest. Joan has also violated verif

—— Application Questions Group B ——

AP-1B (❹)

Match each of the following characteristics of financial information to the appropriate description in the table below.

- Relevance
- Reliability
- Understandability
- Comparability
- Timeliness
- Verifiability

Term (fill in)	Description
	Information is free from material error and bias
	A component of relevance
	The financial statements of a company should be prepared in a similar way year after year
	A component of reliability
	Financial information can be comprehended by users with a reasonable knowledge of the business
	All information for decision making is present in the financial statements

AP-2B (❺)

Match each of the following basic concepts and principles to the appropriate description in the table below.

- Time period concept
- Expense recognition
- Consistency
- Materiality
- Disclosure

Term (fill in)	Description
	Accounting takes place over specific fiscal periods.
	Prevents people from changing accounting methods for the sole purpose of manipulating figures on the financial statements.
	The costs of doing business must be recorded in (or matched to) the same accounting period as the revenues which they helped to generate.
	Any and all information that affects the full understanding of a company's financial statements must be included with the financial statements.
	Accountants should use GAAP except when doing so would be more expensive or complicated relative to the value of the transaction.

AP-3B (❹)

Reflex Sports Inc. is a manufacturer of sports equipment for children. It relies on IFRS to prepare its financial statements. The nature of its accounting transactions can be quite complex at times. However, the financial statements have no additional notes to support them. The company also does not keep all invoices on record to back up expense amounts reported on the financial statements. Which characteristic(s) of information did Reflex Sports fail to represent? Explain.

_____

_____

_____

_____

_____

AP-4B (❺)

Mackenzie Attire is currently preparing its annual financial statements for the past fiscal year. The company uses cash-based accounting. The company's policy includes receiving payment for its services well before the service is performed. The owner recently purchased a fish tank for his home and the transaction included a decrease to Mackenzie Attire's equity (an expense was recorded in the income statement). The value of inventory is adjusted annually to be stated at fair value. Which of the basic accounting principles and/or assumptions has Mackenzie Attire violated? Explain.

_____

_____

_____

_____

_____

_____

_____

_____

_____

AP-5B (⑤)

IMORI is large publicly traded construction company. IMORI has entered into a three-year construction contract with Siano Company. Siano paid upfront for the full value of the contract, and IMORI has recorded the entire amount as revenue immediately. Explain the accounting principle that has been violated.

_____

_____

_____

_____

_____

_____

AP-6B (⑤)

Blossoma Inc. is a private supplier of organic beauty products. The company prepares its financial statements in compliance with ASPE. Due to recent economic difficulties, Blossoma Inc. had to file for bankruptcy. The company's property, plant and equipment are listed on the balance sheet at what they could be sold for, which is lower than their original purchase price. Has Blossoma Inc. violated any of the basic accounting principles and/or assumptions? Explain.

_____

_____

_____

_____

_____

_____

AP-7B (❹ ❺)

Team Toro Inc , a unionized company, is in the business of planning and hosting events for various colleges and universities. Its service includes a wide range of activities such as decor and design, accommodation for guests, and catering. At the end of the year, prior to issuance of its financial statements, the head of the accounting department realized that the union was not able to negotiate a collective agreement with the board and it is planning to go on strike legally at the beginning of next year. After discussing the matter with the board members, the accounting manager decides not to disclose this issue since the strike will happen next year and this year's financial statements are not affected. In addition, the accounting manager thinks the disclosure may have an unnecessarily negative impact on the company's financial position and reputation in the market. Discuss whether any accounting principles or qualitative characteristics have been violated.

AP-8B (❹ ❺)

Imzy Company is a small private company that relies on ASPE to prepare financial statements. During the year, the company has experienced a number of tax disputes with the government. This issue was not included in the notes to the financial statements as the bookkeeper believes this type of tax dispute is common for a small business. In addition, the bookkeeper does not keep purchase invoices because he thinks the costs of holding all those receipts would outweigh their benefits for a small company. Explain whether any accounting principles or qualitative characteristics have been violated by the bookkeeper.

_____

_____

_____

_____

_____

_____

_____

_____

AP-9B (❹)

Identify the qualitative characteristic that describes each of the following scenarios.

a) Titus Group presented its financial information in a way that allowed informed users to comprehend the meaning of the information.

_____

b) Hunt Manufacturing included references to source documents to explain where certain financial figures originated from.

_____

c) Arloc Games Company uses the same accounting methods each year when preparing the financial statements.

_____

d) Crypt Technologies reported all financial information that could have an impact on the decisions of the users of the financial statements.

_____

AP-10B (5)

Identify the accounting principle that describes each of the following scenarios.

a) Pangea Construction recorded revenue for a five-year construction contract evenly over the five years.

_____

b) Athena Spa has committed to opening a second location in the next eight months. Details regarding this expansion were included in the financial information.

_____

c) Zeus Electric used the same accounting policy for depreciation as last year, even though it could have reported a higher net income by switching to a different method.

_____

d) Neptune Water Supply grouped small assets such as pens, staplers, and notepads together as office supplies because the cost of separating them outweighed the benefits.

_____

e) Hermes Athletics had its land appraised at $60,000. The land was listed on the balance sheet at $50,000 which was the price originally paid for it.

_____

f) Hera Consulting prepaid cash for its annual insurance policy. The amount was expensed on a monthly basis as it was used up.

_____

AP-11B (❺ ❻)

The accountant for GYC Consultants is facing an important accounting decision. The company recently incurred a material transaction that can be accounted for in three different ways (options A, B, and C). The effect on the company's net income and total assets for each option is shown below. Under ASPE, which option should GYC's accountant choose to account for the transaction and why?

Effect on	Option A	Option B	Option C
Net Income	+$5,200	+$4,100	+$4,600
Total Assets	+$1,100	+$900	+$1,000

AP-12B (❻)

Starks Instruments Company has five different asset accounts: property, plant & equipment, inventory, cash, accounts receivable and prepaid expenses. Shown below is the level of liquidity of each asset.

Assset	Liquidity Level
Property, plant & equipment	Very low
Inventory	Medium
Cash	Very high
Accounts receivable	High
Prepaid expenses	Low

Required

a) If Starks Instruments Company's financial statements were prepared using APSE, in which order will the assets be presented on the balance sheet?

---

b) If Starks Instruments Company's financial statements were prepared using IFRS instead, in which order will the assets be presented on the balance sheet?

_____

_____

_____

AP-13B (❼)

Marcus is the senior accountant for a small accounting firm. He is currently performing the year-end audit of a particular client: Le Jardin Oak Inc. (LJO), a manufacturer of high quality furniture. After Marcus met with Le Jardin's CEO in a restaurant, the CEO noticed that Le Jardin's financial records, which were provided to Marcus, were scattered on the ground. The CEO was extremely disappointed because the records were meant for internal use only. Which ethical standard did Marcus violate? Explain.

_____

_____

_____

_____

_____

Case Study

CS-1 (❹ ❺)

Gordon is the majority owner of Gordon House Restaurant (GHR), a publicly traded chain of family restaurants. The company is owned by hundreds of shareholders who expect timely, reliable and accurate financial statements. GHR produces financial statements periodically. It is now June 15, 2016. The accountant has prepared the financial statements for the eight-month period ended May 31, 2016. The previous financial statements covered a one-year period.

GHR was recently sued by another company, the details of which are not disclosed in the financial statements. The court proceedings have not yet ended. However, as of May 31, 2016, it was believed that GHR is very likely to lose the case and eventually pay a significant amount in damages to the plaintiff.

Also consider the following additional information:

- Cash disbursements are not supported by additional source documents
- GHR has recognized revenue in a different accounting period than the costs associated with producing that revenue

Required

a) Which of the four qualitative characteristics of financial information has GHR failed to apply? Explain.

_____

_____

_____

_____

_____

_____

_____

_____

_____

_____

_____

_____

_____

_____

b) Which of the basic concepts and principles of accounting has GHR violated? Explain.

_____

_____

_____

_____

_____

_____

_____

_____

_____

_____

Chapter 4

THE ACCOUNTING CYCLE: JOURNALS AND LEDGERS

LEARNING OUTCOMES

❶ Distinguish between debits and credits

❷ Describe the accounting cycle

❸ Explain how to analyze a transaction

❹ Record transactions in the general journal

❺ Post journal entries to the general ledger

❻ Prepare a trial balance

AMEENGAGE™ *Access ameengage.com for integrated resources including tutorials, practice exercises, the digital textbook and more.*

Assessment Questions

AS-1 (❶)

What does the term debit refer to?

_____

_____

AS-2 (❶)

True or False: A credit will always be an increase to any account.

_____

_____

AS-3 (❶)

Which three types of accounts use the debit side of the T-account to increase their value?

_____

_____

AS-4 (❶)

Which three types of accounts use the credit side of the T-account to increase their value?

_____

_____

AS-5 (❶)

What is the normal balance of an asset?

_____

_____

AS-6 (❶)

What is the normal balance of a liability?

_____

_____

AS-7 (❹)

Explain the purpose of a chart of accounts.

_____

_____

_____

AS-8 (❷ ❸ ❹ ❺ ❻)

List and describe the first four steps of the accounting cycle.

_____

_____

_____

_____

AS-9 (❹)

In the accounting cycle, what is the purpose of creating journals?

_____

_____

_____

AS-10 (❺)

In the accounting cycle, what is the purpose of the general ledger?

_____

_____

_____

AS-11 (❻)

In the accounting cycle, what is the purpose of the trial balance?

_____

_____

_____

AS-12 (❹)

In the journal, what information will be entered in the PR (posting reference) column?

_____

_____

_____

AS-13 (❺)

What is the relationship between the closing balance and the opening balance for an asset?

_____

_____

_____

AS-14 (❻)

If the trial balance balances, were all transactions correctly recorded? Explain.

_____

_____

_____

Application Questions Group A

AP-1A (❶ ❸)

Esteem Fitness provides fitness services for its customers. During June 2016, Esteem Fitness had the following transactions.

Jun 1   Sold one-month memberships to customers for $4,500 on account.

Jun 3   Received a telephone bill for $250 which will be paid next month.

Jun 6   Paid an employee's salary of $1,200.

Jun 10   Received $3,000 cash from customers paying in advance for upcoming one-year memberships.

Jun 15   Paid $6,000 cash in advance for six months of rent.

Jun 20   Received a $10,000 loan from the bank.

Jun 26   Purchased equipment with $8,000 cash.

Required

Complete the table to analyze each transaction.

	Account Name	Category	Increase or Decrease	Debit or Credit
Jun 1				
Jun 3				
Jun 6				
Jun 10				
Jun 15				
Jun 20				
Jun 26				

AP-2A (❶ ❸)

Have-a-Bash, owned by Finn Tymes, provides party planning services. During October 2016, Have-a-Bash had the following transactions.

Oct 1   Finn invested $5,000 cash into the business.

Oct 2   Planned a party for a customer and received $900 cash.

Oct 4   Received a $500 utilities bill which will be paid later.

Oct 10   Paid $200 cash for maintenance for the month.

Oct 12   Paid $400 towards the bank loan principal.

Oct 18   Received cash from a customer who owed $1,100.

Oct 22   Paid the utilities bill received earlier.

Oct 28   Paid $3,000 cash in advance for office rent.

Required

Complete the table to analyze each transaction.

	Account Name	Category	Increase or Decrease	Debit or Credit
Oct 1				
Oct 2				
Oct 4				
Oct 10				
Oct 12				
Oct 18				
Oct 22				
Oct 28				

AP-3A (❶)

For the following list of accounts, indicate which side of the T-account causes an increase or decrease. The first account has been done for you.

Account	Debit	Credit
Cash	Increase	Decrease
Advertising Expense		
Service Revenue		
Unearned Revenue		
Accounts Receivable		
Accounts Payable		
Owner's Capital		
Owner's Drawings		
Prepaid Rent		
Rent Expense		

AP-4A (❸ ❹)

Kick-off Sports Training helps train children in various sporting activities. During May 2016, the following transactions took place.

May 3   Received maintenance bill for $500 which will be paid next month.

May 3   Received $2,750 cash for training services provided.

May 4   Borrowed $4,000 cash from the bank.

May 4   Received $220 from a customer who owed money on training services already provided.

May 10   Prepaid $1,200 cash for insurance for one year.

May 10   Paid telephone expenses of $150 for the month with cash.

May 11   Paid $700 cash to reduce the amount owed to a supplier.

May 15   Paid $25 interest on the bank loan.

Required

Prepare the journal entries for the above transactions.

JOURNAL				Page 1
Date	Account Title and Explanation	PR	Debit	Credit

JOURNAL					Page 1
Date	Account Title and Explanation	PR	Debit	Credit	

AP-5A (❸ ❹)

Rejuvenation Spa is a sole proprietorship owned by Claire Sawyer. The company provides a relaxing retreat for people wishing to relax and unwind. During the month of July 2016, the following transactions took place.

July 3	Provided services to a customer on account worth $3,600.
July 4	Borrowed $2,000 cash from the bank.
July 6	Provided services to a customer and received cash of $2,400.
July 10	Received the telephone bill for $250 which will be paid later.
July 11	Paid $600 cash to reduce the amount owed to a supplier.
July 15	Collected $1,800 cash from customers owing on account.
July 20	Paid the telephone bill from July 10.
July 21	Paid a portion of bank loan principal with $1,500 cash.
July 31	Paid salaries for the month with $1,600 cash.
July 31	Purchased equipment for $1,900 which will be paid later.

Required

Prepare the journal entries for the above transactions.

JOURNAL				Page 1
Date	Account Title and Explanation	PR	Debit	Credit

AP-6A (❸ ❹)

Noel Dy opened an automobile repair shop. The following transactions occurred during the month of March 2016.

Mar 1   Noel Dy invested $10,000 cash and $8,000 worth of equipment in the business.

Mar 3   Paid $1,000 cash to rent the shop space.

Mar 5   Purchased $1,200 worth of shop tools using cash.

Mar 7   Received $2,000 cash for repair work done for MJ Gonzales.

Mar 8   Purchased additional shop tools from Adrian Cruz worth $1,000, on account.

Mar 15   Paid half of the amount due to Adrian Cruz with cash.

Mar 18   Paid $200 cash to local publication for advertising.

Mar 19   Paid $1,000 of salaries with cash.

Mar 20   Noel Dy withdrew $1,500 cash for personal use.

Mar 29   Bought $1,000 worth of chairs and tables for the shop on account.

Mar 31   Noel Dy personally invested additional equipment worth $5,000 for business use.

Mar 31   Received $3,000 cash from various customers for repairs done on their automobiles.

Required

Prepare journal entries for the above transactions.

JOURNAL				Page 1
Date	**Account Title and Explanation**	**PR**	**Debit**	**Credit**

JOURNAL				Page 1
Date	Account Title and Explanation	PR	Debit	Credit

AP-7A (❸ ❹ ❺ ❻)

Thomas Topology provides surveying services to construction companies and municipalities. The company is owned and operated by Thomas Edwards. The closing balances at the end of March 2016 and the chart of accounts are shown below.

Thomas Topology Balance Sheet As at March 31, 2016			
Assets		**Liabilities**	
Cash	$22,000	Accounts Payable	$10,500
Accounts Receivable	9,000	Unearned Revenue	4,500
Equipment	8,000	Bank Loan	6,000
		Total Liabilities	21,000
		Owner's Equity	
		Edwards, Capital	18,000
Total Assets	$39,000	**Total Liabilities & Owner's Equity**	$39,000

Account Description	Account #
ASSETS	
Cash	101
Accounts Receivable	105
Prepaid Insurance	110
Equipment	120
LIABILITIES	
Accounts Payable	200
Unearned Revenue	210
Bank Loan	215
OWNER'S EQUITY	
Edwards, Capital	300
Edwards, Drawings	310

Account Description	Account #
REVENUE	
Service Revenue	400
EXPENSES	
Insurance Expense	515
Interest Expense	520
Rent Expense	540
Salaries Expense	545
Telephone Expense	550
Travel Expense	555

During the month of April, Thomas Topology had the following transactions.

Apr 1   Purchased office equipment on account worth $7,000.

Apr 2   Received $25,000 cash for services provided.

Apr 3   Paid $1,000 cash for April's rent.

Apr 4   Prepaid $1,200 for insurance for one year.

Apr 10   Paid $200 cash to reduce the balance of accounts payable.

Apr 14   Paid $8,000 cash for employee's salaries.

Apr 22   Received telephone bill for $250 which will be paid next month.

Apr 24   Recorded travel expenses for $8,000 to be paid next month.

Apr 30   Paid $4,550 to bank for the bank loan principal and interest. Interest was $50 and
          remainder was principal.

Required

a) Prepare the journal entries for the month of April.

b) Post the journal entries to the ledger accounts.

c) Prepare a trial balance at the end of April.

JOURNAL				Page 1
Date	Account Title and Explanation	PR	Debit	Credit

JOURNAL				Page 1
Date	**Account Title and Explanation**	**PR**	**Debit**	**Credit**

Account: Cash   GL No:

Date	**Description**	**PR**	**DR**	**CR**	**Balance**	

Account: GL No:

Date	**Description**	**PR**	**DR**	**CR**	**Balance**	

Account:					GL No:	
Date	Description	PR	DR	CR	Balance	

Account:					GL No:	
Date	Description	PR	DR	CR	Balance	

Account:					GL No:	
Date	Description	PR	DR	CR	Balance	

Account:					GL No:	
Date	Description	PR	DR	CR	Balance	

Account:					GL No:	
Date	**Description**	**PR**	**DR**	**CR**	**Balance**	

Account:					GL No:	
Date	**Description**	**PR**	**DR**	**CR**	**Balance**	

Account:					GL No:	
Date	**Description**	**PR**	**DR**	**CR**	**Balance**	

Account:					GL No:	
Date	**Description**	**PR**	**DR**	**CR**	**Balance**	

Account:					GL No:	
Date	Description	PR	DR	CR	Balance	

Account:					GL No:	
Date	Description	PR	DR	CR	Balance	

Account:					GL No:	
Date	Description	PR	DR	CR	Balance	

Account:					GL No:	
Date	Description	PR	DR	CR	Balance	

Account:					GL No:	
Date	Description	PR	DR	CR	Balance	

Account:					GL No:	
Date	Description	PR	DR	CR	Balance	

Account Titles	DR	CR

AP-8A (❸ ❹ ❺ ❻)

High Flying Biplane provides sightseeing tours in vintage biplanes. The company is owned by Sky Bridges. The closing balances at the end of May 2016 and the chart of accounts are shown below.

High Flying Biplane Balance Sheet As at May 31, 2016			
Assets		**Liabilities**	
Cash	$8,000	Accounts Payable	$8,200
Accounts Receivable	6,000	Unearned Revenue	3,200
Prepaid Insurance	1,200	Bank Loan	20,000
Equipment	60,000	**Total Liabilities**	31,400
		Owner's Equity	
		Bridges, Capital	43,800
Total Assets	$75,200	**Total Liabilities & Owner's Equity**	$75,200

Account Description	Account #
ASSETS	
Cash	101
Accounts Receivable	105
Prepaid Insurance	110
Equipment	120
LIABILITIES	
Accounts Payable	200
Interest Payable	205
Unearned Revenue	210
Bank Loan	215
OWNER'S EQUITY	
Bridges, Capital	300
Bridges, Drawings	310

Account Description	Account #
REVENUE	
Service Revenue	400
EXPENSES	
Advertising Expense	500
Insurance Expense	515
Interest Expense	520
Telephone Expense	550

During the month of June, High Flying Biplane had the following transactions.

Jun 1	The owner invested $5,000 cash into the business.
Jun 2	Received $1,500 cash for tours that will be provided in August.
Jun 3	Received an advertising bill for $400 which will be paid next month.
Jun 4	Paid the telephone bill with $200 cash.
Jun 10	Provided tours worth $2,400 to a customer who will pay next month.
Jun 14	Purchased equipment with $4,000 cash.
Jun 20	Received payments totalling $1,600 from customers paying their accounts.
Jun 22	Paid $900 towards accounts payable.
Jun 24	Paid $1,000 towards the bank loan principal.
Jun 30	The owner withdrew $1,200 cash for personal use.

Required

a) Prepare the journal entries for the month of June.
b) Post the journal entries to the ledger accounts.
c) Prepare a trial balance at the end of June.

JOURNAL				Page 1
Date	Account Title and Explanation	PR	Debit	Credit

Account: Cash					GL No:	
Date	Description	PR	DR	CR	Balance	

Account:					GL No:	
Date	Description	PR	DR	CR	Balance	

Account:					GL No:	
Date	Description	PR	DR	CR	Balance	

Account:					GL No:	
Date	Description	PR	DR	CR	Balance	

Account:					GL No:	
Date	Description	PR	DR	CR	Balance	

Account:						GL No:	
Date	**Description**	**PR**	**DR**	**CR**	**Balance**		

Account:						GL No:	
Date	**Description**	**PR**	**DR**	**CR**	**Balance**		

Account:						GL No:	
Date	**Description**	**PR**	**DR**	**CR**	**Balance**		

Account:						GL No:	
Date	**Description**	**PR**	**DR**	**CR**	**Balance**		

Account:						GL No:	
Date	**Description**	**PR**	**DR**	**CR**	**Balance**		

Account:					GL No:	
Date	Description	PR	DR	CR	Balance	

Account:					GL No:	
Date	Description	PR	DR	CR	Balance	

Account:					GL No:	
Date	Description	PR	DR	CR	Balance	

Account:					GL No:	
Date	Description	PR	DR	CR	Balance	

Account:					GL No:	
Date	Description	PR	DR	CR	Balance	

Account Titles	DR	CR

AP-9A (6)

Micro Company, owned by Steven Upton, showed these accounts and their corresponding normal balances on May 31, 2016.

Account Titles	Balance
Upton, Capital	$23,500
Insurance Expense	900
Accounts Payable	15,500
Service Revenue	8,900
Equipment	34,500
Supplies Expense	3,000
Cash	6,400
Salaries Expense	4,000
Rent Expense	3,000
Upton, Drawings	3,000
Utilities Expense	1,300
Bank Loan	10,200
Prepaid Insurance	2,000

Debit then Credit

Required

Prepare Micro Company's trial balance at May 31, 2016.

Micro Company Trial balance May 31, 2016		
Account Titles	**DR**	**CR**
Cash	6,400	
Prepaid insurance	2,000	
Equipment	34,500	
Accounts Payable		15,500
Bank loan		10,200
Upton, Capital		23,500
Upton Drawings	3,000	
Service Revenue		8,900
Insurance Expense	900	
Rent expense	3,000	
Salaries Expense	4,000	
Supplies Expense	3,000	
Utilities expense	1,300	

Assets 459,000

Liabilities 257,000

AP-10A (6)

Home Circus is owned by Laura Roberts and provides acrobatic entertainment at children's parties and other events. Its complete general ledger for March 2016 is shown below.

Account:	Cash				GL No:	101
Date	Description	PR	DR	CR	Balance	
Mar 1	Opening Balance				7,800	DR
Mar 1		J1		1,800	6,000	DR
Mar 2		J1	2,900		8,900	DR
Mar 3		J1		1,440	7,460	DR
Mar 10		J1		10	7,450	DR
Mar 10		J1		780	6,670	DR
Mar 20		J1	2,600		9,270	DR
Mar 22		J1	800		10,070	DR
Mar 24		J1		710	9,360	DR
Mar 31		J1		2,000	7,360	DR

Account:	Accounts Receivable				GL No:	105
Date	Description	PR	DR	CR	Balance	
Mar 1	Opening Balance				2,460	DR
Mar 22		J1		800	1,660	DR

Account:	Prepaid Insurance				GL No:	110
Date	Description	PR	DR	CR	Balance	
Mar 1	Opening Balance				0	DR
Mar 1		J1	1,800		1,800	DR

Account:	Office Supplies				GL No:	115
Date	Description	PR	DR	CR	Balance	
Mar 1	Opening Balance				640	DR
Mar 4		J1	250		890	DR

Account:	Equipment				GL No:	120
Date	Description	PR	DR	CR	Balance	
Mar 1	Opening Balance				10,500	DR
Mar 20		J1		2,600	7,900	DR

Account:	Accounts Payable				GL No:	200
Date	Description	PR	DR	CR	Balance	
Mar 1	Opening Balance				2,900	CR
Mar 4		J1		250	3,150	CR
Mar 24		J1	710		2,440	CR

Account:	Unearned Revenue				GL No:	210
Date	Description	PR	DR	CR	Balance	
Mar 1	Opening Balance				1,800	CR

Account:	Bank Loan				GL No:	215
Date	Description	PR	DR	CR	Balance	
Mar 1	Opening Balance				5,100	CR
Mar 10		J1	780		4,320	CR

Account:	Roberts, Capital				GL No:	300
Date	Description	PR	DR	CR	Balance	
Mar 1	Opening Balance				11,600	CR

Account:	Roberts, Drawing				GL No:	310
Date	Description	PR	DR	CR	Balance	
Mar 31		J1	2,000		2,000	DR

Account:	Service Revenue				GL No:	400
Date	Description	PR	DR	CR	Balance	
Mar 2		J1		2,900	2,900	CR

Account:	Office Supplies Expense				GL No:	520
Date	Description	PR	DR	CR	Balance	
Mar 10		J1	10		10	DR

Account:	Rent Expense				GL No:	540
Date	Description	PR	DR	CR	Balance	
Mar 3		J1	1,440		1,440	DR

Required

Prepare a trial balance. Place the accounts in the order shown in the general ledger.

Account Titles	DR	CR

AP-11A (❶ ❻)

A part-time bookkeeper for Wombat Tours has created the trial balance at the end of the year and cannot get it to balance.

Account Titles	DR	CR
Wombat Tours		
Trial Balance		
December 31, 2016		
Accounts Payable	$3,150	
Accounts Receivable	2,350	
Advertising Expense		$2,100
Bank Loan		5,200
Sharpe, Capital		6,170
Cash	6,200	
Interest Expense	560	
Maintenance Expense	240	
Office Supplies		1,600
Sharpe, Drawings		2,300
Prepaid Insurance	1,200	
Equipment	13,500	
Rent Expense	6,200	
Salaries Expense	5,300	
Service Revenue		25,800
Telephone Expense	450	
Unearned Revenue	1,680	
Total	$40,830	$43,170

All the entries have been journalized and posted to the general ledger properly, and all the accounts should have normal balances.

Required

Recreate the trial balance for Wombat Tours so that the accounts are listed in the order they would typically appear in a chart of accounts, and ensure that debits equal credits.

Account Titles	DR	CR

AP-12A (❸ ❹)

Greg Carlin is the owner of Carlin Consulting. During the month of April 2016 he had the following transactions.

Apr 1   Greg invested $5,000 cash and equipment valued at $3,000 into the business.
Apr 3   Provided consulting services to a customer. The customer paid $1,000 now and will pay $1,500 later.
Apr 6   Received a loan from the bank for $6,000.
Apr 8   Paid $1,300 for utilities for the month.
Apr 17 Purchased equipment with $4,000 cash.
Apr 20 Paid employee salaries with $2,100 cash.
Apr 22 Provided consulting services to a customer on account for $1,600.
Apr 28 Received the balance owing from the customer on April 3.

Required

Record the transactions in the journal.

JOURNAL				Page 1
Date	Account Title and Explanation	PR	Debit	Credit

Application Questions Group B

AP-1B (❶ ❸)

Have-a-Bash is owned by Shelly Fisher and provides party planning services. During April 2016, Have-a-Bash had the following transactions.

Apr 1	The owner invested $5,800 cash into the business.
Apr 4	Planned a party for a customer for $740. The customer will pay later.
Apr 6	Paid $600 cash for rent for the month.
Apr 8	Received a $370 telephone bill which will be paid later.
Apr 15	Paid $300 towards the bank loan principal.
Apr 19	Received cash from a customer who owed $840.
Apr 27	Paid the telephone bill received earlier.

Required

Complete the table to analyze each transaction.

	Account Name	Category	Increase or Decrease	Debit or Credit
Apr 1				
Apr 4				
Apr 6				
Apr 8				
Apr 15				
Apr 19				
Apr 27				

AP-2B (❶ ❸)

Bendari Tutoring Services had the following transactions for the month of November 2016.

Nov 1	Purchased supplies for $100 on account.
Nov 4	Received $4,200 cash from clients as payment for tutoring.
Nov 9	Received a telephone bill in the mail for $150.
Nov 16	Paid an employee's salary of $3,500 in cash.
Nov 25	Collected $500 from clients who owed money for previous services.

Required

Complete the table to analyze each transaction.

	Account Name	Category	Increase or Decrease	Debit or Credit
Nov 1				
Nov 4				
Nov 9				
Nov 16				
Nov 25				

AP-3B (❶)

For the accounts listed below, determine if the normal balance is a debit or a credit. Also, indicate if a debit or a credit will be needed to decrease the account balance.

	Account Title	Normal Balance	Decrease
1	Cash		
2	Accounts Receivable		
3	Accounts Payable		
4	Loan Payable		
5	Owner's Capital		
6	Service Revenue		
7	Insurance Expense		
8	Prepaid Insurance		
9	Equipment		
10	Unearned Revenue		
11	Owner's Drawings		
12	Salaries Expense		
13	Office Supplies		

AP-4B (❸ ❹)

Exhale Spa provides a relaxing retreat for people wishing to relax and unwind. During the month of July 2016, the following transactions took place.

Jul 3	Provided services to a customer and received $3,100 cash.
Jul 4	Borrowed $2,500 from the bank.
Jul 6	Provided services worth $2,800 to a customer on account.
Jul 10	Received the utilities bill for $240, which will be paid later.
Jul 11	Paid $690 cash to reduce the balance of accounts payable.
Jul 15	Collected $1,900 cash from customers owing on account.
Jul 20	Paid $2,600 towards the bank loan principal.
Jul 21	Paid the amount owing from July 10.
Jul 27	Paid salaries of $1,700 for the month with cash.
Jul 31	Purchased equipment worth $3,100 which will be paid later.

Required

Prepare the journal entries for the above transactions.

JOURNAL					Page 1
Date	Account Title and Explanation	PR	Debit	Credit	

JOURNAL				Page 1
Date	Account Title and Explanation	PR	Debit	Credit

AP-5B (❸ ❹)

Tracts of Land provides surveying services to construction companies and municipalities. During the month of February 2016, Tracts of Land had the following transactions.

Feb 1   Purchased equipment worth $8,200, which will be paid later.

Feb 2   Provided services worth $20,200 to a customer on account.

Feb 3   Paid $1,900 cash for February's utilities.

Feb 4   Paid $1,600 for four months of insurance coverage.

Feb 10   Paid $2,000 cash to reduce the balance of accounts payable.

Feb 14   Paid $6,600 cash for monthly maintenance contract.

Feb 22   Billed for $5,800 in travel expenses to be paid next month.

Feb 24   Received an advertising bill for $400 which will be paid next month.

Feb 28   Paid $2,730 to the bank to reduce the bank loan principal. Interest was $30 and the remainder was principal.

Required

Prepare the journal entries for the above transactions.

JOURNAL					Page 1
Date	**Account Title and Explanation**		**PR**	**Debit**	**Credit**

AP-6B (❸ ❹)

Cherry Consulting Firm is owned by Ron Cherry and offers consulting services for small businesses. During June 2016, the following transactions occurred.

Jun 2   Received a deposit of $3,000 from a customer for services to be provided in the future.
Jun 3   Paid a $495 utility bill that was received and recorded last month.
Jun 8   Charged $1,400 in travel costs to a credit card.
Jun 17   Paid $1,000 cash to reduce the bank loan. Of that amount, $75 is interest and the remainder is principal.
Jun 19   Ron withdrew $2,100 cash from the business for personal use.
Jun 28   Paid $4,900 for salaries for the month.

Required

Prepare the journal entries for the above transactions.

JOURNAL					Page 1
Date	**Account Title and Explanation**	**PR**	**Debit**	**Credit**	

AP-7B (❸ ❹ ❺ ❻)

Limbo Lower provides acrobatic entertainment at children's parties and other events. The company is a sole proprietorship owned by Leslie Lowe. The closing balances at the end of August 2016 and the chart of accounts are shown below.

Limbo Lower Balance Sheet As at August 31, 2016			
Assets		**Liabilities**	
Cash	$7,200	Accounts Payable	$3,400
Accounts Receivable	2,300	Unearned Revenue	1,400
Office Supplies	850	Bank Loan	5,600
Equipment	11,500	**Total Liabilities**	10,400
		Owner's Equity	
		Lowe, Capital	11,450
Total Assets	$21,850	**Total Liabilities & Owner's Equity**	$21,850

Account Description	Account #
ASSETS	
Cash	101
Accounts Receivable	105
Prepaid Insurance	110
Office Supplies	115
Equipment	120
LIABILITIES	
Accounts Payable	200
Unearned Revenue	210
Bank Loan	215
OWNER'S EQUITY	
Lowe, Capital	300
Lowe, Drawings	310

Account Description	Account #
REVENUE	
Service Revenue	400
EXPENSES	
Insurance Expense	515
Interest Expense	520
Office Supplies Expense	530
Rent Expense	540

During the month of September, Limbo Lower had the following transactions.

Sep 1   Paid $1,800 cash in advance for a one-year insurance policy.

Sep 2   Received $1,900 cash for services provided.

Sep 3   Paid $1,350 cash for September's rent.

Sep 4   Purchased office supplies on account worth $250.

Sep 10   Paid $960 towards the bank loan principal and $40 of interest on the loan.

Sep 20   Received $2,200 cash from a customer booking a party in advance.

Sep 22   Collected $850 from a customer paying their account.

Sep 24   Paid $600 towards accounts payable.

Sep 30   The owner withdrew $1,600 cash for personal use.

Required

a) Prepare the journal entries for the month of September.

b) Post the journal entries to the ledger accounts.

c) Prepare a trial balance at the end of September.

JOURNAL				Page 1
Date	Account Title and Explanation	PR	Debit	Credit

Account: Cash						GL No:	
Date	**Description**	**PR**	**DR**	**CR**	**Balance**		

Account:						GL No:	
Date	**Description**	**PR**	**DR**	**CR**	**Balance**		

Account:						GL No:	
Date	**Description**	**PR**	**DR**	**CR**	**Balance**		

Account:						GL No:	
Date	**Description**	**PR**	**DR**	**CR**	**Balance**		

Account:						GL No:	
Date	**Description**	**PR**	**DR**	**CR**	**Balance**		

Account:					GL No:	
Date	**Description**	**PR**	**DR**	**CR**	**Balance**	

Account:					GL No:	
Date	**Description**	**PR**	**DR**	**CR**	**Balance**	

Account:					GL No:	
Date	**Description**	**PR**	**DR**	**CR**	**Balance**	

Account:					GL No:	
Date	**Description**	**PR**	**DR**	**CR**	**Balance**	

Account:					GL No:	
Date	**Description**	**PR**	**DR**	**CR**	**Balance**	

Account:					GL No:	
Date	Description	PR	DR	CR	Balance	

Account:					GL No:	
Date	Description	PR	DR	CR	Balance	

Account:					GL No:	
Date	Description	PR	DR	CR	Balance	

Account:					GL No:	
Date	Description	PR	DR	CR	Balance	

Account:					GL No:	
Date	Description	PR	DR	CR	Balance	

Account Titles	DR	CR

AP-8B (❸ ❹ ❺ ❻)

Sokatoa, owned by Susan Wethers, had the following transactions for the month of July 2016.

Jul 1	Purchased a new machine with $12,000 cash.
Jul 5	Provided services worth $10,000 to clients who will pay later.
Jul 12	Susan withdrew $5,000 cash from the business.
Jul 19	Received a maintenance bill for $1,100 which will be paid later.
Jul 31	Got a loan from the bank for $25,000.

Required

Journalize the transactions, post them to the general ledger, and prepare a trial balance.

JOURNAL					Page 1
Date	Account Title and Explanation	PR	Debit		Credit

Account:	Cash				GL No:	101
Date: 2016	Description	PR	DR	CR	Balance (DR or CR)	
	Opening Balance				31,800	DR

Account:	Accounts Receivable				GL No:	105
Date: 2016	Description	PR	DR	CR	Balance (DR or CR)	
	Opening Balance				5,000	DR

Account:	Machine				GL No:	120
Date: 2016	Description	PR	DR	CR	Balance (DR or CR)	
	Opening Balance				6,000	DR

Account:	Accounts Payable				GL No:	200
Date: 2016	Description	PR	DR	CR	Balance (DR or CR)	
	Opening Balance				3,500	CR

Account:	Bank Loan				GL No:	215
Date: 2016	Description	PR	DR	CR	Balance (DR or CR)	
	Opening Balance				0	CR

Account:	Wethers, Capital				GL No:	300
Date: 2016	Description	PR	DR	CR	Balance (DR or CR)	
	Opening Balance				39,300	CR

Account:	Wethers, Drawings				GL No:	310
Date: 2016	Description	PR	DR	CR	Balance (DR or CR)	

Account:	Sales Revenue				GL No:	400
Date: 2016	Description	PR	DR	CR	Balance (DR or CR)	

Account:	Maintenance Expense				GL No:	520
Date: 2016	Description	PR	DR	CR	Balance (DR or CR)	

Account:	Salaries Expense				GL No:	540
Date: 2016	Description	PR	DR	CR	Balance (DR or CR)	

Account Titles	DR	CR

Analysis

Explain how the general ledger is similar to the T-accounts used in earlier chapters.

_____

_____

_____

_____

AP-9B (❶ ❻)

The following are the accounts of DRAM Company and their corresponding normal balances on October 31, 2016.

Account	Balance
David, Capital	$20,400
Accounts Payable	13,200
Insurance Expense	1,000
Service Revenue	6,800
Equipment	30,500
Supplies Expense	2,900
Cash	5,700
Salaries Expense	4,100
David, Drawings	3,100
Rent Expense	2,200
Telephone Expense	1,200
Bank Loan	11,700
Prepaid Rent	1,400

Required

Prepare DRAM Company's trial balance for the month ended October 31, 2016.

Account Titles	DR	CR

AP-10B (⑥)

The following account balances were taken from Macro Company's general ledger on February 29, 2016.

Account	Balance
Chalmers, Capital	$10,050
Accounts Payable	13,000
Prepaid Expenses	5,000
Interest Payable	825
Vehicle	32,000
Computer Equipment	19,000
Salary Expense	31,000
Unearned Revenue	8,000
Depreciation Expense	1,700
Rent Expense	2,400
Cash	15,275
Service Revenue	74,500

Required

Prepare Macro Company's trial balance.

Account Titles	DR	CR

Analysis

The accountant at Macro Company was worried that he may have recorded some entries incorrectly in the journal, but upon seeing that the trial balance is in balance, realized that he must have done everything correctly. Is this true or false? Explain.

_____

_____

_____

_____

AP-11B (❶)

Indicate whether increases and decreases in the following groups of accounts correspond to debits or credits.

	Increase	Decrease
Liabilities		
Owner's Equity		
Expenses		
Owner's Drawings		
Revenues		
Assets		

Analysis

What is a normal balance?

_____

_____

_____

AP-12B (❸ ❹)

Helen Long owns and operates Long Landscaping which provides landscaping and gardening services. During the month of August 2016, she had the following transactions.

Aug 1	Provided services to a customer who paid $800 cash.
Aug 3	Paid $1,000 to the bank to repay a bank loan. Of that amount, $100 was interest.
Aug 6	Received a maintenance bill for $500 which will be paid later.
Aug 8	Paid $1,600 for a one-year insurance policy.
Aug 17	Paid $2,200 for rent for the month.
Aug 20	Provided services to a customer for $1,300 and the customer will pay later.
Aug 22	Paid the maintenance bill received on August 6.
Aug 28	Received payment from the customer from August 20.

Required

Record the transactions in the journal.

JOURNAL					Page 1
Date	Account Title and Explanation	PR	Debit	Credit	

JOURNAL				Page 1
Date	Account Title and Explanation	PR	Debit	Credit

Notes

Chapter 5

THE ACCOUNTING CYCLE: ADJUSTMENTS

LEARNING OUTCOMES

❶ Describe the purpose of adjustments

❷ Prepare adjusting entries for accrued revenue

❸ Prepare adjusting entries for accrued expenses

❹ Prepare adjusting entries for unearned revenue

❺ Prepare adjusting entries for prepaid expenses

❻ Prepare adjusting entries for depreciation

❼ Prepare an adjusted trial balance

Appendix

❽ Prepare correcting entries

AMEENGAGE™ Access **ameengage.com** for integrated resources including tutorials, practice exercises, the digital textbook and more.

Assessment Questions

AS-1 (❼)

What is the purpose of a worksheet?

_____

_____

AS-2 (❶)

Why must adjustments be made at the end of the accounting period?

_____

_____

AS-3 (❹)

When making an adjustment to record unearned revenue that is now earned, which accounts are used and how are they affected?

_____

_____

AS-4 (❻)

When making an adjustment to record depreciation on equipment, which accounts are used and how are they affected?

_____

_____

AS-5 (❻)

What is the purpose of a contra account?

_____

_____

_____

AS-6 (❻)

True or False: All assets that are part of property, plant and equipment depreciate.

_____

_____

_____

AS-7 (❺)

When making an adjustment to record the used portion of prepaid insurance, which accounts are used and how are they affected?

_____

_____

AS-8 (❸)

When making an adjustment to record accrued interest on a bank loan, which accounts are used and how are they affected?

_____

_____

AS-9 (❼)

What is an adjusted trial balance?

_____

_____

AS-10 (❻)

How does accumulated depreciation affect the value of property, plant and equipment?

_____

_____

AS-11 (❶)

What is an accounting period?

_____

_____

AS-12 (❶)

What does accrual-based accounting state regarding revenue and expenses?

_____

_____

_____

AS-13 (❷ ❸ ❹ ❺ ❻)

Provide five examples of adjustments.

_____

_____

_____

AS-14 (❸)

Define accrued expenses.

_____

_____

_____

AS-15 (❸)

What is the entry to recognize accrued interest expense?

_____

_____

_____

Application Questions Group A

AP-1A (④ ⑤ ⑥ ⑦)

Swordfish Programming is owned by Mark Kulak and provides computer solutions to the security industry. At the end of April 2016, Swordfish had the following adjustments.

Apr 30   A count of office supplies showed that there was $550 remaining in the office.

Apr 30   The balance of prepaid insurance is for a 12-month policy, one month of insurance has been used.

Apr 30   During April, Swordfish Programming earned $900 of unearned revenue.

Apr 30   The computers were purchased on April 1, 2016 and have an expected useful life of five years, after which they will have no residual value. Record the depreciation for April.

OE
O/B ———→ 10,235
+ NI ———→ 3,515
13,750
+ invest
− Drawings   1500
= c/B
12,250 − capital

Required

Using the following trial balance, complete the adjustments and the adjusted trial balance in the worksheet.

owners equity
Opening balance
+Net Income
+ investment
− Drawings
=Closing balance

Swordfish Programming Worksheet April 30, 2016						
	Unadjusted Trial Balance		Adjustments		Adjusted Trial Balance	
Account Titles	DR	CR	DR	CR	DR	CR
Cash	$4,200					
Accounts Receivable	2,300					
Prepaid Insurance	1,800					
Office Supplies	800					
Computers	9,600					
Accumulated Depreciation		$0				
Accounts Payable		1,640				
Unearned Revenue		1,950				
Bank Loan		3,200				
Kulak, Capital		10,235				
Kulak, Drawings	1,500					
Service Revenue		4,750				
Depreciation Expense	0					
Insurance Expense	0					
Office Supplies Expense	0					
Rent Expense	1,300					
Telephone Expense	275					
Total	$21,775	$21,775				

AP-2A (③ ④ ⑤ ⑥ ⑦)

Chirp Hearing is owned by Christina Earring and provides hearing aids and other auditory services. At the end of November 2016, the company had the following adjustments.

Nov 30 Interest on the bank loan is set at 10%. One month of interest has accrued.

Nov 30 The balance of the prepaid insurance is for the remaining 10 months of the insurance policy. One month of insurance has been used.

Nov 30 The equipment was purchased on September 1, 2016 and will have a useful life of 7 years, after which it will have no residual value. Depreciation is recorded every month. Record depreciation for November.

Nov 30 Chirp Hearing completed $650 of work that was previously unearned.

Nov 30 Office supplies used during the month totalled $400.

Required

Using the following trial balance, complete the adjustments and the adjusted trial balance in the worksheet.

220 per month

	Unadjusted Trial Balance		Adjustments		Adjusted Trial Balance	
Chirp Hearing Worksheet November 30, 2016						
Account Titles	**DR**	**CR**	**DR**	**CR**	**DR**	**CR**
Cash	$6,250				6250	
Accounts Receivable	3,440				3440	
Prepaid Insurance	2,200			220	1980	
Office Supplies	1,140			400	740	
Equipment	15,120				1520	
Accumulated Depreciation		$360		180		540
Accounts Payable		2,260				2260
Interest Payable		0		40		40
Unearned Revenue		1,240	650			590
Bank Loan		4,800				4800
Earring, Capital		12,640				12640
Earring, Drawings	2,100				2100	
Service Revenue		12,500		650		13150
Depreciation Expense	0		180		180	
Insurance Expense	0		220		220	
Interest Expense	0		40		40	
Office Supplies Expense	0		400		400	
Rent Expense	1,650				1650	
Salaries Expense	1,900				1900	
Total	**$33,800**	**$33,800**	1490=1490		34020	34020

AP-3A (❷ ❸ ❺ ❻)

Mr. Allan Poe operates an advertising business called A Advertising. He had the following adjustments for the month of December 2016.

Dec 31   Recognized $1,250 rent expense used for the month.

Dec 31   An annual magazine subscription was prepaid on December 1, 2016 for $600. By December 31, one issue had been received.

Dec 31   Depreciation for the month is $400.

Dec 31   Salaries for employees have accrued by $1,300 by the end of the month.

Dec 31   A 30-day contract was started on December 16. The customer will pay $5,000 at the end of the contract in January. Accrue the revenue earned by the end of December.

Required

Prepare the journal entries for the adjustments.

JOURNAL					Page 1
Date	**Account Titles and Explanation**		**PR**	**Debit**	**Credit**

AP-4A (❸ ❹ ❺ ❻)

MJ Sandblasting is in its second year of operations. At the end of April 2016, it had the following adjustments.

Apr 30   Recognized $300 of prepaid insurance expense for the month.

Apr 30   Depreciation on equipment for the month was $200.

Apr 30   A count of office supplies showed that $650 had been used.

Apr 30   Accrued interest on a bank loan was $30.

Apr 30   Outstanding work for a client worth $800 was completed during the month. The client had paid for the work in March.

Required

Prepare the journal entries for the adjustments.

JOURNAL					Page 1
Date	**Account Titles and Explanation**	**PR**	**Debit**	**Credit**

AP-5A (❹ ❺ ❻ ❼)

Sigmund Services has completed all its journal entries for the month of April 2016 and posted them to the general ledger. Based on the ledger balances, an unadjusted trial balance has been prepared.

Sigmund Services Unadjusted Trial Balance April 30, 2016		
Account Titles	**DR**	**CR**
Cash	$32,050	
Accounts Receivable	9,000	
Prepaid Insurance	1,200	
Equipment	15,000	
Accounts Payable		$25,550
Unearned Revenue		4,500
Bank Loan		1,500
Sigmund, Capital		18,000
Service Revenue		25,000
Interest Expense	50	
Rent Expense	1,000	
Salaries Expense	8,000	
Telephone Expense	250	
Travel Expense	8,000	
Total	$74,550	$74,550

The following adjustments must be made at the end of April.

Apr 30 The balance of prepaid insurance represents a 12-month policy. One month has been used.

Apr 30 Depreciation of equipment for the month is $120.

Apr 30 Sigmund Services has earned $1,300 that was previously unearned.

Required

a) Fill in the unadjusted trial balance on the worksheet and complete the rest of the worksheet.

b) Create the journal entries for the adjustments from the worksheet.

Account Titles	Unadjusted Trial Balance		Adjustments		Adjusted Trial Balance	
	DR	CR	DR	CR	DR	CR

JOURNAL				Page 2
Date	Account Titles and Explanation	PR	Debit	Credit

AP-6A (③④⑤⑥⑦)

High Flying Biplane has completed all its journal entries for the month of June 2016 and posted them to the general ledger. Based on the ledger balances, an unadjusted trial balance has been prepared.

High Flying Biplane Unadjusted Trial Balance June 30, 2016		
Account Titles	**DR**	**CR**
Cash	$8,800	
Accounts Receivable	6,800	
Prepaid Insurance	1,200	
Equipment	64,000	
Accounts Payable		$7,700
Unearned Revenue		4,700
Bank Loan		19,000
High, Capital		48,800
High, Drawings	1,200	
Service Revenue		2,400
Advertising Expense	400	
Telephone Expense	200	
Total	$82,600	$82,600

The following adjustments must be made at the end of June.

Jun 30   One month of insurance worth $100 has been used.
Jun 30   Depreciation on the equipment was $450 this month.
Jun 30   Of the unearned revenue amount, $4,080 still remains unearned.
Jun 30   Interest accrued on the bank loan was $75.

Required

a) Fill in the unadjusted trial balance on the worksheet and complete the rest of the worksheet.

b) Create the journal entries for the adjustments from the worksheet.

| | Unadjusted Trial Balance | | Adjustments | | Adjusted Trial Balance | |
Account Titles	DR	CR	DR	CR	DR	CR

| JOURNAL | | | | | Page 2 |
Date	Account Titles and Explanation	PR	Debit	Credit

AP-7A (④⑤⑥⑦)

Limbo Lower has completed all its journal entries for the month of September 2016 and posted them to the general ledger. Based on the ledger balances, an unadjusted trial balance has been prepared.

Limbo Lower **Unadjusted Trial Balance** **September 30, 2016**		
Account Titles	**DR**	**CR**
Cash	$5,800	
Accounts Receivable	1,450	
Prepaid Insurance	1,800	
Office Supplies	1,100	
Equipment	9,300	
Accounts Payable		$3,050
Unearned Revenue		1,400
Bank Loan		4,640
Roberts, Capital		11,450
Roberts, Drawings	1,600	
Service Revenue		1,900
Interest Expense	40	
Rent Expense	1,350	
Total	$22,440	$22,440

The following adjustments must be made at the end of September.

Sep 30 The amount of prepaid insurance is for 12 months. Once month has been used.

Sep 30 Depreciation for the month on equipment was $120.

Sep 30 Unearned revenue of $360 has now been earned.

Sep 30 A count of office supplies shows that $650 remains.

Required

a) Fill in the unadjusted trial balance on the worksheet and complete the rest of the worksheet.

b) Create the journal entries for the adjustments from the worksheet.

Account Titles	Unadjusted Trial Balance		Adjustments		Adjusted Trial Balance	
	DR	CR	DR	CR	DR	CR

JOURNAL				Page 2
Date	Account Titles and Explanation	PR	Debit	Credit

AP-8A (❸ ❹ ❺ ❻ ❼)

Zig Zag Robotics has the following adjustments to make at the end of September 2016, the end of its fiscal year.

Sep 30   Unearned revenue of $850 has now been earned.

Sep 30   A count of the office supplies shows that $430 worth still remains on hand.

Sep 30   Salaries accrued but not yet paid amount to $2,430.

Sep 30   Monthly depreciation on equipment was $600.

The chart of accounts is shown below.

Account Description	Account #
ASSETS	
Cash	101
Accounts Receivable	105
Office Supplies	110
Equipment	120
Accumulated Depreciation	130
LIABILITIES	
Accounts Payable	200
Unearned Revenue	210
Salaries Payable	220

Account Description	Account #
OWNER'S EQUITY	
Rizzo, Capital	300
Rizzo, Drawings	310
REVENUE	
Service Revenue	400
EXPENSES	
Salaries Expense	530
Depreciation Expense	535
Supplies Expense	540

Required

a) Complete the six-column worksheet.

b) Journalize the adjustments.

c) Post the transactions to the general ledger accounts provided.

	Zig Zag Robotics Worksheet September 30, 2016					
	Unadjusted Trial Balance		Adjustments		Adjusted Trial Balance	
Account Titles	DR	CR	DR	CR	DR	CR
Cash	$3,000					
Accounts Receivable	950					
Office Supplies	830					
Equipment	5,500					
Accumulated Depreciation		$1,800				
Accounts Payable		1,250				
Unearned Revenue		1,700				
Rizzo, Capital		4,030				
Rizzo, Drawings	500					
Service Revenue		4,200				
Salaries Expense	2,200					
Total	$12,980	$12,980				

JOURNAL				Page 1
Date	Account Title and Explanation	PR	Debit	Credit

Account:	Office Supplies				GL No:	110
Date: 2016	Description	PR	DR	CR	Balance (DR or CR)	
	Opening Balance					

Account:	Accumulated Depreciation				GL No:	130
Date: 2016	Description	PR	DR	CR	Balance (DR or CR)	
	Opening Balance					

Account:	Unearned Revenue				GL No:	210
Date: 2016	Description	PR	DR	CR	Balance (DR or CR)	
	Opening Balance					

Account:	Salaries Payable				GL No:	220
Date: 2016	Description	PR	DR	CR	Balance (DR or CR)	
	Opening Balance					

Account:	Service Revenue				GL No:	400
Date: 2016	Description	PR	DR	CR	Balance (DR or CR)	
	Opening Balance					

Account:	Salaries Expense				GL No:	530
Date: 2016	Description	PR	DR	CR	Balance (DR or CR)	
	Opening Balance					

Account:	Depreciation Expense				GL No:	535
Date: 2016	Description	PR	DR	CR	Balance (DR or CR)	
	Opening Balance					

Account:	Supplies Expense				GL No:	540
Date: 2016	Description	PR	DR	CR	Balance (DR or CR)	
	Opening Balance					

Analysis

What is the purpose of preparing a worksheet before journalizing and posting adjusting entries, and before preparing financial statements?

_____

_____

_____

_____

AP-9A (❻)

On January 1, 2016, Precision Machinery purchased a new piece of equipment for $100,000. The equipment is expected to last five years and will have no residual value. Precision Machinery has a December 31 year end. Prepare the table below showing the yearly depreciation, accumulated depreciation and net book value of the equipment.

Year	Original Cost of Equipment	Depreciation Expense	Accumulated Depreciation	Net Book Value
2016				
2017				
2018				
2019				
2020				
Total				

AP-10A (❻)

On March 1, 2016, Jefferson Consulting purchased new computers for $19,000. The computers are expected to last three years and have an estimated residual value of $1,000. Jefferson has a December 31 year end. Prepare the table below showing the yearly depreciation, accumulated depreciation and net book value of the computers.

Year	Original Cost of Computers	Depreciation Expense	Accumulated Depreciation	Net Book Value
2016				
2017				
2018				
2019				
Total				

AP-11A (8)

On June 23, 2016, the bookkeeper for Henson Company discovered an error in the journal entries. On June 2, equipment was purchased on account for $9,000, however it was recorded in the journals and ledgers for $90,000. Prepare the entries to correct this error.

JOURNAL				Page 1
Date	Account Titles and Explanation	PR	Debit	Credit
June 2	Ac. payable		90000	
	Equipment			90000
June 23	Equipment		9000	
	Ac. payable			9000

AP-12A (8)

On November 22, 2016, the bookkeeper for Fraggle Company discovered an error in the journal entries. On November 16, an entry was made for the cash purchase of office supplies for $550 that in error debited equipment. Prepare the entries to correct this error.

JOURNAL				Page 1
Date	Account Titles and Explanation	PR	Debit	Credit

Applicaton Questions Group B

AP-1B (④⑤⑥⑦)

Decodely Programming provides custom computer programming and web design. At the end of December 2016, it had four adjustments.

Dec 31   During December, Decodely Programming earned $830 of unearned revenue.

Dec 31 $1,250 of office supplies was used during the month.

Dec 31   The balance of prepaid insurance represents 11 months remaining on the policy. One month of insurance has been used.

Dec 31   Equipment depreciated $110 during December.

Required

Using the following trial balance, complete the adjustments and the adjusted trial balance in the worksheet.

Decodely Programming Worksheet December 31, 2016						
	Unadjusted Trial Balance		Adjustments		Adjusted Trial Balance	
Account Titles	DR	CR	DR	CR	DR	CR
Cash	$4,000					
Accounts Receivable	2,620					
Prepaid Insurance	2,750					
Office Supplies	1,790					
Equipment	9,400					
Accumulated Depreciation		$400				
Accounts Payable		1,900				
Unearned Revenue		4,500				
Bank Loan		3,410				
Singh, Capital		9,930				
Singh, Drawings	1,560					
Service Revenue		4,090				
Depreciation Expense	0					
Insurance Expense	0					
Office Supplies Expense	0					
Rent Expense	1,970					
Utilities Expense	140					
Total	$24,230	$24,230				

AP-2B (❸ ❺ ❻ ❼)

Counterpoint Studios has completed all the entries for the month of November 2016, except the monthly adjusting entries. The following information is available to make the adjustments.

Nov 30   Annual depreciation on equipment totals $9,000.

Nov 30   Interest accrued on the bank loan is $500.

Nov 30   Office supplies on hand are valued at $2,300.

Nov 30   The annual insurance policy was purchased on December 1, 2015 for $21,900.

Required

Complete the six-column worksheet for Counterpoint Studios.

Counterpoint Studios Worksheet November 30, 2016						
	Unadjusted Trial Balance		Adjustments		Adjusted Trial Balance	
Account Titles	DR	CR	DR	CR	DR	CR
Cash	$52,250					
Accounts Receivable	24,800					
Office Supplies	10,400					
Prepaid Insurance	1,825					
Equipment	295,400					
Accumulated Depreciation		$107,250				
Accounts Payable		31,500				
Bank Loan		140,000				
Jones, Capital		96,750				
Jones, Drawings	60,000					
Service Revenue		382,500				
Advertising Expense	100,000					
Salaries Expense	185,000					
Insurance Expense	20,075					
Depreciation Expense	8,250					
Total	$758,000	$758,000				

AP-3B (❸ ❹ ❺ ❻)

Sprig Gardening Service provides seasonal gardening services. At the end of August 2016, the company must make the following adjustments.

Aug 31	Depreciation for equipment is $120.
Aug 31	Interest due on a bank loan is $50. It will be paid next month.
Aug 31	Accrued salary expense for an employee at the end of the month. The company owes the employee $450.
Aug 31	One month of prepaid insurance at $70 per month has been used.
Aug 31	A physical count of office supplies shows that $300 was used during August.
Aug 31	Sprig Gardening earned $670 that was previously unearned.

Required

Prepare the adjusting journal entries.

JOURNAL					Page 1
Date	**Account Titles and Explanation**	**PR**	**Debit**	**Credit**	

AP-4B (❸ ❹ ❺ ❻)

Speak Up sells voice recognition software. At the end of March 2016, it had the following account balances and adjustments.

Speak Up		
Trial Balance		
March 31, 2016		
Account Titles	**DR**	**CR**
Cash	$6,380	
Accounts Receivable	3,590	
Prepaid Insurance	999	
Office Supplies	1,120	
Equipment	15,170	
Accumulated Depreciation		$400
Accounts Payable		2,120
Unearned Revenue		1,570
Bank Loan		4,930
Jones, Capital		12,659
Jones, Drawings	2,930	
Service Revenue		12,570
Rent Expense	1,920	
Salaries Expense	2,140	
Total	**$34,249**	**$34,249**

Mar 31   Accrued $43 interest on the bank loan.
Mar 31   The balance of the prepaid insurance is for the remaining nine months of the insurance policy. The insurance coverage for March has not been recorded.
Mar 31   Speak Up completed $942 of work that was previously unearned.
Mar 31   One month of depreciation is $250.
Mar 31   Office supplies used during the month totalled $448.

Required

Complete the adjusting entries.

JOURNAL				Page 1
Date	Account Titles and Explanation	PR	Debit	Credit

AP-5B (❹❺❻❼)

Thomas Topology has completed journal entries for the month of October and posted them to the general ledger. Based on the ledger balances, an unadjusted trial balance has been prepared.

The following adjustments must be made at the end of October.

Oct 31	One month of prepaid rent worth $720 has been used.
Oct 31	Depreciation on equipment for the month was $340.
Oct 31	Unearned revenue worth $1,330 has now been earned.

Required

a) Fill in the unadjusted trial balance on the worksheet and complete the rest of the worksheet.

b) Create the journal entries for the adjustments from the worksheet.

	Thomas Topology Worksheet October 31, 2016					
	Unadjusted Trial Balance		Adjustments		Adjusted Trial Balance	
Account Titles	DR	CR	DR	CR	DR	CR
Cash	$32,000					
Accounts Receivable	9,500					
Prepaid Rent	5,760					
Equipment	15,000					
Accumulated Depreciation		$950				
Accounts Payable		27,800				
Unearned Revenue		5,800				
Bank Loan		1,960				
Thomas, Capital		9,330				
Service Revenue		30,000				
Depreciation Expense						
Insurance Expense	570					
Interest Expense	150					
Rent Expense	0					
Salaries Expense	6,400					
Supplies Expense	360					
Utilities Expense	6,100					
Total	$75,840	$75,840				

JOURNAL				Page 1
Date	Account Titles and Explanation	PR	Debit	Credit

AP-6B (❸ ❹ ❺ ❻ ❼)

Floating Speed Boat has completed its journal entries for the month of September and posted them to the general ledger. Based on the ledger balances, an unadjusted trial balance has been prepared.

The following adjustments must be made at the end of September.

Sep 30   Depreciation on equipment for the month is $390.

Sep 30   Prepaid insurance of $250 has been used up this month.

Sep 30   Interest of $150 has accrued on the bank loan.

Sep 30   Unearned revenue of $570 has now been earned.

Required

a) Complete the worksheet.

b) Create the journal entries for the adjustments from the worksheet.

	Floating Speed Boat Worksheet September 30, 2016					
	Unadjusted Trial Balance		**Adjustments**		**Adjusted Trial Balance**	
Account Titles	**DR**	**CR**	**DR**	**CR**	**DR**	**CR**
Cash	$8,800					
Accounts Receivable	7,900					
Prepaid Insurance	1,500					
Equipment	64,000					
Accumulated Depreciation		$870				
Accounts Payable		9,900				
Interest Payable		0				
Unearned Revenue		6,500				
Bank Loan		15,500				
Fathom, Capital		49,000				
Fathom, Drawings	1,200					
Service Revenue		3,400				
Advertising Expense	430					
Depreciation Expense	0					
Insurance Expense	0					
Interest Expense	0					
Rent Expense	1,340					
Total	**$85,170**	**$85,170**				

JOURNAL				Page 1
Date	**Account Titles and Explanation**	**PR**	**Debit**	**Credit**

AP-7B (③④⑤⑥⑦)

Space Jam Storage offers storage space and transportation services for customers. Space Jam Storage has already completed the transactions for the month and posted them to the general ledger. The adjustments for December 2016 have not yet been prepared.

Dec 31   Provided services worth $1,500 to customer who had paid in advance.

Dec 31   One month of insurance of $1,000 was used.

Dec 31   Depreciation for the month was $500.

Dec 31   Salaries accrued at the end of December amounted to $3,370.

Required

a) Prepare the six-column worksheet.

b) Record the journal entries for the adjusting entries.

<table>
<tr><td colspan="7" align="center">**Space Jam Storage**
Worksheet
December 31, 2016</td></tr>
<tr><td></td><td colspan="2" align="center">**Unadjusted Trial Balance**</td><td colspan="2" align="center">**Adjustments**</td><td colspan="2" align="center">**Adjusted Trial Balance**</td></tr>
<tr><td>**Account Titles**</td><td>**DR**</td><td>**CR**</td><td>**DR**</td><td>**CR**</td><td>**DR**</td><td>**CR**</td></tr>
<tr><td>Cash</td><td>$3,250</td><td></td><td></td><td></td><td>3250</td><td></td></tr>
<tr><td>Accounts Receivable</td><td>2,750</td><td></td><td></td><td></td><td>2750</td><td></td></tr>
<tr><td>Prepaid Insurance</td><td>13,000</td><td></td><td></td><td>1000</td><td>12000</td><td></td></tr>
<tr><td>Equipment</td><td>285,000</td><td></td><td></td><td></td><td>285000</td><td></td></tr>
<tr><td>Accumulated Depreciation</td><td></td><td>$45,000</td><td></td><td>500</td><td></td><td>45500</td></tr>
<tr><td>Accounts Payable</td><td></td><td>5,500</td><td></td><td></td><td></td><td>5500</td></tr>
<tr><td>Salaries Payable</td><td></td><td>0</td><td></td><td>3370</td><td></td><td>3370</td></tr>
<tr><td>Unearned Revenue</td><td></td><td>3,600</td><td>1500</td><td></td><td></td><td>2100</td></tr>
<tr><td>Bank Loan</td><td></td><td>191,680</td><td></td><td></td><td></td><td>191680</td></tr>
<tr><td>Jordan, Capital</td><td></td><td>46,200</td><td></td><td></td><td></td><td>46200</td></tr>
<tr><td>Jordan, Drawings</td><td>13,500</td><td></td><td></td><td></td><td>13500</td><td></td></tr>
<tr><td>Service Revenue</td><td></td><td>78,000</td><td></td><td>1500</td><td></td><td>79500</td></tr>
<tr><td>Maintenance Expense</td><td>5,200</td><td></td><td></td><td></td><td>5200</td><td></td></tr>
<tr><td>Depreciation Expense</td><td>4,000</td><td></td><td>500</td><td></td><td>4500</td><td></td></tr>
<tr><td>Interest Expense</td><td>1,280</td><td></td><td></td><td></td><td>1280</td><td></td></tr>
<tr><td>Insurance Expense</td><td>11,000</td><td></td><td>1000</td><td></td><td>12000</td><td></td></tr>
<tr><td>Salaries Expense</td><td>31,000</td><td></td><td>3370</td><td></td><td>34370</td><td></td></tr>
<tr><td>Total</td><td>$369,980</td><td>$369,980</td><td>6370</td><td>6370</td><td>373,850</td><td>373,850</td></tr>
</table>

186-187
Chapter 7
153-154-
Classified
Balance
Sheet

Determin what you dont know office suplys used - howmuch used   Intrest bank loan - balance sheet   Read ?s dates AP13 A + B and Notes

JOURNAL					Page 2
Date	**Account Titles and Explanation**		**PR**	**Debit**	**Credit**

AP-8B (❸ ❹ ❺ ❻ ❼)

Presto Chango has the following adjustments to make at the end of December 2016, the end of its fiscal year.

Dec 31   Salaries accrued but not yet paid amount to $750.

Dec 31   Unearned revenue of $620 has now been earned.

Dec 31   A count of the office supplies shows that $320 worth still remains on hand.

Dec 31   Interest accrued on the bank loan but not yet paid amount to $70.

Dec 31   Monthly depreciation on equipment was $400.

Presto Chango Chart of Accounts (GL No.)

Account Description	Account #
ASSETS	
Cash	101
Accounts Receivable	105
Office Supplies	110
Property, Plant & Equipment	120
Accumulated Depreciation	130
LIABILITIES	
Accounts Payable	200
Unearned Revenue	205
Interest Payable	210
Salaries Payable	220
Bank Loan	225

Account Description	Account #
OWNER'S EQUITY	
Presto, Capital	300
Presto, Drawings	310
REVENUE	
Service Revenue	400
EXPENSES	
Salaries Expense	520
Depreciation Expense	525
Interest Expense	530
Supplies Expense	535

Required

a) Complete the six-column worksheet.

b) Journalize the adjustments.

c) Post the transactions to the general ledger accounts provided.

Presto Chango Worksheet December 31, 2016						
	Unadjusted Trial Balance		Adjustments		Adjusted Trial Balance	
Account Titles	DR	CR	DR	CR	DR	CR
Cash	$4,200					
Accounts Receivable	1,350					
Office Supplies	680					
Property, Plant and Equipment	14,500					
Accumulated Depreciation		$800				
Accounts Payable		1,300				
Unearned Revenue		1,250				
Bank Loan		6,000				
Presto, Capital		4,880				
Presto, Drawings	800					
Service Revenue		8,700				
Salaries Expense	1,400					
Total						

JOURNAL				Page 2
Date	**Account Titles and Explanation**	**PR**	**Debit**	**Credit**

Account:					GL No:	
Date: 2016	**Description**	**PR**	**DR**	**CR**	**Balance (DR or CR)**	
	Opening Balance					

Account:					GL No:	
Date: 2016	**Description**	**PR**	**DR**	**CR**	**Balance (DR or CR)**	
	Opening Balance					

Account:					GL No:	
Date: 2016	**Description**	**PR**	**DR**	**CR**	**Balance (DR or CR)**	
	Opening Balance					

Account:					GL No:	
Date: 2016	**Description**	**PR**	**DR**	**CR**	**Balance (DR or CR)**	
	Opening Balance					

Account:					GL No:	
Date: 2016	**Description**	**PR**	**DR**	**CR**	**Balance (DR or CR)**	
	Opening Balance					

Account:					GL No:	
Date: 2016	**Description**	**PR**	**DR**	**CR**	**Balance (DR or CR)**	
	Opening Balance					

Account:					GL No:	
Date: 2016	**Description**	**PR**	**DR**	**CR**	**Balance (DR or CR)**	
	Opening Balance					

Account:					GL No:	
Date: 2016	**Description**	**PR**	**DR**	**CR**	**Balance (DR or CR)**	
	Opening Balance					

Account:					GL No:	
Date: 2016	**Description**	**PR**	**DR**	**CR**	**Balance (DR or CR)**	
	Opening Balance					

Account:					GL No:	
Date: 2016	**Description**	**PR**	**DR**	**CR**	**Balance (DR or CR)**	
	Opening Balance					

AP-9B (6)

On January 1, 2016, Hackerton purchased a new machine for $60,000. The machine is expected to last six years and will have no residual value. Hackerton has a December 31 year end. Prepare the table below showing the yearly depreciation, accumulated depreciation and net book value of the machine.

Year	Original Cost of Machine	Depreciation Expense	Accumulated Depreciation	Net Book Value
2016				
2017				
2018				
2019				
2020				
2021				
Total				

AP-10B (6)

On November 1, 2016, Gregory Accounting refurnished the entire office for $25,000. The furniture is expected to last four years and has an estimated residual value of $1,000. Gregory Accounting has a December 31 year end. Prepare the table below showing the yearly depreciation, accumulated depreciation and net book value of the furniture.

Year	Original Cost of Furniture	Depreciation Expense	Accumulated Depreciation	Net Book Value
2016				
2017				
2018				
2019				
2020				
Total				

AP-11B (⑧)

On August 16, 2016, the bookkeeper for Reliable Administration discovered an error in the journal entries. On August 9, an entry was made to pay for a one-year insurance policy for $1,800, however accounts payable was used in error, instead of cash. Prepare the entries to correct this error.

JOURNAL					Page 2
Date	Account Titles and Explanation	PR	Debit	Credit	

AP-12B (⑧)

On February 21, 2016, the bookkeeper for Balsdon Consulting discovered an error in the journal entries. On February 6, an entry was made to pay for repairs expense with $800 cash, however rent expense was debited in error. Prepare the entries to correct this error.

JOURNAL					Page 2
Date	Account Titles and Explanation	PR	Debit	Credit	

Case Study

CS-1 (❷ ❸ ❹ ❺ ❻)

One Stop Consulting is preparing year-end financial statements dated December 31, 2016 and has to make several adjustments before the financial statements can be prepared. The owner has approached the accountant with the following information.

1. A large contract worth a lot of money was started in November of this year that will be completed in early January. The customer will not pay until the contract is completed in January. The owner does not want to include any work already completed in revenue and would rather record the entire amount earned in January when the contract is complete.

2. Interest, utilities and salaries expense will be accrued on December 31, 2016. Utility bills are usually received on the 15th of the month and are usually the same amounts each month. The owner wants to accrue the full amount of the utilities on December 31, 2016 instead of just half that would normally be accrued.

3. An insurance policy was purchased in September covering one year. The owner wants to include the entire amount of the policy as an expense for the 2016 year end.

4. A customer paid a deposit in October for work to be completed in December and January. The initial receipt of cash was recorded in unearned revenue. The majority of the work was completed by December 31, 2016. The owner wants to wait until the work is 100% complete in January before recording any of it as revenue.

5. Equipment and furniture are depreciated using the straight-line method over five years. The owner wants to change the estimate from five years to three years for the depreciation calculation on December 31, 2016.

Required

a) For each action the owner wants, discover if there is any violation of ASPE principles or characteristics.

_____

_____

_____

_____

_____

_____

_____

_____

_____

_____

b) For each action the owner wants, identify how this would affect the financial statements.

_____

_____

_____

_____

_____

_____

_____

_____

c) What are some possible reasons the owner would want to make these changes to the adjustment process?

_____

_____

_____

_____

_____

_____

_____

AS-9 (❷)

What are the four steps to close the accounts using the income summary?

_____

_____

_____

AS-10 (❷)

If a company has a net income for the period and closes its books using the income summary account, will the income summary account have a debit or credit balance before it is closed to the capital account?

_____

_____

AS-11 (❸)

Which categories of accounts appear on the post-closing trial balance?

_____

_____

AS-12 (❼)

Identify two benefits of a computerized accounting system.

_____

_____

_____

AS-13 (❹)

Define current assets.

_____

_____

AS-14 (④)

Define long-term assets.

_____

_____

_____

AS-15 (④)

What are current liabilities? Provide two examples of current liabilities.

_____

_____

_____

AS-16 (④)

What are long-term liabilities? Provide two examples of long-term liabilities.

_____

_____

_____

AS-17 (⑤)

What is one difference between a non-classified balance sheet and a classified balance sheet?

_____

_____

_____

AS-18 (⑥)

How do you calculate the current ratio and what does it measure?

_____

_____

_____

Application Questions Group A

AP-1A (❶)

Floating Speed Boat has completed all its journal entries and adjusting entries for the month of September 2016. The adjusted trial balance is shown below.

Note: During the month of September, the owner of Floating Speed Boat invested $6,900 into the business.

Floating Speed Boat Adjusted Trial Balance September 30, 2016		
Account Titles	**DR**	**CR**
Cash	$8,800	
Accounts Receivable	7,900	
Prepaid Insurance	1,150	
Equipment	64,000	
Accumulated Depreciation		$1,260
Accounts Payable		9,900
Interest Payable		150
Unearned Revenue		5,930
Bank Loan		15,400
Murray, Capital		49,000
Murray, Drawings	1,200	
Service Revenue		3,970
Advertising Expense	430	
Depreciation Expense	390	
Insurance Expense	250	
Interest Expense	150	
Rent Expense	1,340	
Total	**$85,610**	**$85,610**

Required

Prepare the income statement, statement of owner's equity and the balance sheet from the adjusted trial balance.

Floating Speed Boat		
Income Statement		
For the Month Ended September		

Floating Speed boat Balance Sheet As at September 30, 2016		
Assets		
Cash		
Accounts receivible		
Pre paid insurance		
Equipment		

AP-2A (❶ ❷ ❸)

Regina Consulting has completed all its journal entries and adjusting entries for the month of October 2016. The adjusted trial balance is shown below.

Regina Consulting Adjusted Trial Balance October 31, 2016		
Account Titles	**DR**	**CR**
Cash	$32,000	
Accounts Receivable	9,500	
Prepaid Rent	4,680	
Equipment	15,000	
Accumulated Depreciation		$1,290
Accounts Payable		27,800
Unearned Revenue		4,470
Bank Loan		1,600
Regina, Capital		9,330
Service Revenue		31,330
Depreciation Expense	340	
Insurance Expense	570	
Interest Expense	150	
Rent Expense	720	
Salaries Expense	6,400	
Supplies Expense	360	
Utilities Expense	6,100	
Total	**$75,820**	**$75,820**

Required

a) Prepare the income statement, statement of owner's equity and the balance sheet from the adjusted trial balance.
b) Create the closing entries using the income summary account.
c) Prepare the post-closing trial balance.

a) Prepare the financial statements.

Regina Consulting		
Income Summary Account		

b) Prepare the closing entries.

JOURNAL					Page 1
Date	Account Title and Explanation	PR	Debit	Credit

c) Prepare the post-closing trial balance.

Account Titles	DR	CR

AP-3A (❷ ❸)

Keynote Consulting has journalized its adjusting entries and prepared its adjusted trial balance.

Keynote Consulting Adjusted Trial Balance August 31, 2016		
Account Titles	**DR**	**CR**
Cash	$6,200	
Accounts Receivable	1,750	
Prepaid Insurance	1,650	
Office Supplies	1,150	
Equipment	10,650	
Accumulated Depreciation		$320
Accounts Payable		1,640
Interest Payable		50
Unearned Revenue		1,420
Bank Loan		3,000
Nichols, Capital		14,290
Nichols, Drawings	2,000	
Service Revenue		4,100
Depreciation Expense	150	
Insurance Expense	170	
Interest Expense	50	
Rent Expense	800	
Telephone Expense	250	
Total	$24,820	$24,820

Required

a) Prepare the closing entries using the income summary account for the month of August.
b) Prepare the post-closing trial balance.

a) Closing entries

JOURNAL				Page 1
Date	**Account Title and Explanation**	**PR**	**Debit**	**Credit**

b) Post-closing trial balance

Account Titles	**DR**	**CR**

AP-4A (❷ ❸)

Frank's Custom Framing has journalized its adjusting entries and prepared its adjusted trial balance.

Frank's Custom Framing Adjusted Trial Balance October 31, 2016		
Account Titles	**DR**	**CR**
Cash	$8,620	
Accounts Receivable	2,340	
Prepaid Insurance	2,650	
Office Supplies	1,840	
Equipment	23,400	
Accumulated Depreciation		$1,640
Accounts Payable		3,540
Interest Payable		120
Unearned Revenue		2,110
Bank Loan		5,500
Frank, Capital		24,080
Frank, Drawings	3,200	
Service Revenue		8,750
Depreciation Expense	260	
Insurance Expense	185	
Interest Expense	120	
Rent Expense	1,200	
Telephone Expense	275	
Salaries Expense	1,650	
Total	**$45,740**	**$45,740**

Required

a) Prepare the closing entries using the income summary account for the month of October.
b) Prepare the post-closing trial balance.

a) Closing entries

JOURNAL				Page 1
Date	Account Title and Explanation	PR	Debit	Credit

b) Post-closing trial balance

AP-5A (❷ ❸)

Home Protector has journalized its adjusting entries and prepared its adjusted trial balance.

Home Protector Adjusted Trial Balance December 31, 2016		
Account Titles	**DR**	**CR**
Cash	$12,650	
Accounts Receivable	5,420	
Prepaid Insurance	2,820	
Office Supplies	2,240	
Equipment	25,600	
Accumulated Depreciation		$2,340
Accounts Payable		6,250
Salaries Payable		650
Unearned Revenue		4,250
Bank Loan		7,500
Holmes, Capital		21,645
Holmes, Drawings	4,300	
Service Revenue		16,875
Depreciation Expense	320	
Insurance Expense	220	
Interest Expense	160	
Rent Expense	1,890	
Telephone Expense	350	
Salaries Expense	3,540	
Total	**$59,510**	**$59,510**

Required

a) Prepare the closing entries directly to owner's capital for the month of December.
b) Prepare the post-closing trial balance.

a) Closing entries

JOURNAL				Page 1
Date	**Account Title and Explanation**	**PR**	**Debit**	**Credit**
	Income summary account		6480	
	DE			320
	I F			220
	I E			160
	R E			1890
	T E			350
	SE			3540
	Closing of Expense accounts			
	Service Revenue		16875	
	Income summary account			16875
	Holmes, Drawings			4300
	Income summary account		4300	
	Income summary account		6095	
	Capital			6095

b) Post-closing trial balance

Account Titles	DR	CR

AP-6A (❷ ❸)

Luminary Electric has journalized its adjusting entries and prepared its adjusted trial balance.

Luminary Electric Adjusted Trial Balance March 31, 2016		
Account Titles	**DR**	**CR**
Cash	$10,420	
Accounts Receivable	6,350	
Prepaid Insurance	2,350	
Office Supplies	1,860	
Equipment	32,500	
Accumulated Depreciation		$5,480
Accounts Payable		4,870
Salaries Payable		840
Unearned Revenue		5,340
Bank Loan		9,000
Watts, Capital		23,745
Watts, Drawings	5,200	
Service Revenue		17,850
Depreciation Expense	410	
Insurance Expense	195	
Interest Expense	210	
Office Supplies Expense	670	
Rent Expense	2,150	
Telephone Expense	450	
Salaries Expense	4,360	
Total	**$67,125**	**$67,125**

Required

a) Prepare the closing entries directly to owner's capital for the month of March.
b) Prepare the post-closing trial balance.

a) Closing entries

| JOURNAL | | | | Page 1 |
Date	Account Title and Explanation	PR	Debit	Credit

b) Post-closing trial balance

Account Titles	DR	CR

AP-7A (❶ ❷ ❸)

Thomas Topology has completed all its journal entries and adjusting entries for the month of April 2016. The chart of accounts and adjusted trial balance are shown below.

Account Description	Account #
ASSETS	
Cash	101
Accounts Receivable	105
Prepaid Insurance	110
Equipment	120
Accumulated Depreciation	125
LIABILITIES	
Accounts Payable	200
Unearned Revenue	210
Bank Loan	215
OWNER'S EQUITY	
Thompson, Capital	300
Thompson, Drawings	310
Income Summary	315

Account Description	Account #
REVENUE	
Service Revenue	400
EXPENSES	
Depreciation Expense	510
Insurance Expense	515
Interest Expense	520
Rent Expense	540
Salaries Expense	545
Telephone Expense	550
Travel Expense	555

Thomas Topology Adjusted Trial Balance April 30, 2016		
Account Titles	**DR**	**CR**
Cash	$32,050	
Accounts Receivable	9,000	
Prepaid Insurance	1,100	
Equipment	15,000	
Accumulated Depreciation		$120
Accounts Payable		25,550
Unearned Revenue		3,200
Bank Loan		1,500
Thompson, Capital		18,000
Service Revenue		26,300
Depreciation Expense	120	
Insurance Expense	100	
Interest Expense	50	
Rent Expense	1,000	
Salaries Expense	8,000	
Telephone Expense	250	
Travel Expense	8,000	
Total	$74,670	$74,670

Required

a) Prepare the income statement, statement of owner's equity and the balance sheet.
b) Create the closing entries using the income summary account and post the closing entries to the ledger accounts. The ledger accounts are presented at the end of this question.
c) Prepare the post-closing trial balance.

Note: The daily transactions and adjustments for the month of April have already been posted in the general ledger. You are only responsible for posting the closing entries.

a) Prepare the financial statements.

Income Statement

Revenue	26,300	
Expenses	17,520	
Net income	8,780	

Statement of owner's equity

Tompson capital	18,000	
Net income	8,780	
Cash balance =	26,780	

b) Prepare the closing entries.

JOURNAL				Page 3
Date	Account Title and Explanation	PR	Debit	Credit

c) Prepare the post-closing trial balance.

Account Titles	DR	CR

GENERAL LEDGER

Account:	Cash				GL. No: 101	
Date	**Description**	**PR**	**DR**	**CR**	**Balance**	
2016						
Apr 1	Opening Balance				22,000	DR
Apr 2		J1	25,000		47,000	DR
Apr 3		J1		1,000	46,000	DR
Apr 4		J1		1,200	44,800	DR
Apr 10		J1		200	44,600	DR
Apr 14		J1		8,000	36,600	DR
Apr 20		J1		50	36,550	DR
Apr 30		J1		4,500	32,050	DR

Account:	Accounts Receivable				GL No: 105	
Date	**Description**	**PR**	**DR**	**CR**	**Balance**	
2016						
Apr 1	Opening Balance				9,000	DR

Account:	Prepaid Insurance				GL No: 110	
Date	**Description**	**PR**	**DR**	**CR**	**Balance**	
2016						
Apr 1	Opening Balance				0	DR
Apr 4		J1	1,200		1,200	DR
Apr 30	Adjustment	J2		100	1,100	DR

Account:	Equipment				GL No: 120	
Date	**Description**	**PR**	**DR**	**CR**	**Balance**	
2016						
Apr 1	Opening Balance				8,000	DR
Apr 1		J1	7,000		15,000	DR

Account:	Accumulated Depreciation				GL No: 125	
Date	**Description**	**PR**	**DR**	**CR**	**Balance**	
2016						
Apr 30	Adjustment	J2		120	120	CR

Account:	Accounts Payable				GL No: 200	
Date	Description	PR	DR	CR	Balance	
2016						
Apr 1	Opening Balance				10,500	CR
Apr 1		J1		7,000	17,500	CR
Apr 10		J1	200		17,300	CR
Apr 22		J1		250	17,550	CR
Apr 24		J1		8,000	25,550	CR

Account:	Unearned Revenue				GL No: 210	
Date	Description	PR	DR	CR	Balance	
2016						
Apr 1	Opening Balance				4,500	CR
Apr 30	Adjustment	J2	1,300		3,200	CR

Account:	Bank Loan				GL No: 215	
Date	Description	PR	DR	CR	Balance	
2016						
Apr 1	Opening Balance				6,000	CR
Apr 30		J1	4,500		1,500	CR

Account:	Thompson, Capital				GL No: 300	
Date	Description	PR	DR	CR	Balance	
2016						
Apr 1	Opening Balance				18,000	CR

Account:	Thompson, Drawings				GL No: 310	
Date	Description	PR	DR	CR	Balance	

Account:	Income Summary				GL No: 315	
Date	Description	PR	DR	CR	Balance	

Account:	Service Revenue				GL No: 400	
Date	Description	PR	DR	CR	Balance	
2016						
Apr 2		J1		25,000	25,000	CR
Apr 30	Adjustment	J2		1,300	26,300	CR

Account:	Depreciation Expense				GL No: 510	
Date	Description	PR	DR	CR	Balance	
2016						
Apr 30	Adjustment	J2	120		120	DR

Account:	Insurance Expense				GL No: 515	
Date	Description	PR	DR	CR	Balance	
2016						
Apr 30	Adjustment	J2	100		100	DR

Account:	Interest Expense				GL No: 520	
Date	Description	PR	DR	CR	Balance	
2016						
Apr 20		J1	50		50	DR

Account:	Rent Expense				GL No: 540	
Date	Description	PR	DR	CR	Balance	
2016						
Apr 3		J1	1,000		1,000	DR

Account: Salaries Expense					GL No: 545	
Date	Description	PR	DR	CR	Balance	
2016						
Apr 14		J1	8,000		8,000	DR

Account: Telephone Expense					GL No: 550	
Date	Description	PR	DR	CR	Balance	
2016						
Apr 22		J1	250		250	DR

Account: Travel Expense					GL No: 555	
Date	Description	PR	DR	CR	Balance	
2016						
Apr 24		J1	8,000		8,000	DR

AP-8A (❶ ❷ ❸)

Space Jam Storage offers storage space and transportation services for customers. Space Jam Storage has already completed most of the transactions for the month and posted them to the general ledger. The following transactions during December 2016 have not yet been prepared.

Dec 2   Prepaid $12,000 for one year of insurance in advance.

Dec 5   Paid $1,400 cash for regular maintenance on delivery vehicles.

Dec 12   The owner, Stephen Bugs, withdrew $3,500 cash from the business for personal use.

Dec 18   Received $2,200 cash payment from a customer for future storage services.

Dec 23   Paid $1,000 to reduce the bank loan, of which $870 was principal and the rest was interest.

Dec 28   Received $450 cash from a customer who owed money for previous services.

Required

a) Prepare the journal entries for the above transactions.

JOURNAL				Page 1
Date	**Account Title and Explanation**	**PR**	**Debit**	**Credit**

b) Post the above journal entries to the general ledger. The chart of accounts is shown below for your reference.

Account Description	Account #
ASSETS	
Cash	101
Accounts Receivable	105
Prepaid Insurance	110
Equipment	120
Accumulated Depreciation	125
LIABILITIES	
Accounts Payable	200
Salaries Payable	210
Unearned Revenue	220
Bank Loan	250

Account Description	Account #
OWNER'S EQUITY	
Bugs, Capital	300
Bugs, Drawings	310
Income Summary	315
REVENUE	
Service Revenue	400
EXPENSES	
Maintenance Expense	500
Depreciation Expense	520
Interest Expense	540
Insurance Expense	560
Salaries Expense	570

GENERAL LEDGER

Account:	Cash				GL No: 101	
Date	**Description**	**PR**	**DR**	**CR**	**Balance (DR or CR)**	
2016	Opening Balance				18,500	DR

Account:	Accounts Receivable				GL No: 105	
Date	**Description**	**PR**	**DR**	**CR**	**Balance (DR or CR)**	
2016	Opening Balance				3,200	DR

Account:	Prepaid Insurance				GL No: 110	
Date	**Description**	**PR**	**DR**	**CR**	**Balance (DR or CR)**	
2016	Opening Balance				1,000	DR

Account:	Equipment				GL No: 120	
Date	**Description**	**PR**	**DR**	**CR**	**Balance (DR or CR)**	
2016	Opening Balance				285,000	DR

Account:	Accumulated Depreciation				GL No: 125	
Date	Description	PR	DR	CR	Balance (DR or CR)	
2016	Opening Balance				45,000	CR

Account:	Accounts Payable				GL No: 200	
Date	Description	PR	DR	CR	Balance (DR or CR)	
2016	Opening Balance				5,500	CR

Account:	Salaries Payable				GL No: 210	
Date	Description	PR	DR	CR	Balance (DR or CR)	
2016	Opening Balance				0	CR

Account:	Unearned Revenue				GL No: 220	
Date	Description	PR	DR	CR	Balance (DR or CR)	
2016	Opening Balance				1,400	CR

Account:	Bank Loan				GL No: 250	
Date	Description	PR	DR	CR	Balance (DR or CR)	
2016	Opening Balance				192,550	CR

Account:	Bugs, Capital				GL No: 300	
Date	Description	PR	DR	CR	Balance (DR or CR)	
2016	Opening Balance				46,200	CR

Account:	Bugs, Drawings				GL No: 310	
Date	Description	PR	DR	CR	Balance (DR or CR)	
2016	Opening Balance				10,000	DR

Account:	Income Summary				GL No: 315	
Date	Description	PR	DR	CR	Balance (DR or CR)	
2016	Opening Balance				0	CR

Account:	Service Revenue				GL No: 400	
Date	Description	PR	DR	CR	Balance (DR or CR)	
2016	Opening Balance				78,000	CR

Account:	Maintenance Expense				GL No: 500	
Date	Description	PR	DR	CR	Balance (DR or CR)	
2016	Opening Balance				3,800	DR

Account:	Depreciation Expense				GL No: 520	
Date	Description	PR	DR	CR	Balance (DR or CR)	
2016	Opening Balance				4,000	DR

Account:	Interest Expense				GL No: 540	
Date	Description	PR	DR	CR	Balance (DR or CR)	
2016	Opening Balance				1,150	DR

Account:	Insurance Expense				GL No: 560	
Date	Description	PR	DR	CR	Balance (DR or CR)	
2016	Opening Balance				11,000	DR

Account:	Salaries Expense				GL No: 570	
Date	Description	PR	DR	CR	Balance (DR or CR)	
2016	Opening Balance				31,000	DR

c) Prepare a six-column worksheet, starting with the account balances from the general ledger above. Space Jam Storage had the following year-end adjustments.

Dec 31   Provided $1,500 worth of services to customer who paid in advance.

Dec 31   One month of insurance worth $1,000 has been used.

Dec 31   One month of depreciation is $500.

Dec 31   Accrued salaries owed to employees worth $3,370.

Account Titles	Unadjusted Trial Balance		Adjustments		Adjusted Trial Balance	
	DR	CR	DR	CR	DR	CR

d)   Prepare the financial statements for Space Jam Storage.

e) Record the journal entries for the adjusting and closing transactions. Use the income summary method. Post these entries in the general ledger above from part (b).

JOURNAL				Page 2
Date	Account Title and Explanation	PR	Debit	Credit

f) Prepare the post-closing trial balance for Space Jam Storage.

Account Titles	DR	CR

Analysis

The accountant for Space Jam Storage found that a journal entry back in November had been entered incorrectly. The account that should have been debited was credited and vice versa. Why wasn't this error detected during the preparation of trial balances and financial statements?

_____

_____

_____

_____

_____

Classified balance sheet
long term and short term
Assets split up

AP-9A (❹)

The following information is taken from the records of Ginger Consulting.

Accounts Payable	$19,000
Short-Term Investment	12,000
Land	52,000
Cash	23,000
Factory Equipment	29,000
Loans Payable	30,000
Office Furniture	18,000
Prepaid Expense	9,000
Unearned Revenue	6,000

Required

a) Calculate total current assets.

_____

_____

_____

b) Calculate total long-term assets.

_____

_____

_____

c) Calculate total assets.

_____

_____

AP-10A (❹)

Suppose a business has a $400,000 long-term bank loan on December 31, 2016. The borrowing arrangement requires the business to pay $100,000 of this debt by September 2017. Show how the business will report both current and long-term liabilities on its December 31, 2016 balance sheet.

_____

_____

_____

AP 3- 5 chapters

AP-11A (④)

Pelican Accounting borrowed a $1,000,000 interest-free bank loan on January 1, 2016. Payment is agreed to be made in four years in four equal annual installments. Calculate the current and long-term liabilities as at December 31 for the following years.

	As at December 31			
	2016	**2017**	**2018**	**2019**
Current portion of loan payable				
Long-term loan payable				

AP-12A (④)

Renegade Landscaping's general ledger includes the following account balances on December 31, 2016.

Accounts Payable	$12,000
Interest Payable	3,000
Salaries Payable	2,000
Bank Loan	
Current Portion	10,000
Long-Term Portion	20,000

Required

a) Calculate current liabilities.

_____

_____

_____

b) Calculate long-term liabilities.

_____

_____

AP-13A (❹)

For the following independent transactions, determine the amount of current and long-term liabilities.

year ends 2017

	Transaction	Current Liability	Long-Term Liability
1.	On December 31, 2016, Frankie Flowershop borrowed $300,000 from the bank. The entire amount is due on December 30, 2017.	300000	—
2.	KLM Company purchased a small building at a cost of $190,000. The down payment is $100,000. The remaining balance is payable in three years with an annual payment of $30,000, starting next year.	30 000	60 000
3.	During June 2016, a business owner obtained an interest-free loan from a financing company. The loan amount was $60,000. The agreed terms of payment is four annual installments of $15,000.	15 000	45 000
4.	A business owner borrowed $20,000 from his close friend for a business expansion. They both signed an agreement that the payment will be made after two years.	—	20 000

AP-14A (❹ ❺ ❻)

Empowered Solutions has the following balances as at May 31, 2016.

Cash	$22,000
Accounts Receivable	15,000
Inventory	12,000
Equipment	73,000
Accounts Payable	13,000
Unearned Revenue	8,000
Current Portion of Bank Loan	10,000
Long-Term Portion of Bank Loan	20,000
Powers, Capital	71,000

Required

a)   Prepare a classified balance sheet using the balances listed above.

b) Calculate the working capital for Empowered Solutions.

_____

c) Calculate the current ratio for Empowered Solutions.

_____

d) Calculate the quick ratio for Empowered Solutions.

_____

AP-15A (❹ ❺ ❻)

Below is Preston Services' financial accounting information for the year ending September 30, 2016. Assume all accounts have a normal balance.

Cash	$7,500
Accounts Receivable	2,400
Inventory	6,000
Prepaid Insurance	1,800
Equipment	35,000
Accumulated Depreciation	800
Accounts Payable	5,100
Unearned Revenue	1,100
Bank Loan	18,000
Presto, Capital	27,700

The bank loan is payable over 3 years and $6,000 will be paid by September 30, 2017.

Required

a) Prepare a classified balance sheet.

b) Calculate the working capital for Preston Services.

c) Calculate the current ratio for Preston Services.

d) Calculate the quick ratio for Preston Services.

AP-16A (❽)

Below, is Coleson Services' unadjusted trial balance at the end of December 2016. Adjusting entries have not yet been made. Use the trial balance and the information below to complete the worksheet.

Dec 31   A physical count showed that $320 of supplies is still on hand.

Dec 31   The equipment was purchased at the beginning of the year and is expected to last four years and no residual value.

Dec 31   Of the balance of unearned revenue, $600 has been earned.

Dec 31   The amount in prepaid insurance is for an annual policy that was paid on September 1, 2016.

	Coleson Services Worksheet December 31, 2016									
	Unadjusted Trial Balance		Adjustments		Adjusted Trial Balance		Income Statement		Balance Sheet	
Account Titles	DR	CR	DR	CR	DR	CR	DR	CR	DR	CR
Cash	$1,500									
Accounts Receivable	3,000									
Prepaid Insurance	1,800									
Office Supplies	800									
Equipment	6,000									
Accumulated Depreciation		$0								
Accounts Payable		4,000								
Unearned Revenue		1,000								
Bank Loan		2,500								
Coleson, Capital		2,850								
Coleson, Drawings	1,200									
Service Revenue		8,000								
Depreciation Expense	0									
Insurance Expense	0									
Interest Expense	0									
Maintenance Expense	900									
Supplies Expense	0									
Rent Expense	1,900									
Salaries Expense	150									
Telephone Expense	700									
Travel Expense	400									
Total	$18,350	$18,350								
Net Income										
Total										

——————— **Application Questions Group B** ———————

AP-1B (❶)

Below is Caprio Services' adjusted trial balance for the year ending December 31, 2016. Using this information, prepare the income statement, statement of owner's equity and then the balance sheet for the end of December 31, 2016.

Caprio Services Adjusted Trial Balance December 31, 2016		
Account Titles	DR	CR
Cash	$90,200	
Accounts Receivable	47,800	
Prepaid Insurance	32,000	
Equipment	415,000	
Accumulated Depreciation		$145,000
Accounts Payable		26,000
Unearned Revenue		15,800
Bank Loan		260,000
Caprio, Capital		108,200
Caprio, Drawings	40,000	
Service Revenue		545,000
Advertising Expense	100,000	
Insurance Expense	40,000	
Maintenance Expense	5,900	
Rent Expense	78,000	
Salaries Expense	228,500	
Telephone Expense	3,200	
Travel Expense	19,400	
Total	**$1,100,000**	**$1,100,000**

Note: During the year, the owner contributed $20,000 to the business. This has been included in Caprio, Capital already.

Analysis

In the accounting cycle, why is the income statement prepared first, then the statement of owner's equity, and finally the balance sheet?

_____

_____

_____

_____

AP-2B (❶)

Counterpoint Studios has completed all the entries for the month of November 2016, except the monthly adjusting entries. The following information is available to make the adjustments.

- Annual depreciation on property, plant, and equipment totals $9,000.
- Interest accrued on the bank loan is $500.
- Office supplies on hand are valued at $2,300.
- The annual insurance policy was purchased December 1, 2015 for $21,900.
- The balance of owner's equity at the beginning of November was $86,750.

Required

a) Complete the six-column worksheet for Counterpoint Studios.

	Counterpoint Studios Worksheet November 30, 2016					
	Unadjusted Trial Balance		**Adjustments**		**Adjusted Trial Balance**	
Account Titles	**DR**	**CR**	**DR**	**CR**	**DR**	**CR**
Cash	$52,250					
Accounts Receivable	24,800					
Office Supplies	10,400					
Prepaid Insurance	1,825					
Equipment	295,400					
Accumulated Depreciation		$107,250				
Accounts Payable		31,500				
Bank Loan		140,000				
Wu, Capital		96,750				
Wu, Drawings	60,000					
Service Revenue		382,500				
Advertising Expense	100,000					
Salaries Expense	185,000					
Insurance Expense	20,075					
Depreciation Expense	8,250					
Total	$758,000	$758,000				

b) Prepare the income statement, statement of owner's equity and balance sheet.

AP-3B (❷ ❸)

Jim's Custom Painting has journalized its adjusting entries and prepared its adjusted trial balance.

Jim's Custom Painting Adjusted Trial Balance August 31, 2016		
Account Titles	**DR**	**CR**
Cash	$8,400	
Accounts Receivable	2,900	
Prepaid Rent	2,100	
Office Supplies	2,400	
Equipment	20,700	
Accumulated Depreciation		$2,700
Accounts Payable		3,200
Interest Payable		300
Unearned Revenue		2,900
Mortgage Payable		5,400
Gordon, Capital		22,360
Gordon, Drawings	4,000	
Service Revenue		7,600
Depreciation Expense	150	
Insurance Expense	240	
Interest Expense	300	
Rent Expense	1,420	
Supplies Expense	350	
Travel Expense	1,500	
Total	**$44,460**	**$44,460**

Required

a) Prepare the closing entries using the income summary account for the month of August.
b) Prepare the post-closing trial balance.

a) Closing entries

JOURNAL				Page 1
Date	**Account Title and Explanation**	**PR**	**Debit**	**Credit**

b) Post-closing trial balance

Account Titles	DR	CR

AP-4B (❷)

Portal Delivery Services has prepared its income statement and statement of owner's equity.

Portal Delivery Services Income Statement For the Year Ended October 31, 2016		
Service Revenue		$500,000
Expenses		
Transportation Expense	$95,000	
Salaries Expense	240,000	
Maintenance Expense	70,000	
Depreciation Expense	45,000	
Total Expenses		450,000
Net Income (Loss)		$50,000

Portal Delivery Services Statement of Owner's Equity For the Year Ended October 31, 2016		
Jones, Capital at November 1, 2015		$120,000
Add		
Additional Investments	$30,000	
Net Income (Loss)	50,000	80,000
Subtotal		200,000
Less		
Jones, Drawings		100,000
Jones, Capital at October 31, 2016		$100,000

Required

Prepare the closing entries using the income summary method for Portal Delivery Services.

JOURNAL				Page 1
Date	**Account Title and Explanation**	**PR**	**Debit**	**Credit**

Analysis

What is the purpose of preparing closing entries at the end of each period? Explain.

_____

_____

_____

_____

_____

AP-5B (❷ ❸)

Home Protector has journalized its adjusting entries and prepared its adjusted trial balance.

Home Protector Adjusted Trial Balance January 31, 2016		
Account Titles	DR	CR
Cash	$14,200	
Accounts Receivable	6,900	
Prepaid Services	4,000	
Office Supplies	2,000	
Equipment	37,700	
Accumulated Depreciation		$5,700
Accounts Payable		4,800
Salaries Payable		950
Unearned Revenue		4,800
Mortgage Payable		8,800
Sherlock, Capital		32,750
Sherlock, Drawings	4,900	
Service Revenue		18,200
Depreciation Expense	350	
Insurance Expense	290	
Maintenance Expense	470	
Rent Expense	1,500	
Telephone Expense	490	
Utilities Expense	3,200	
Total	$76,000	$76,000

Required

a) Prepare the closing entries directly to owner's capital for the month of January.
b) Prepare the post-closing trial balance.

a) Closing entries

JOURNAL				Page 1
Date	**Account Title and Explanation**	**PR**	**Debit**	**Credit**

b) Post-closing trial balance

Account Titles	**DR**	**CR**

AP-6B (❷ ❸)

Health Foods has journalized its adjusting entries and prepared its adjusted trial balance.

Health Foods Adjusted Trial Balance May 31, 2016		
Account Titles	DR	CR
Cash	$14,800	
Accounts Receivable	7,600	
Prepaid Rent	3,300	
Office Supplies	2,300	
Equipment	39,300	
Accumulated Depreciation		$5,200
Accounts Payable		4,200
Salaries Payable		980
Unearned Revenue		4,800
Mortgage Payable		11,000
Schmitt, Capital		34,820
Schmitt, Drawings	4,400	
Service Revenue		17,000
Depreciation Expense	140	
Insurance Expense	140	
Maintenance Expense	160	
Office Supplies Expense	880	
Rent Expense	1,400	
Telephone Expense	280	
Utilities Expense	3,300	
Total	$78,000	$78,000

Required

a) Prepare the closing entries directly to owner's capital for the month of May.
b) Prepare the post-closing trial balance.

a) Closing entries

JOURNAL				Page 1
Date	Account Title and Explanation	PR	Debit	Credit

b) Post-closing trial balance

Account Titles	DR	CR

AP-7B (❶ ❷ ❸)

High Flying Biplane has completed all its journal entries and adjusting entries for the month of June 2016. The chart of accounts and adjusted trial balance are shown below.

Account Description	Account #
ASSETS	
Cash	101
Accounts Receivable	105
Prepaid Insurance	110
Equipment	120
Accumulated Depreciation	125
LIABILITIES	
Accounts Payable	200
Interest Payable	205
Unearned Revenue	210
Bank Loan	215
OWNER'S EQUITY	
Singh, Capital	300
Singh, Drawings	310
Income Summary	315

Account Description	Account #
REVENUE	
Service Revenue	400
EXPENSES	
Advertising Expense	500
Depreciation Expense	510
Insurance Expense	515
Interest Expense	520
Telephone Expense	550

High Flying Biplane Adjusted Trial Balance June 30, 2016		
Account Titles	**DR**	**CR**
Cash	$8,800	
Accounts Receivable	6,800	
Prepaid Insurance	1,100	
Equipment	64,000	
Accumulated Depreciation		$450
Accounts Payable		7,700
Interest Payable		75
Unearned Revenue		4,080
Bank Loan		19,000
Singh, Capital		48,800
Singh, Drawings	1,200	
Service Revenue		3,020
Advertising Expense	400	
Depreciation Expense	450	
Insurance Expense	100	
Interest Expense	75	
Telephone Expense	200	
Total	$83,125	$83,125

Required

a) Prepare the income statement, statement of owner's equity and the balance sheet.
b) Create the closing entries using the income summary account and post the closing entries to the ledger accounts.
c) Prepare the post-closing trial balance.

Note: The daily transactions and adjustments for the month of June have already been posted in the general ledger. You are only responsible for posting the closing entries.

a) Prepare financial statements.

b) Prepare the closing entries.

JOURNAL					Page 3
Date	**Account Title and Explanation**	**PR**	**Debit**	**Credit**	

c) Prepare the post-closing trial balance.

Account Titles	DR	CR

GENERAL LEDGER

Account: Cash   GL. No: 101

Date	Description	PR	DR	CR	Balance	
2016						
Jun 1	Opening Balance				8,000	DR
Jun 1		J1	5,000		13,000	DR
Jun 2		J1	1,500		14,500	DR
Jun 4		J1		200	14,300	DR
Jun 14		J1		4,000	10,300	DR
Jun 20		J1	1,600		11,900	DR
Jun 22		J1		900	11,000	DR
Jun 24		J1		1,000	10,000	DR
Jun 30		J1		1,200	8,800	DR

Account: Accounts Receivable   GL No: 105

Date	Description	PR	DR	CR	Balance	
2016						
Jun 1	Opening Balance				6,000	DR
Jun 10		J1	2,400		8,400	DR
Jun 20		J1		1,600	6,800	DR

Account: Prepaid Insurance   GL No: 110

Date	Description	PR	DR	CR	Balance	
2016						
Jun 1	Opening Balance				1,200	DR
Jun 30	Adjustment	J2		100	1,100	DR

Account: Equipment   GL No: 120

Date	Description	PR	DR	CR	Balance	
2016						
Jun 1	Opening Balance				60,000	DR
Jun 14		J1	4,000		64,000	DR

Account: Accumulated Depreciation   GL No: 125

Date	Description	PR	DR	CR	Balance	
2016						
Jun 30	Adjustment	J2		450	450	CR

Account:	Accounts Payable				GL No: 200	
Date	**Description**	**PR**	**DR**	**CR**	**Balance**	
2016						
Jun 1	Opening Balance				8,200	CR
Jun 3		J1		400	8,600	CR
Jun 22		J1	900		7,700	CR

Account:	Interest Payable				GL No: 205	
Date	**Description**	**PR**	**DR**	**CR**	**Balance**	
2016						
Jun 30	Adjustment	J2		75	75	CR

Account:	Unearned Revenue				GL No: 210	
Date	**Description**	**PR**	**DR**	**CR**	**Balance**	
2016						
Jun 1	Opening Balance				3,200	CR
Jun 2		J1		1,500	4,700	CR
Jun 30	Adjustment	J2	620		4,080	CR

Account:	Bank Loan				GL No: 215	
Date	**Description**	**PR**	**DR**	**CR**	**Balance**	
2016						
Jun 1	Opening Balance				20,000	CR
Jun 24		J1	1,000		19,000	CR

Account:	Singh, Capital				GL No: 300	
Date	**Description**	**PR**	**DR**	**CR**	**Balance**	
2016						
Jun 1	Opening Balance				43,800	CR
Jun 1		J1		5,000	48,800	CR

Account: Singh, Drawings   **GL No: 310**

Date	Description	PR	DR	CR	Balance	
2016						
Jun 30		J1	1,200		1,200	DR

Account: Income Summary   **GL No: 315**

Date	Description	PR	DR	CR	Balance

Account: Service Revenue   **GL No: 400**

Date	Description	PR	DR	CR	Balance	
2016						
Jun 10		J1		2,400	2,400	CR
Jun 30	Adjustment	J2		620	3,020	CR

Account: Advertising Expense   **GL No: 500**

Date	Description	PR	DR	CR	Balance	
2016						
Jun 3		J1	400		400	DR

Account: Depreciation Expense   **GL No: 510**

Date	Description	PR	DR	CR	Balance	
2016						
Jun 30	Adjustment	J2	450		450	DR

Account: Insurance Expense   **GL No: 515**

Date	Description	PR	DR	CR	Balance	
2016						
Jun 30	Adjustment	J2	100		100	DR

Account:	Interest Expense					GL No: 520	
Date	**Description**	**PR**	**DR**	**CR**	**Balance**	
2016						
Jun 30	Adjustment	J2	75		75	DR

Account:	Telephone Expense					GL No: 550	
Date	**Description**	**PR**	**DR**	**CR**	**Balance**	
2016						
Jun 4		J1	200		200	DR

AP-8B (❶ ❷ ❸)

Limbo Lower has completed all its journal entries and adjusting entries for the month of September 2016. The chart of accounts and adjusted trial balance are shown below.

Account Description	Account #
ASSETS	
Cash	101
Accounts Receivable	105
Prepaid Insurance	110
Office Supplies	115
Equipment	120
Accumulated Depreciation	125
LIABILITIES	
Accounts Payable	200
Unearned Revenue	210
Bank Loan	215
OWNER'S EQUITY	
Patel, Capital	300
Patel, Drawings	310
Income Summary	315

Account Description	Account #
REVENUE	
Service Revenue	400
EXPENSES	
Depreciation Expense	510
Insurance Expense	515
Interest Expense	520
Office Supplies Expense	530
Rent Expense	540

Limbo Lower Adjusted Trial Balance September 30, 2016		
Account Titles	**DR**	**CR**
Cash	$5,800	
Accounts Receivable	1,450	
Prepaid Insurance	1,650	
Office Supplies	650	
Equipment	9,300	
Accumulated Depreciation		$120
Accounts Payable		3,050
Unearned Revenue		1,040
Bank Loan		4,640
Patel, Capital		11,450
Patel, Drawings	1,600	
Service Revenue		2,260
Depreciation Expense	120	
Insurance Expense	150	
Interest Expense	40	
Office Supplies Expense	450	
Rent Expense	1,350	
Total	$22,560	$22,560

Required

a) Prepare the income statement, statement of owner's equity and the balance sheet.

b) Create the closing entries using the income summary account and post the closing entries to the ledger accounts.

c) Prepare the post-closing trial balance.

Note: The daily transactions and adjustments for the month of September have already been posted in the general ledger. You are only responsible for posting the closing entries.

a) Prepare the financial statements.

b) Prepare the closing entries.

JOURNAL				Page 3
Date	Account Title and Explanation	PR	Debit	Credit

c) Prepare the post-closing trial balance.

Account Titles	DR	CR

GENERAL LEDGER

Account:	Cash				GL. No: 101	
Date	**Description**	**PR**	**DR**	**CR**	**Balance**	
2016						
Sep 1	Opening Balance				7,200	DR
Sep 1		J1		1,800	5,400	DR
Sep 2		J1	1,900		7,300	DR
Sep 3		J1		1,350	5,950	DR
Sep 10		J1		40	5,910	DR
Sep 10		J1		960	4,950	DR
Sep 20		J1	2,200		7,150	DR
Sep 22		J1	850		8,000	DR
Sep 24		J1		600	7,400	DR
Sep 30		J1		1,600	5,800	DR

Account:	Accounts Receivable				GL No: 105	
Date	**Description**	**PR**	**DR**	**CR**	**Balance**	
2016						
Sep 1	Opening Balance				2,300	DR
Sep 22		J1		850	1,450	DR

Account:	Prepaid Insurance				GL No: 110	
Date	**Description**	**PR**	**DR**	**CR**	**Balance**	
2016						
Sep 1	Opening Balance				0	DR
Sep 1		J1	1,800		1,800	DR
Sep 30	Adjustment	J2		150	1,650	DR

Account:	Office Supplies				GL No: 115	
Date	**Description**	**PR**	**DR**	**CR**	**Balance**	
2016						
Sep 1	Opening Balance				850	DR
Sep 4		J1	250		1,100	DR
Sep 30	Adjustment	J2		450	650	DR

Account:	Equipment				GL No: 120	
Date	Description	PR	DR	CR	Balance	
2016						
Sep 1	Opening Balance				11,500	DR
Sep 20		J1		2,200	9,300	DR

Account:	Accumulated Depreciation				GL No: 125	
Date	Description	PR	DR	CR	Balance	
2016						
Sep 30	Adjustment	J2		120	120	CR

Account:	Accounts Payable				GL No: 200	
Date	Description	PR	DR	CR	Balance	
2016						
Sep 1	Opening Balance				3,400	CR
Sep 4		J1		250	3,650	CR
Sep 24		J1	600		3,050	CR

Account:	Unearned Revenue				GL No: 210	
Date	Description	PR	DR	CR	Balance	
2016						
Sep 1	Opening Balance				1,400	CR
Sep 30	Adjustment	J2	360		1,040	CR

Account:	Bank Loan				GL No: 215	
Date	Description	PR	DR	CR	Balance	
2016						
Sep 1	Opening Balance				5,600	CR
Sep 10		J1	960		4,640	CR

Account:	Patel, Capital				GL No: 300	
Date	Description	PR	DR	CR	Balance	
2016						
Sep 1	Opening Balance				11,450	CR

Account:	Patel, Drawings					GL No: 310	
Date	**Description**	**PR**	**DR**	**CR**	**Balance**	
2016						
Sep 30		J1	1,600		1,600	DR

Account:	Income Summary					GL No: 315	
Date	**Description**	**PR**	**DR**	**CR**	**Balance**	

Account:	Service Revenue					GL No: 400	
Date	**Description**	**PR**	**DR**	**CR**	**Balance**	
2016						
Sep 2		J1		1,900	1,900	CR
Sep 30	Adjustment	J2		360	2,260	CR

Account:	Depreciation Expense					GL No: 510	
Date	**Description**	**PR**	**DR**	**CR**	**Balance**	
2016						
Sep 30	Adjustment	J2	120		120	DR

Account:	Insurance Expense					GL No: 515	
Date	**Description**	**PR**	**DR**	**CR**	**Balance**	
2016						
Sep 30	Adjustment	J2	150		150	DR

Account:	Interest Expense					GL No: 520	
Date	**Description**	**PR**	**DR**	**CR**	**Balance**	
2016						
Sep 10		J1	40		40	DR

Account:	Office Supplies Expense				GL No: 530	
Date	Description	PR	DR	CR	Balance	
2016						
Sep 30	Adjustment	J2	450		450	DR

Account:	Rent Expense				GL No: 540	
Date	Description	PR	DR	CR	Balance	
2016						
Sep 3		J1	1,350		1,350	DR

AP-9B (❹)

The following information is taken from the records of Basil Cleaning.

Accounts Payable	$18,000
Inventory	14,000
Land	55,000
Cash	31,000
Factory Equipment	20,000
Current Loans Payable	21,000
Office Furniture	18,000
Prepaid Insurance	13,000
Unearned Revenue	8,000

Required

a) Calculate total current assets.

b) Calculate total long-term assets.

c)   Calculate total assets.

_____

_____

AP-10B (④)

Manuel Consulting borrowed a $1,180,000 interest-free bank loan on January 1, 2016. Payment is agreed to be made in four years in four equal annual instalments (paid on each subsequent January 1). Calculate the current and long-term liabilities as at December 31 before the annual instalments are made for the following years.

	December 31			
	2016	**2017**	**2018**	**2019**
Current portion of loan				
Long-term portion of loan				

AP-11B (④)

On July 1, 2016, Bryte Services took out a $200,000 bank loan. The loan will be repaid in equal annual installments over the next 10 years. Show how the bank loan will appear on Bryte Services' classified balance sheet on June 30, 2022.

_____

_____

_____

Analysis

Show the journal entries required to record the receipt of the loan and the first principal payment.

JOURNAL					Page 1
Date	**Account Title and Explanation**	**PR**	**Debit**		**Credit**

AP-12B (❹)

On January 1, 2016, Detmore Consulting took out a $100,000 bank loan. The loan will be repaid in two equal payments; one on December 31, 2017, and the other on December 31, 2019. Complete the table below with the correct balances for the accounts at the dates listed.

	Bank Loan	
	Current	**Long-Term**
Dec. 31, 2016		
Dec. 31, 2017		
Dec. 31, 2018		
Dec. 31, 2019		

Analysis

Why is it helpful to split some liabilities into current and long-term portions for reporting purposes?

_____

_____

_____

_____

_____

AP-13B (❹)

Identify the following accounts as either current or long-term, and as either assets or liabilities.

Account Name	Current or Long-Term	Asset or Liability
Accounts Receivable		
Salaries Payable		
Equipment		
Cash		
Bank Loan due in six months		
Office Furniture		
Accounts Payable		
Prepaid Rent		
Bank Loan due in two years		
Inventory		

AP-14B (❹❺❻)

Below is Bravolo's adjusted trail balance for the year ending September 30, 2016. Assume all accounts have a normal balance.

Cash	$17,400
Accounts Receivable	5,800
Prepaid Insurance	1,800
Equipment	23,000
Accumulated Depreciation	1,100
Accounts Payable	7,600
Unearned Revenue	1,500
Bank Loan	18,000
Bravolo, Capital	19,800

The bank loan is payable over three years and $6,000 will be paid by September 30, 2017.

Required

a) Prepare a classified balance sheet.

Bravolo Classified Balance Sheet As at September 30, 2016		

b) Calculate the working capital for Bravolo.

_____

_____

c) Calculate the current ratio for Bravolo.

_____

_____

d) Calculate the quick ratio for Bravolo.

_____

_____

AP-15B (❹ ❺ ❻)

Below is Canduro's financial information for the year ending June 30, 2016. Assume all accounts have a normal balance.

Accounts Payable	$8,900
Accounts Receivable	6,100
Accumulated Depreciation	1,200
Bank Loan	21,000
Cash	19,000
Prepaid Insurance	3,250
Equipment	25,000
Canduro, Capital	20,550
Unearned Revenue	1,700

The bank loan is payable over five years and $4,200 will be paid by June 30, 2017.

Required

a) Prepare a classified balance sheet.

Canduro Classified Balance Sheet As at June 30, 2016		

b) Calculate the working capital for Canduro.

_____

c) Calculate the current ratio for Canduro.

_____

d) Calculate the quick ratio for Canduro.

_____

AP-16B (❽)

Charles Ly is the owner of Gamma Services. He has hired you to prepare the financial statements for his company on April 30, 2016. As part of the process, you need to create the worksheet. Use the unadjusted trial balance and the adjustments to complete the worksheet.

Apr 30   Recognized prepaid insurance worth $100 for this month.

Apr 30   Recorded $400 deprecation on equipment.

Apr 30   Recognized $1,800 of unearned revenue that has now become earned.

	Gamma Services Worksheet April 30, 2016									
	Unadjusted Trial Balance		Adjustments		Adjusted Trial Balance		Income Statement		Balance Sheet	
Account Titles	DR	CR	DR	CR	DR	CR	DR	CR	DR	CR
Cash	$21,750									
Accounts Receivable	13,000									
Prepaid Insurance	1,200									
Equipment	17,500									
Accumulated Depreciation		$2,000								
Accounts Payable		10,300								
Unearned Revenue		4,500								
Bank Loan		18,000								
Ly, Capital		14,000								
Service Revenue		9,000								
Insurance Expense	0									
Salaries Expense	4,000									
Telephone Expense	200									
Depreciation Expense	0									
Interest Expense	150									
Totals	$57,800	$57,800								
Net Profit (Loss)										
Total										

Case Study

CS-1 (① ② ③ ④ ⑤)

Grindstone Paving provides residential and commercial paving services. Its balance sheet at the end of June 2016 is shown below, along with its chart of accounts.

Grindstone Paving Balance Sheet As at June 30, 2016			
Assets		**Liabilities**	
Cash	$7,580	Accounts Payable	$15,800
Accounts Receivable	6,000	Unearned Revenue	6,200
Prepaid Insurance	1,800	Bank Loan	22,000
Equipment	55,000	Total Liabilities	44,000
		Owner's Equity	
		Stone, Capital	26,380
Total Assets	$70,380	**Total Liabilities and Owner's Equity**	$70,380

Account Description	Account #
ASSETS	
Cash	101
Accounts Receivable	105
Prepaid Insurance	110
Equipment	120
Accumulated Depreciation	125
LIABILITIES	
Accounts Payable	200
Interest Payable	205
Salary Payable	210
Unearned Revenue	215
Bank Loan	220
OWNER'S EQUITY	
Stone, Capital	300
Stone, Drawings	310
Income Summary	315

Account Description	Account #
REVENUE	
Service Revenue	400
EXPENSES	
Advertising Expense	500
Depreciation Expense	510
Insurance Expense	515
Interest Expense	520
Salaries Expense	545
Telephone Expense	550

For the month of July 2016, Grindstone Paving had the following transactions.

Jul 1   The owner invested $8,000 cash into the business.
Jul 2   Received $2,530 cash for work that will be provided in August.
Jul 5   Received an advertising bill for $600 which will be paid next month.
Jul 8   Paid the $350 telephone bill with cash.
Jul 10   Provided $4,680 worth of services to customers who will pay later.
Jul 14   Purchased equipment with $8,200 cash.
Jul 20   Received $2,350 in payment from customers paying their account.
Jul 22   Paid $1,970 toward accounts payable.
Jul 24   Paid $1,300 toward bank loan principal.
Jul 28   Paid salary of $2,400 to an employee.
Jul 30   The owner withdrew $2,200 cash for personal use.

At the end of July, the following adjustments had to be journalized to properly report the balances of the company's accounts.

Jul 31   One month of prepaid insurance worth $100 has been used.
Jul 31   Monthly depreciation on the equipment was $450.
Jul 31   Unearned revenue worth $620 has now been earned.
Jul 31   Interest of $75 has accrued on the bank loan.
Jul 31   Accrued salary expense of $500 for an employee.

Note: Of the remaining balance of the bank loan, $5,000 will be paid within the next year.

Required

a) Enter the opening balances from the June 2016 balance sheet into the general ledger accounts (the ledger accounts are presented at the end of this question).
b) Prepare the journal entries for the month of July and post them to the appropriate general ledger accounts.
c) Create the trial balance in the worksheet and then complete the remaining section of the worksheet.
d) Create the income statement, statement of owner's equity and the classified balance sheet.
e) Prepare the journal entries for the adjustments and post them to the appropriate general ledger accounts.
f) Prepare the journal entries to close the books for the month of July 2016 (use the income summary account), and post the journal entries to the appropriate general ledger accounts.
g) Create the post-closing trial balance.

a) Enter opening balances in the ledgers located at the end of the question.

b) Journal entries

JOURNAL					Page 1
Date	Account Title and Explanation	PR	Debit	Credit	

c) Worksheet

Account Titles	Unadjusted Trial Balance		Adjustments		Adjusted Trial Balance	
	DR	CR	DR	CR	DR	CR

d) Financial statements

e) Adjusting entries

JOURNAL				Page 2
Date	Account Title and Explanation	PR	Debit	Credit

f) Closing entries

JOURNAL				Page 3
Date	Account Title and Explanation	PR	Debit	Credit

g) Create the post-closing trial balance.

Account Titles	DR	CR

GENERAL LEDGER

Account: Cash					GL. No.	
Date	Description	PR	DR	CR	Balance	

Account:					GL. No.	
Date	**Description**	**PR**	**DR**	**CR**	**Balance**	

Account:					GL. No.	
Date	**Description**	**PR**	**DR**	**CR**	**Balance**	

Account:					GL. No.	
Date	**Description**	**PR**	**DR**	**CR**	**Balance**	

Account:					GL. No.	
Date	**Description**	**PR**	**DR**	**CR**	**Balance**	

Account:					GL. No.	
Date	**Description**	**PR**	**DR**	**CR**	**Balance**	

Account:					GL. No.	
Date	**Description**	**PR**	**DR**	**CR**	**Balance**	

Account:					GL. No.	
Date	**Description**	**PR**	**DR**	**CR**	**Balance**	

Account:					GL. No.	
Date	**Description**	**PR**	**DR**	**CR**	**Balance**	

Account:					GL. No.	
Date	**Description**	**PR**	**DR**	**CR**	**Balance**	

Account:					GL. No.	
Date	**Description**	**PR**	**DR**	**CR**	**Balance**	

Account:						GL. No.	
Date	**Description**	**PR**	**DR**	**CR**	**Balance**		

Account:						GL. No.	
Date	**Description**	**PR**	**DR**	**CR**	**Balance**		

Account:						GL. No.	
Date	**Description**	**PR**	**DR**	**CR**	**Balance**		

Account:						GL. No.	
Date	**Description**	**PR**	**DR**	**CR**	**Balance**		

Account:						GL. No.	
Date	**Description**	**PR**	**DR**	**CR**	**Balance**		

Account:						GL. No.	
Date	Description	PR	DR	CR	Balance		

Account:						GL. No.	
Date	Description	PR	DR	CR	Balance		

Account:						GL. No.	
Date	Description	PR	DR	CR	Balance		

Account:						GL. No.	
Date	Description	PR	DR	CR	Balance		

Chapter 7

INVENTORY: MERCHANDISING TRANSACTIONS

LEARNING OUTCOMES

❶ Define a merchandising business

❷ Differentiate between the perpetual and the periodic inventory systems

❸ Record journal entries related to inventory purchases under the perpetual inventory system

❹ Record journal entries related to inventory sales under the perpetual inventory system

❺ Calculate gross profit and gross margin percentage

❻ Prepare a multistep income statement and classified multistep income statement

❼ Prepare closing entries for a merchandising business under the perpetual inventory system

❽ Identify inventory controls

Appendix

❾ Record journal entries related to inventory purchases under the periodic inventory system

❿ Record journal entries related to inventory sales under the periodic inventory system

⓫ Calculate cost of goods sold under the periodic inventory system

⓬ Prepare closing entries for a merchandising business under the periodic inventory system

AMEENGAGE™ *Access **ameengage.com** for integrated resources including tutorials, practice exercises, the digital textbook and more.*

Assessment Questions

AS-1 (❶)

What is a merchandising business?

_____

_____

_____

AS-2 (❶)

What is COGS and what type of account is it?

_____

_____

_____

AS-3 (❺)

How is gross profit calculated? What is the difference between gross profit and net profit?

_____

_____

_____

AS-4 (❷)

In a perpetual inventory system, how often are inventory levels updated?

_____

_____

AS-5 (❷)

In a periodic inventory system, how often are inventory levels updated?

_____

_____

AS-6 (❶)

Define inventory in the context of a merchandising business.

_____

_____

_____

AS-7 (❺)

Define operating expenses.

_____

_____

_____

AS-8 (❸)

What are some reasons purchase returns occur?

_____

_____

_____

AS-9 (❸)

When does a purchase allowance occur?

_____

_____

_____

AS-10 (❸ ❹)

Provide three common reasons why a seller gives a purchase discount.

_____

_____

_____

_____

AS-11 (❸ ❹)

If a discount term is written as 3/10, n/30, what does this mean?

_____

_____

AS-12 (❸)

Explain the difference between a purchase return and a purchase allowance.

_____

_____

_____

AS-13 (❹)

Explain the difference between a sales allowance and a sales discount.

_____

_____

_____

AS-14 (❶)

Explain how cost of goods available for sale is calculated in a periodic inventory system.

_____

_____

_____

AS-15 (❸)

What are the two possible Freight on Board (FOB) points?

_____

_____

AS-16 (❸)

What does FOB shipping point indicate?

_____

_____

AS-17 (❸)

What does FOB destination indicate?

_____

_____

_____

AS-18 (❹)

What type of account is sales returns and allowances and what is it used for?

_____

_____

_____

AS-19 (❺)

What is the formula for gross profit margin?

_____

_____

_____

AS-20 (❷ ❹)

In a perpetual inventory system, describe the transaction(s) required to record the sale of inventory.

_____

_____

_____

AS-21 (❷ ❾)

In a periodic inventory system, describe the transaction(s) required to record the sale of inventory.

_____

_____

AS-22 (❻ ⓫)

What is one difference between a single-step income statement and a multistep income statement?

_____

_____

AS-23 (❻)

What are administrative expenses?

_____

_____

AS-24 (❻)

In a typical multistep income statement, which category do items such as interest revenue and loss from a lawsuit fall under?

_____

_____

AS-25 (❽)

Provide an example of how an accountant can manage inventory in order to ensure the economical and efficient use of resources.

_____

_____

_____

Application Questions Group A

AP-1A (❸ ❹)

Super Shirt Wholesalers spent $10,000 to produce 1,000 shirts as inventory. Hip Top Retailers paid $15,000 for the 1,000 shirts from Super Shirt Wholesalers on March 15, 2016. Payment is due on April 15. Assume both companies use the perpetual inventory system.

Required

a) Prepare the journal entry or entries for Hip Top Shirt Retailers on March 15.

JOURNAL			Page 1	
Date	Account Title and Explanation		Debit	Credit

b) Prepare the journal entry or entries for Super Shirt Wholesalers on March 15.

JOURNAL			Page 1	
Date	Account Title and Explanation		Debit	Credit

AP-2A (❸)

JB Supermarkets bought $3,000 worth of groceries on account from a produce supplier on May 10, 2016. On May 11, JB's bookkeeper was informed that $200 worth of tomatoes was substandard and returned to the supplier. Prepare the journal entry to record the purchase return using the perpetual inventory system.

JOURNAL			Page 1
Date	Account Title and Explanation	Debit	Credit

AP-3A (❾)

Refer to AP-2A above and record the purchase return assuming JB Supermarkets uses a periodic inventory system.

JOURNAL			Page 1
Date	Account Title and Explanation	Debit	Credit

AP-4A (❸)

On January 12, 2016, Corner-Mart received a shipment of T-shirts from Promo Novelties for an event. The invoice amounted to $5,000 and was recorded in the accounting system. Soon after the delivery was made, the marketing manager discovered that the logo was printed incorrectly. The goods were returned to Promo Novelties on January 31. Prepare the journal entry for Corner-Mart to record the return using the perpetual inventory system.

JOURNAL			Page 1
Date	Account Title and Explanation	Debit	Credit

AP-5A (❾)

Refer to AP-4A above. Record the purchase return assuming Corner-Mart uses a periodic inventory system.

JOURNAL			Page 1
Date	Account Title and Explanation	Debit	Credit

AP-6A (❸)

a) Beds Unlimited received a shipment of bed sheets on April 3, 2016. The value of the bed sheets was $8,000, and the sheets were shipped FOB shipping point. Freight charges came to $100. Prepare the journal entry to record the receipt of goods by Beds Unlimited, assuming payment will be made in May, using the perpetual inventory system.

JOURNAL			Page 1
Date	Account Title and Explanation	Debit	Credit

b) The bed sheets delivered to Beds Unlimited were the wrong colour. After some negotiation, the manager agreed to keep the products with a 10% allowance. Prepare the entry on April 10, 2016 to record the purchase allowance. (Assume all bed sheets were still in inventory). Allowances are not granted on freight charges.

JOURNAL			Page 1
Date	Account Title and Explanation	Debit	Credit

c)   Journalize the transaction for Beds Unlimited when the payment is made on May 3, 2016.

JOURNAL			Page 1
Date	Account Title and Explanation	Debit	Credit

AP-7A (❸)

The following is written on an invoice relating to goods that were purchased: 5/10, n/30. What does it mean?

_____

_____

AP-8A (❺)

If a computer company bought computers for $10,000 and sold them for $14,000, how much would the gross profit be on the entire shipment if the business took advantage of the early cash payment terms of 2/15, n/30 from its supplier?

_____

AP-9A (❸)

Shoe Retailers uses the perpetual inventory system. It purchased $10,000 of shoes from Runner Wear Supplies on March 1, 2016. Runner Wear's invoice shows terms of 2/10, n/30.

Required

a)   What is the latest date Shoe Retailers could pay the bill and apply the discount?

_____

b) As bookkeeper for Shoe Retailers, prepare the journal entry to record the March 1 purchase.

JOURNAL			Page 1
Date	Account Title and Explanation	Debit	Credit

c) Journalize the transaction for payment of the invoice, assuming the payment was made on March 5.

JOURNAL			Page 1
Date	Account Title and Explanation	Debit	Credit

d) Journalize the transaction for payment of the invoice, assuming the payment was made on April 3.

JOURNAL			Page 1
Date	Account Title and Explanation	Debit	Credit

AP-10A (❸ ❹)

On May 1, 2016, Food Wholesalers purchased $3,000 worth of dried fruit inventory and paid $100 for freight charges on account. On May 15, 2016, Food Wholesalers sold all of the dried fruit inventory to Retail Grocers for $4,000 on account. As the bookkeeper for Food Wholesalers, journalize the transactions using the perpetual inventory system.

JOURNAL			Page 1
Date	Account Title and Explanation	Debit	Credit

AP-11A (❸)

Johson is a maker of cotton garments that are sold to various retailers. On September 1, 2016, Craig's Retailers sent back a shipment of goods that was unsatisfactory. The goods were sold on account for $7,700 originally and cost $4,620. Johson returned the goods to inventory. Johson uses a perpetual inventory system.

Required

a) As Johson's bookkeeper prepare the journal entries to reflect the return.

JOURNAL			Page 1
Date	Account Title and Explanation	Debit	Credit

b) Journalize the entry if Craig's only returned half of the shipment.

JOURNAL			Page 1
Date	**Account Title and Explanation**	**Debit**	**Credit**

AP-12A (❹ ❺)

Assume you are the bookkeeper for Moira's Wholesalers, a distributor of kitchen furniture. Your sales manager informed you that Ted's Retailers is unhappy with the quality of some tables delivered on August 12, 2016, and will be shipping back all the goods. The original invoice amounted to $1,500 and the goods cost Moira's $1,000. Using a perpetual inventory system, complete the journal entries for each of the following independent scenarios.

Required

a) Rather than taking back the tables, your sales manager agreed to allow Ted's Retailers a 10% discount if it agrees to keep the goods. Record Ted's payment in settlement of the invoice on September 12.

JOURNAL			Page 1
Date	**Account Title and Explanation**	**Debit**	**Credit**

b) Suppose that Ted's shipped back all the goods on August 15 and the inventory was put back on the sales floor. Journalize the transactions.

JOURNAL			Page 1
Date	Account Title and Explanation	Debit	Credit

c) Suppose that Ted's shipped back half the goods on August 15 and kept the other half with a 10% allowance. Journalize the transactions that took place on August 15.

JOURNAL			Page 1
Date	Account Title and Explanation	Debit	Credit

d) Continue from part b). Since all the goods were sold and returned in the same period, what happened to Moira's gross profit? (Disregard the additional shipping and administration costs). Explain your answer.

_____

_____

_____

AP-13A (❸ ❹ ❺)

The following information pertains to Wicked Kitchen Supplies for the month of March 2016.

Mar 1   Purchased merchandise for $16,000 on credit from Hotel Supplies terms 1/20, n/30.

Mar 1   Wicked paid $35 cash to have the merchandise from Hotel Supplies delivered.

Mar 5   Sold merchandise on credit to Four Boars Restaraunt for $8,000, terms 2/10, n/30; cost of goods $5,500.

Mar 5   Paid $25 cash to ship the goods to Four Boars Restaurant.

Mar 8   Four Boars returned $1,900 (sales price) of merchandise purchased March 5, cost $800. There was nothing wrong with the merchandise and it will be resold.

Mar 12   Returned $500 of the merchandise purchased March 1 as it was the wrong design.

Mar 15   Received payment from Four Boars Restaraunt for March 5 sale.

Mar 15   Paid for merchandise purchased from Hotel Supplies on March 1.

Mar 23   Sold merchandise on credit to Black Kettle Kitchen for $4,000, terms 2/10, n/30; cost of goods was $2,000.

Mar 26   Black Kettle Kitchen returned $200 (sales price) of merchandise purchased March 23; cost of goods was $50. The merchandise was returned to inventory.

Mar 31   Received payment from Black Kettle Kitchen for the March 23 sale.

Journalize the above transactions assuming that Wicked Kitchen Supplies uses a perpetual inventory system. Round all calculations to the nearest whole dollar.

JOURNAL			Page 1
Date	Account Title and Explanation	Debit	Credit

JOURNAL			Page 2
Date	**Account Title and Explanation**	**Debit**	**Credit**

Analysis

Calculate Wicked Kitchen Supplies' gross profit for the month.

_____

_____

_____

_____

_____

_____

_____

_____

_____

AP-14A (❸ ❹)

The following information was presented by the bookkeeper for Switch Company for the month of January 2016.

Jan 5	Purchased merchandise for $12,000 on credit from Outdoor Pursuits terms 1/10, n/30.
Jan 5	Switch Company paid $25 to have the merchandise delivered.
Jan 12	Purchased merchandise for $7,000 on credit from Cambleback terms 2/10, n/30.
Jan 14	Returned $300 of the merchandise purchased January 5 from Outdoor Pursuits as it was defective.
Jan 15	Paid for merchandise purchased from Outdoor Pursuits on January 5.
Jan 26	Paid for merchandise purchased from Cambleback on January 12.

Journalize the above transactions assuming that Switch Company uses a perpetual inventory system. Round all calculations to the nearest whole dollar.

JOURNAL			Page 1
Date	Account Title and Explanation	Debit	Credit

AP-15A (② ③ ④ ⑨ ⑩)

For each business transaction in the table below, identify which accounts are debited and credited. Do this for both the perpetual and periodic inventory system.

	Transaction	Perpetual Inventory System		Periodic Inventory System	
		DR	CR	DR	CR
1.	Purchased inventory on account.				
2.	Returned a portion of the inventory purchased in transaction 1.				
3.	Paid for remaining invoice balance after taking advantage of the early payment discount.				
4.	Sold inventory on account.				
5.	Customer found that a portion of goods sold in transaction 4 were of lower quality. However, he agreed to keep them at 10% discount.				
6.	Customer paid the remaining invoice balance after taking the advantage of an early payment discount.				

AP-16A (⑤)

If sales revenue is $300,000 and cost of goods sold is $180,000, what is the gross profit and gross margin percentage?

_____

_____

_____

_____

lookup formulas

Chapter 7-13A

AP-17A (❸ ❹)

The following transactions took place at Science Supplies during May 2016.

May 14   Sold merchandise on credit to Elements for $10,000, terms 2/10, n/30; cost of goods $8,500.

May 14   Science Supplies paid $50 to ship the goods to Elements.

May 16   Elements returned $500 (sales price) of merchandise purchased May 14, cost $375. The goods were returned to the stock of inventory.

May 17   Received payment from Elements for May 14 sale.

May 18   Sold merchandise on credit to Litmus for $6,000, terms 2/10, n/30; cost of goods $3,600.

May 26   Litmus kept the merchandise purchased May 18. However, some of it was defective so Science Supplies agreed to a 50% allowance on the total sale.

May 31   Received payment from Litmus for the May 18 sale.

Journalize the above transactions assuming that Science Supplies uses a perpetual inventory system. Round all calculations to the nearest dollar.

JOURNAL			Page 1
Date	Account Title and Explanation	Debit	Credit

JOURNAL			Page 2
Date	Account Title and Explanation	Debit	Credit

AP-18A (❷)

Suppose that on March 15, 2016, both Company A and Company B sold inventory with a cost of $40,000. The updated balance of inventory as at March 1 for both companies was $90,000. Company A uses the perpetual inventory system. Company B uses the periodic inventory system and performs an inventory count at the end of each month. What is the value of inventory on record as at March 15 for each of Company A and Company B?

AP-19A (⑨ ⑩ ⑪ ⑫)

Crystal Crockery, owned by Crystal Kleer, has provided you with the following information about the transactions occurring in March 2016.

Mar 2   Crystal Crockery received a shipment of gift mugs for resale from Cup Makers. The amount on the invoice is $7,000 and the stated terms are: 2/15, n/45.

Mar 2   Crystal Crockery paid $400 cash for shipping charges.

Mar 5   The manager of Crystal Crockery checked the shipped cups and found that goods worth $700 were defective. The defective goods were returned to the supplier.

Mar 13   Crystal Crockery paid the remaining invoice balance and, in doing so, took advantage of the early payment discount.

Mar 20   Crystal Crockery sold the goods costing $6,227 to AS Supermarket for $9,500.

Mar 22   AS Supermarket found 10% of items to be defective and returned these to Crystal Crockery. The goods cannot be resold.

Mar 28   The invoice showed terms 2/10, n/60. AS Supermarket paid the remaining invoice balance after taking advantage of the early settlement discount.

Opening inventory balance was $500 and the closing inventory balance was $847.

Required

Assume Crystal Crockery uses the periodic inventory system.

a) Prepare the journal entries to record the purchase and sales transactions.

JOURNAL			Page 1
Date	Account Title and Explanation	Debit	Credit

JOURNAL			Page 1
Date	Account Title and Explanation	Debit	Credit

b) Prepare the journal entries to record the closing entries for the month. Assume that the accounting period for Crystal Crockery is one month.

JOURNAL			Page 1
Date	Account Title and Explanation	Debit	Credit

c) Prepare the cost of goods sold section of the income statement.

Net Purchases

AP-20A (❼)

The following is Glueman Industries' adjusted trial balance **in account order** for the year ended September 30, 2016.

Glueman Industries Adjusted Trial Balance September 30, 2016		
Account Titles	**DR**	**CR**
Cash	$3,800	
Accounts Receivable	2,800	
Prepaid Insurance	4,500	
Prepaid Rent	8,100	
Property, Plant and Equipment	43,800	
Accumulated Depreciation		$1,000
Accounts Payable		2,330
Unearned Revenue		2,000
Wages Payable		2,820
Kiefer, Capital		48,800
Sales Revenue		79,000
Sales Discounts	1,750	
Sales Returns and Allowances	430	
Cost of Goods Sold	36,780	
Rent Expense	9,300	
Utilities Expense	8,240	
Wages Expense	15,800	
Depreciation Expense	650	
	$135,950	$135,950

Required

a) Prepare the journal entries to close the appropriate accounts using the income summary.

JOURNAL			Page 1
Date	**Account Title and Explanation**	**Debit**	**Credit**

b) Prepare journal entries to close appropriate accounts directly to the capital account.

JOURNAL			Page 1
Date	**Account Title and Explanation**	**Debit**	**Credit**

AP-21A (6)

Glent Company prepared the following trial balance at its year-end of September 30, 2016. The company is owned by Wayne Glent.

Glent Company Trial Balance September 30, 2016		
Account Titles	**DR**	**CR**
Cash	$14,600	
Accounts Receivable	6,000	
Inventory	6,600	
Prepaid Expenses	2,000	
Equipment	40,000	
Accumulated Depreciation		$2,500
Accounts Payable		8,000
Unearned Revenue		6,000
Bank Loan		9,000
Glent, Capital		38,750
Glent, Drawings	1,000	
Sales Revenue		61,750
Gain on Sale of Equipment		4,000
Cost of Goods Sold	30,000	
Depreciation Expense	500	
Interest Expense	600	
Maintenance Expense	1,200	
Rent Expense	15,000	
Salaries Expense	12,500	
Total	**$130,000**	**$130,000**

Notes:
1. Assume the balance of owner's equity is the opening balance
2. The bank loan is payable over the next nine years in equal annual installments

Required

Prepare a multi-step income statement, statement of owner's equity, and classified balance sheet using the balances listed above.

AP-22A (6)

A Bit of Fit operates several retail stores that specialize in products for a healthy lifestyle. Some of its financial information is shown below for its fiscal year ended December 31, 2016.

Cost of Goods Sold	$60,000
Depreciation Expense	10,000
Gain on Sale of Equipment	3,000
Interest Expense	500
Insurance Expense	7,000
Salaries Expense	50,000
Sales Discounts	2,500
Sales Returns and Allowances	6,500
Sales Revenue	154,000
Supplies Expense	2,000
Utilities Expense	9,000

Required

a) Create a multistep income statement for A Bit of Fit.

b) Create a classified multistep income statement for A Bit of Fit using the following information.

	Selling	Administrative	Total
Salaries Expense	80%	20%	100%
Depreciation Expense	100%	0%	100%
Insurance Expense	75%	25%	100%
Utilities Expense	75%	25%	100%
Supplies Expense	0%	100%	100%

Analysis

Give a reason why revenues and expenses are categorized into "operating" and "other" on the multistep income statement.

_____

_____

_____

_____

_____

_____

AP-23A (⑪ ⑫)

The following information was taken from the financial records of Bell Distribution, owned by Marcus Bell, at its year-end of December 31, 2016. The company uses the periodic inventory system.

Freight-In	$1,400
Interest Expense	3,200
Inventory, January 1, 2016	150,000
Inventory, December 31, 2016	120,000
Purchase Returns and Allowances	13,800
Purchases	100,000
Rent Expense	30,000
Salaries Expense	44,000
Sales Discounts	9,200
Sales Revenue	250,000

Required

a) Calculate the cost of goods sold for Bell Distribution for 2016.

b) Prepare the closing entries for Bell Distribution for 2016.

a) Cost of Goods Sold

_____

_____

_____

_____

_____

_____

b) Closing entries

JOURNAL			Page 1
Date	Account Title and Explanation	Debit	Credit

Application Questions Group B

AP-1B (❸ ❹)

On September 1, 2016, Fruit Wholesalers purchased $3,700 worth of dried fruit inventory and paid $120 for freight charges on account. On September 16, Fruit Wholesalers sold all of the dried fruit inventory to Retail Grocers for $5,920 on account. As the bookkeeper for Fruit Wholesalers, journalize the transactions under the perpetual inventory system.

JOURNAL			Page 1
Date	**Account Title and Explanation**	**Debit**	**Credit**

AP-2B (❸)

JB Supermarkets bought $2,140 worth of groceries on account from a produce supplier on December 8, 2016. On December 9, JB's bookkeeper was informed that 15% of the produce was substandard and returned to the supplier. Prepare the journal entry to record the purchase return using the perpetual inventory system.

JOURNAL			Page 1
Date	**Account Title and Explanation**	**Debit**	**Credit**

AP-3B (❸)

Top Mop Retailers bought $12,900 worth of mops from Super Mop Wholesalers Ltd. on March 15, 2016. Payment was due in April.

Required

a) Prepare the journal entry for Top Mop Retailers using the perpetual inventory system.

JOURNAL				Page 1
Date	Account Title and Explanation		Debit	Credit

b) Prepare the journal entry for Top Mop Retailers for the payment of $12,900 made to Super Mop Wholesalers Ltd. on April 15.

JOURNAL				Page 1
Date	Account Title and Explanation		Debit	Credit

AP-4B (❸)

a) Signs Unlimited received a shipment of plastic sheets on February 15, 2016. The sheets were shipped FOB shipping point. The value of the plastic was $9,000, and the shipping charges totalled $110. Prepare the journal entry to record the receipt of goods by Signs Unlimited, assuming the payments for the inventory and freight will be made in March, using the perpetual inventory system.

JOURNAL				Page 1
Date	Account Title and Explanation		Debit	Credit

b) The plastic sheets delivered to Signs Unlimited were in the wrong colour. After some negotiation, the manager agreed to keep the products with a 6% allowance on the value of the inventory. Prepare the entry on February 22 to record the purchase allowance. (Assume all items were still in inventory). Allowances are not granted on freight charges.

JOURNAL			Page 1
Date	Account Title and Explanation	Debit	Credit

c) Journalize the transaction for Signs Unlimited when the payment is made on March 15.

JOURNAL			Page 1
Date	Account Title and Explanation	Debit	Credit

AP-5B (❸)

a) Sandal Retailers purchased $8,100 of sandals from Comfy Wear Supplies at the end of April 10, 2016. Since Sandal Retailers has good cash reserves, the accountant took advantage of the early payment discount that Comfy Wear offers. Comfy Wear's invoice shows terms of 2/15, n/30. What is the latest date Sandal Retailers could pay the bill to take advantage of the discount?

b) As the bookkeeper for Sandal Retailers, prepare the journal entry to record the purchase on April 10, using a perpetual inventory system.

JOURNAL			Page 1
Date	Account Title and Explanation	Debit	Credit

c) Journalize the transaction for payment of the invoice, assuming the payment was made on April 18.

JOURNAL				Page 1
Date	Account Title and Explanation		Debit	Credit

d) Journalize the transaction for payment of the invoice, assuming the payment was made on April 26.

JOURNAL				Page 1
Date	Account Title and Explanation		Debit	Credit

AP-6B (❾)

a) Boards Unlimited received a shipment of plastic sheets on April 3, 2016. The value of the plastic was $8,000, and the sheets were shipped FOB shipping point. Freight charges came to $100. Prepare the journal entry to record the receipt of goods by Boards Unlimited, assuming payment will be made in May, using the periodic inventory system.

JOURNAL				Page 1
Date	Account Title and Explanation		Debit	Credit

b) The plastic sheets delivered to Boards Unlimited were in the wrong colour. After some
negotiation, the manager agreed to keep the products with a 10% discount. Prepare the
entry on April 10 to record the purchase allowance. (Assume all plastic sheets were still in
inventory.)

JOURNAL			Page 1
Date	Account Title and Explanation	Debit	Credit

c) Journalize the transaction for Boards Unlimited when the payment is made on May 3.

JOURNAL			Page 1
Date	Account Title and Explanation	Debit	Credit

AP-7B (❸)

Rock Retailers purchased $11,200 worth of shoes from Runner Wear Supplies at the end of April
4, 2016. Since Rock Retailers has good cash reserves, the accountant took advantage of the
early payment discount that Runner Wear offers. Runner Wear's invoice shows terms of 2/10,
n/30. What is the latest date that Rock Retailers could pay the bill to take advantage of the
discount? How much cash would be exchanged if the full discount was taken advantage of?

_____

_____

_____

AP-8B (❺)

If a telephone retail business bought telephones for $10,800 and sold them for $14,500, how
much would the gross profit be on the entire shipment assuming the business took advantage
of the early cash payment terms of 3/10, n/30 from its supplier?

_____

_____

AP-9B (⑨ ⑩)

Socks Retailers uses the periodic inventory system. It purchased $10,000 worth of shoes from Jogger Wear Supplies at the end of March 1, 2016. Jogger Wear's invoice terms are 2/15, n/30.

Required

a) What is the latest date Socks Retailers could pay the bill to apply the discount?

b) As Socks Retailers' bookkeeper, prepare the journal entry to record the March 1 purchase.

JOURNAL			Page 1
Date	**Account Title and Explanation**	**Debit**	**Credit**

c) Journalize the transaction for payment of the invoice on March 5.

JOURNAL			Page 1
Date	**Account Title and Explanation**	**Debit**	**Credit**

d) Journalize the transaction for payment of the invoice on April 3.

JOURNAL			Page 1
Date	**Account Title and Explanation**	**Debit**	**Credit**

AP-10B (❸)

At the end of March 20, 2016, Cup-A-Java received a shipment of gift mugs for resale from Cup Makers in the amount of $5,000. The terms stated on the invoice from Cup Makers were 3/15, n/60. Under a perpetual inventory system, journalize the following scenarios.

Required

a) As the bookkeeper for Cup-A-Java, record the purchase of inventory.

JOURNAL			Page 1
Date	Account Title and Explanation	Debit	Credit

b) If Cup-A-Java decided to take advantage of the early payment cash discount, by when should the payment be made to qualify for the discount?

c) The payment by Cup-A-Java to Cup Makers was made on March 31. Prepare the journal entry for the payment of goods.

JOURNAL			Page 1
Date	Account Title and Explanation	Debit	Credit

d) Journalize the entry if payment had instead been made on May 20.

JOURNAL			Page 1
Date	Account Title and Explanation	Debit	Credit

e) On March 25, 20% of the shipment was returned because it was the wrong colour. The invoice has not yet been paid. Prepare the journal entry for this transaction.

JOURNAL			Page 1
Date	Account Title and Explanation	Debit	Credit

f) Continue from (e); journalize the entry if Cup-A-Java took advantage of the early payment cash discount when paying for the balance of the cups on March 31.

JOURNAL			Page 1
Date	Account Title and Explanation	Debit	Credit

AP-11B (❹)

Macks makes garments that are sold to retailers. On June 1, 2016, Cory's Retailers sent back a shipment of goods. The goods sold on account for $6,000 and cost $4,000. Macks put the returned goods back into inventory for resale. Macks uses a perpetual inventory system.

Required

a) As Macks' bookkeeper, prepare the journal entries to reflect the return.

JOURNAL			Page 1
Date	Account Title and Explanation	Debit	Credit

b)   Journalize the entry if Cory's only returned half of the shipment.

JOURNAL			Page 1	
Date	Account Title and Explanation		Debit	Credit

c)   What happened to the value of Macks' owner's equity when Cory's returned the merchandise? Did it increase, decrease or stay the same? Explain your answer.

_____

_____

_____

_____

d)   Explain the logic behind debiting the sales returns and allowances as a contra-account instead of debiting the revenue account directly.

_____

_____

_____

_____

AP-12B (④)

Pete's Wholesalers imports and distributes towels. It sells its products to various retailers throughout the country and offer payment terms of 2/10, n/30. On October 1, 2016, Pete's made a large sale to Ernie's Bathroom Retailers in the amount of $15,000, which cost Pete's $9,000. Pete's uses a perpetual inventory system. Complete the following.

Required

a) Journalize the sale that was made on account.

JOURNAL			Page 1
Date	Account Title and Explanation	Debit	Credit

b) By what date must Ernie's pay the invoice to qualify for the early cash payment discount?

_____

_____

c) Assume Ernie's paid the bill on October 5. Record the journal entry.

JOURNAL			Page 1
Date	Account Title and Explanation	Debit	Credit

d) If Ernie's had returned half the shipment and paid for the balance owing on October 5, how would the transactions be journalized? Assume the inventory was restocked by Pete's Wholesalers.

JOURNAL			Page 1
Date	Account Title and Explanation	Debit	Credit

e) Suppose instead that Ernie's found the goods unsatisfactory and agreed to keep the goods with a 10% allowance. Prepare the journal entries to record the sales allowance and Ernie's payment on October 20.

JOURNAL			Page 1
Date	Account Title and Explanation	Debit	Credit

AP-13B (❸ ❹ ❺)

Wilde Wilderness Supplies had the following transactions during the month of January 2016.

Jan 1   Sold merchandise on credit to Merril for $15,000, terms 2/10, n/30; cost of goods $8,500.

Jan 1   Wilde paid $50 to ship the goods to Merril.

Jan 5   Purchased inventory for $12,000 on credit from Banff Outdoor terms 1/10, n/30.

Jan 5   Wilde paid $25 to have the merchandise from Banff Sales delivered.

Jan 8   Merril returned $1,200 (sales price) of merchandise purchased January 1, cost $800. The inventory will be resold.

Jan 12   Some of the merchandise purchased on January 5 was the wrong size. Wilde decided to keep the merchandise in exchange for a 25% allowance on the purchase. Allowances are not granted on shipping charges.

Jan 15   Received payment from Merril for January 1 sale.

Jan 18   Sold merchandise on credit to Totem Outfitters. for $5,000, terms 2/15, n/30; cost of goods $2,600.

Jan 23   Paid for merchandise purchased from Banff Outdoor on January 5.

Jan 26   Wilde granted Totem Outfitters a 20% allowance on the January 18 sale due to defective products.

Jan 31   Received payment from Totem Outfitters for the January 18 sale.

Journalize the above transactions assuming that Wilde Wilderness Supplies uses a perpetual inventory system. Round all calculations to the nearest whole dollar.

JOURNAL				Page 1
Date	Account Title and Explanation		Debit	Credit

JOURNAL			Page 2
Date	Account Title and Explanation	Debit	Credit

Analysis

Calculate Wilde Wilderness Supplies' gross profit margin for the month.

_____

_____

_____

_____

_____

_____

_____

_____

_____

_____

_____

_____

_____

_____

AP-14B (❸ ❹ ❼)

AB Retailers had the following business transactions during the month of April 2016.

Apr 10	AB Retailers bought $3,500 worth of T-shirts from Unique Designers. The invoice showed payment terms of 2/10, n/30.
Apr 10	Soon after AB Retailers received the products, it was discovered that some of the T-shirts (worth $500) did not meet quality standards. These goods were returned to the supplier.
Apr 20	AB Retailers made payment for the remaining invoice balance.
Apr 22	AB Retailers sold *all* the goods for $4,500 to SK Stores on terms 3/10, n/45.
Apr 28	SK Stores paid for the goods purchased and took advantage of the early payment discount.

Required

a) Prepare the journal entries to record the above transactions. Assume the company uses the perpetual inventory system.

JOURNAL			Page 1
Date	**Account Title and Explanation**	**Debit**	**Credit**

b) Calculate April's ending inventory based on the above transactions. Assume that inventory at the beginning of April amounted to $1,500.

_____

_____

_____

c) At the end of April, an inventory count was performed. The balance of inventory according to the count was $1,300. Management deemed that the difference between the ledger account and physical inventory account is due to theft (shrinkage). Prepare the journal entry to adjust the inventory balance on April 30.

JOURNAL			Page 1
Date	Account Title and Explanation	Debit	Credit

AP-15B (❷ ❸ ❹ ❾ ❿)

On January 1, 2016, a company purchases 1,000 units of inventory at $12 per unit on account. On January 5, the company sells 25 units for $50 per unit on account.

Required

a) Write the journal entries to record the transactions under the perpetual inventory system.

b) Write the journal entries to record the transactions under the periodic inventory system.

JOURNAL			Page 1
Date	**Account Title and Explanation**	**Debit**	**Credit**

AP-16B (⑤)

If sales are $290,000 and cost of goods sold is $130,000, what is the gross profit and gross margin percentage?

_____

_____

_____

_____

AP-17B (⑥)

Phony Accessory is a shop that sells cell phone accessories. The following information is available for the year ending June 30, 2016.

Sales Revenue	$49,000
Maintenance Expense	800
Rent Expense	3,000
Salaries Expense	38,000
Cost of Goods Sold	11,200
Interest Expense	1,000

Prepare the multistep income statement for June 2016.

Analysis

Phony Accessory sold 3,500 phone cases at an average price of $14 each during the year. The company buys phone case inventory at an average price of $3.20 each. If Phony Accessory had sold 4,000 phone cases instead, would it have a positive net income? Assume operating expenses would remain the same. Show your work.

_____

_____

_____

_____

_____

_____

_____

AP-18B (❶ ❹)

Suppose that SCOOP Pet Supplies' gross profit margin is 40% and that all sales are cash sales. Prepare any journal entries required to record sales for the year ended December 31, 2016, assuming that the company had $846,500 in sales revenue for the year and uses a perpetual inventory system.

JOURNAL				Page 1
Date	Account Title and Explanation		Debit	Credit

AP-19B (❼)

The following are the T-accounts for Direct Sales for the year ended September 30, 2016.

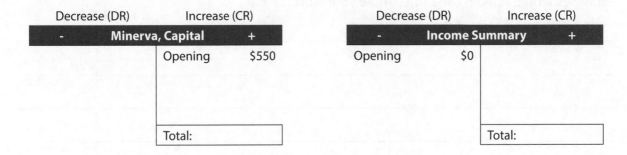

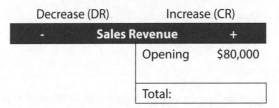

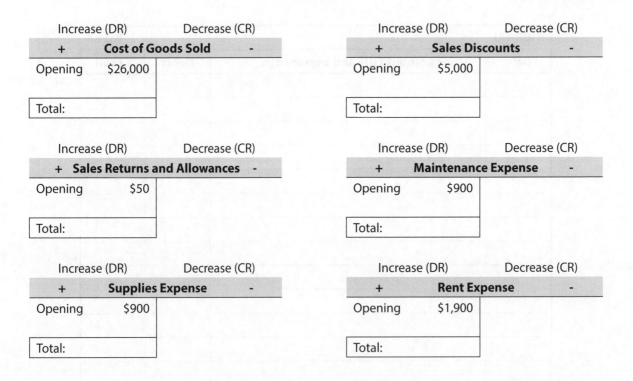

Required

a) Prepare the journal entries to close the appropriate accounts using the income summary (below).

b) Post the entries to the appropriate T-accounts and calculate the totals (above).

JOURNAL			Page 1
Date	**Account Title and Explanation**	**Debit**	**Credit**

AP-20B (❼)

The following is the adjusted trial balance **in alphabetical order** for LCP Construction for the year ended December 31, 2016.

Account Titles	DR	CR
LCP Construction		
Adjusted Trial Balance		
December 31, 2016		
Accounts Payable		$2,330
Accumulated Depreciation		1,140
Cash	$10,800	
Cost of Goods Sold	28,660	
Depreciation Expense	9,080	
Equipment	27,766	
Insurance Expense	5,260	
Interest Revenue		7,650
Pohler, Capital		48,060
Prepaid Insurance	4,675	
Prepaid Rent	18,100	
Rent Expense	9,300	
Sales Discounts	440	
Sales Returns and Allowances	1,749	
Sales Revenue		60,945
Unearned Revenue		1,000
Utilities Expense	2,240	
Wages Expense	5,800	
Wages Payable		2,745
	$123,870	$123,870

Required

Prepare the journal entries to close the appropriate accounts using the income summary.

JOURNAL			Page 1
Date	Account Title and Explanation	Debit	Credit

AP-21B (⑥)

Bugle News operates by selling newspaper and magazines to consumers. Peter has prepared the income statement and balance sheet for Bugle News as shown below.

The bank loan is due in annual payments of $50,000.

Bugle News Income Statement For the Year Ended December 31, 2016		
Revenues		
Sales Revenue	$975,000	
Interest Revenue	25,000	
Total Revenue		$1,000,000
Expenses		
Cost of Goods Sold	150,000	
Salaries Expense	85,000	
Rent Expense	55,800	
Insurance Expense	250,200	
Loss on Property Damage	59,000	
Total Expenses		600,000
Net Income		$400,000

Bugle News Balance Sheet As at December 31, 2016		
Assets		
Cash	$121,000	
Accounts Receivable	5,000	
Prepaid Insurance	514,000	
Inventory	310,000	
Equipment	800,000	
Accumulated Depreciation	(250,000)	
Total Assets		$1,500,000
Liabilities		
Accounts Payable	$15,000	
Unearned Revenue	530,000	
Bank Loan	300,000	
Total Liabilities		845,000
Owner's Equity		
Parker, Capital		655,000
Total Owner's Equity		655,000
Total Liabilities and Owner's Equity		$1,500,000

Required

a) Prepare the multistep income statement for Bugle News.

b) Prepare the classified balance sheet for Bugle News.

Analysis

Calculate and interpret the current ratio for Bugle News.

_____

_____

_____

_____

_____

_____

_____

_____

AP-22B (◉)

Rita Retail is a merchandising business. The store's building contains a large selling area with merchandise displays and shelves, and a smaller back office area where administrative tasks are performed such as payroll, marketing, and HR. The following information is available:

- Salaries for the back office workers amounted to $80,000 for the year.
- The office area is allocated 20% of the utility and insurance costs.
- Depreciation is charged on the merchandise displayers only.

Prepare a classified multistep income statement for Rita Retail.

Rita Retail Income Statement For the Year Ended December 31, 2016		
Sales Revenue		$1,400,000
Expenses		
Cost of Goods Sold	$890,000	
Salaries Expense	210,000	
Office Supplies Expense	12,000	
Insurance Expense	42,000	
Utilities Expense	7,000	
Depreciation Expense	5,000	
Total Expenses		1,166,000
Net Income		$234,000

Analysis

Give a reason why it is useful to separate expenses into selling and administrative categories on the income statement.

_____

_____

_____

AP-23B (⑪ ⑫)

Tommy Greggson, owner of Greggson Retail, prepared the following adjusted trial balance at its year-end of October 31, 2016.

Greggson Retail Trial Balance October 31, 2016		
Account Titles	**DR**	**CR**
Cash	$78,000	
Accounts Receivable	36,000	
Inventory	165,000	
Property, Plant, and Equipment	250,000	
Accumulated Depreciation		$80,000
Accounts Payable		126,000
Unearned Revenue		8,000
Bank Loan		50,000
Greggson, Capital		300,000
Greggson, Drawings	20,000	
Sales Revenue		360,000
Purchase Returns and Allowances		12,000
Purchase Discounts		5,000
Sales Returns and Allowances	30,000	
Sales Discounts	3,000	
Purchases	235,000	
Freight-In	7,000	
Depreciation Expense	4,000	
Interest Expense	1,000	
Salaries Expense	112,000	
Total	**$941,000**	**$941,000**

A year-end inventory count revealed that $210,000 of inventory is on hand.

Required

a) Prepare a multistep income statement for Greggson Retail.
b) Prepare the closing entries for Greggson Retail using the income summary method.

a) Prepare a multistep income statement

b) Prepare the closing entries using the income summary method

JOURNAL			Page 1
Date	Account Title and Explanation	Debit	Credit

Case Study

CS-1 (❸❹❺❻)

George K. Connor is a company that sells goods using a perpetual inventory system. During its first month of operations, the following transactions occurred during February 2016.

Feb 1   Purchased inventory on account for $20,000, terms of 2/10, n/30.

Feb 1   Received a deposit of $10,000 from a customer for products to be delivered later.

Feb 1   Returned damaged inventory worth $3,500.

Feb 5   Sold products for cash of $13,000. The cost of these products was $6,000.

Feb 10 Paid the balance owing to the supplier of inventory from Feb 1.

Feb 16 Received an advertising bill for $3,000 which will be paid next month.

Feb 21 Sold products on account for $31,000. The cost of these products was $10,000.

Feb 22 Paid wages and benefits with $6,000 cash.

Feb 25 Purchased new computers on account for $4,000.

Feb 26 A customer agreed to keep a defective product for a 30% allowance. The customer originally paid $1,000 on account for the product.

Feb 27 A customer returned an incorrect product for cash. This product had a sales price of $500 and a cost of $300. The item was returned to sales floor for resale.

Feb 28 Incurred maintenance expense of $2,000 on account.

The company uses the following chart of accounts to implement its accounting system.

Account Description	Account #
ASSETS	
Cash	101
Accounts Receivable	105
Inventory	115
Computers	120
LIABILITIES	
Accounts Payable	200
Unearned Revenue	215
OWNER'S EQUITY	
Connor, Capital	300
Connor, Drawings	310

Account Description	Account #
REVENUE	
Sales Revenue	400
Sales Returns and Allowances	455
EXPENSES	
Cost of Goods Sold	500
Advertising Expense	505
Maintenance Expense	520
Salaries Expense	545

Required

a) Prepare the journal entries for the period.

b) Post the entries to the general ledger.

c) Prepare a trial balance.

d) Prepare a multistep income statement, statement of owner's equity, and classified balance sheet for the period.

e) Calculate the gross profit margin on product sales.

f) Calculate the current ratio of the company at the end of the period.

a) Prepare the journal entries for the period

JOURNAL				Page 1
Date	Account Title and Explanation	PR	Debit	Credit

Date	Account Title and Explanation	PR	Debit	Credit

b) Post the entries to the General Ledger

Account:					GL. No.
Date	**Description**	**PR**	**DR**	**CR**	**Balance**

Account:					GL. No.
Date	**Description**	**PR**	**DR**	**CR**	**Balance**

Account:					GL. No.
Date	**Description**	**PR**	**DR**	**CR**	**Balance**

Account:					GL. No.
Date	**Description**	**PR**	**DR**	**CR**	**Balance**

Account:						GL. No._____
Date	**Description**	**PR**	**DR**	**CR**	**Balance**	

Account:						GL. No._____
Date	**Description**	**PR**	**DR**	**CR**	**Balance**	

Account:						GL. No._____
Date	**Description**	**PR**	**DR**	**CR**	**Balance**	

Account:						GL. No._____
Date	**Description**	**PR**	**DR**	**CR**	**Balance**	

Account: _____ GL. No._____

Date	Description	PR	DR	CR	Balance

Account: _____ GL. No._____

Date	Description	PR	DR	CR	Balance

Account: _____ GL. No._____

Date	Description	PR	DR	CR	Balance

Account: _____ GL. No._____

Date	Description	PR	DR	CR	Balance

Account:						GL. No._____
Date	**Description**		**PR**	**DR**	**CR**	**Balance**

Account:						GL. No._____
Date	**Description**		**PR**	**DR**	**CR**	**Balance**

c) Prepare a trial balance

Account Titles	**DR**	**CR**

d) Prepare the financial statements for the period

e) Calculate the gross profit margin on product sales

_____

_____

f) Calculate the current ratio at the end of the period

_____

_____

CS-2 (③ ④ ⑤ ⑥ ⑦)

Freestyle Fashion is an urban clothing retailer using the perpetual inventory system. Its balance sheet as at January 1, 2016 is presented below.

Freestyle Fashion Balance Sheet As at January 1, 2016		
Current Assets		
Cash	$28,400	
Inventory	50,000	
Prepaid Rent	12,000	
Total Current Assets		$90,400
Property, Plant & Equipment		
Equipment	32,000	
Total Property, Plant & Equipment		32,000
Total Assets		$122,400
Current Liabilities		
Accounts Payable	$20,500	
Unearned Revenue	12,000	
Total Current Liabilities		$32,500
Long-Term Liabilities		
Bank Loan	60,000	
Total Long-Term Liabilities		60,000
Total Liabilities		92,500
Owner's Equity		
Styles, Capital		29,900
Total Liabilities and Owner's Equity		$122,400

During January 2016, Freestyle Fashion had the following transactions

Jan 2   Purchased 490 jackets at $50 apiece on account (with terms 2/10, n/30).

Jan 5   Sold $50,000 worth of inventory on account. This inventory cost $39,000.

Jan 9   Purchased 100 pairs of jeans at $20 a piece on account (with terms 4/15, n/30).

Jan 11 Paid the balance owed to the supplier for all the jackets purchased on January 2.

Jan 16 Paid hourly store workers $2,000 in wages.

Jan 18 A customer returned products for cash to the store due to a defect. These products were originally sold for $200 and cost $75.

Jan 21 Paid the balance owed to the supplier for jeans purchased on Jan 9.

Jan 24 Received $25,000 cash from sales previously made on account.

Jan 26 Incurred $2,500 in utilities expenses, to be paid next month.

Jan 30 Sold $20,000 worth of inventory for cash. This inventory cost $15,000.

The company uses the following chart of accounts to implement its accounting system.

Account Description	Account #
ASSETS	
Cash	101
Accounts Receivable	105
Prepaid Rent	110
Inventory	115
Property, Plant & Equipment	120
Accumulated Depreciation	125
LIABILITIES	
Accounts Payable	200
Interest Payable	205
Salary Payable	210
Unearned Revenue	215
Bank Loan	220
OWNER'S EQUITY	
Styles, Capital	300
Styles, Drawings	310
Income Summary	315

Account Description	Account #
REVENUE	
Sales Revenue	400
Sales Returns & Allowances	405
Sales Discounts	410
EXPENSES	
Cost of Goods Sold	500
Advertising Expense	505
Depreciation Expense	510
Insurance Expense	515
Interest Expense	520
Maintenance Expense	525
Office Supplies Expense	530
Professional Fees Expense	535
Rent Expense	540
Salaries Expense	545
Utilities Expense	550
Travel Expense	555

Required

a) Journalize the transactions for January 2016.

JOURNAL					Page 1
Date	Account Title and Explanation	PR	Debit	Credit	

JOURNAL				Page 1
Date	Account Title and Explanation	PR	Debit	Credit

b) Journalize the following adjustments (to be recorded on January 31, 2016).

Jan 31   Prepaid rent represents one year of rent. One month of prepaid rent has been used

Jan 31   Depreciation for the month is $2,000

Jan 31 $1,000 of unearned revenue that has now been earned

Jan 31 $100 of interest is accrued and owed on the bank loan

JOURNAL					Page 2
Date	Account Title and Explanation	PR	Debit	Credit

c) Prepare the month-end closing journal entries. Use the income summary account.

JOURNAL				Page 3
Date	Account Title and Explanation	PR	Debit	Credit

d) Post the transactions to the general ledger.

General Ledger

Account:					GL. No._____	
Date	Description	PR	DR	CR	Balance	

Account:					GL. No._____	
Date	Description	PR	DR	CR	Balance	

Account:					GL. No._____	
Date	Description	PR	DR	CR	Balance	

Account:					GL. No._____	
Date	Description	PR	DR	CR	Balance	

Account: GL. No._____

Date	Description	PR	DR	CR	Balance	

Account: GL. No._____

Date	Description	PR	DR	CR	Balance	

Account: GL. No._____

Date	Description	PR	DR	CR	Balance	

Account:					GL. No._____	
Date	Description	PR	DR	CR	Balance	

Account:					GL. No._____	
Date	Description	PR	DR	CR	Balance	

Account:					GL. No._____	
Date	Description	PR	DR	CR	Balance	

Account: GL. No._____

Date	Description	PR	DR	CR	Balance	

Account: GL. No._____

Date	Description	PR	DR	CR	Balance	

Account: GL. No._____

Date	Description	PR	DR	CR	Balance	

Account:					GL. No._____	
Date	Description	PR	DR	CR	Balance	

Account:					GL. No._____	
Date	Description	PR	DR	CR	Balance	

Account:					GL. No._____	
Date	Description	PR	DR	CR	Balance	

Account:					GL. No._____	
Date	**Description**	**PR**	**DR**	**CR**	**Balance**	

Account:					GL. No._____	
Date	**Description**	**PR**	**DR**	**CR**	**Balance**	

Account:					GL. No._____	
Date	**Description**	**PR**	**DR**	**CR**	**Balance**	

Account:					GL. No.	
Date	**Description**	**PR**	**DR**	**CR**	**Balance**	

e) Prepare a multistep income statement, statement of owner's equity, and a classified balance sheet for January 2016.

Notes

Chapter 8

INVENTORY VALUATION

LEARNING OUTCOMES

❶ Determine the value of inventory using the specific identification method under the perpetual inventory system

❷ Determine the value of inventory using the first-in, first-out (FIFO) method under the perpetual inventory system

❸ Determine the value of inventory using the weighted-average cost method under the perpetual inventory system

❹ Explain the impact of inventory errors

❺ Apply the lower of cost and net realizable value (LCNRV) rule to value inventory

❻ Estimate the value of inventory using the gross profit method under the periodic inventory system

❼ Estimate the value of inventory using the retail method under the periodic inventory system

❽ Measure a company's management of inventory using inventory ratios

Appendix

❾ Determine the value of inventory using the specific identification method under the periodic inventory system

❿ Determine the value of inventory using the first-in, first-out (FIFO) method under the periodic inventory system

⓫ Determine the value of inventory using the weighted-average cost method under the periodic inventory system

AMEENGAGE™ Access **ameengage.com** for integrated resources including tutorials, practice exercises, the digital textbook and more.

──── **Assessment Questions** ────

AS-1 (❶ ❷ ❸)

List the three different inventory valuation methods allowed under ASPE and IFRS.

_____

_____

AS-2 (❶ ❷ ❸)

In times of rising prices, which inventory valuation method results in the highest closing inventory? Explain your answer.

_____

_____

_____

AS-3 (❶ ❷ ❸)

Different inventory valuation methods result in different inventory values. What factors may cause a company to select FIFO, weighted-average cost or specific identification?

_____

_____

_____

_____

_____

_____

_____

_____

AS-4 (❺)

Which accounting principle is the use of lower of cost and net realizable value based on?

_____

_____

_____

AS-5 (❻ ❼)

Name two methods which can be used to estimate inventory for interim statement purposes.

_____

_____

_____

AS-6 (❽)

What is the benefit to a company of using a perpetual inventory system?

_____

_____

_____

_____

_____

_____

_____

AS-7 (❶ ❷ ❸)

How does the actual flow of inventory affect the choice of inventory valuation method? How often can the inventory valuation method be changed?

_____

_____

_____

_____

AS-8 (❹)

Describe the impact of inventory errors.

_____

_____

_____

_____

_____

_____

_____

_____

_____

_____

AS-9 (❶ ❷ ❸)

Which of the inventory valuation methods show more ending inventory and less COGS in the case of rising prices?

_____

_____

_____

_____

AS-10 (❽)

How can a company monitor and prevent inventory shrinkage?

_____

_____

_____

_____

_____

_____

_____

_____

AS-11 (❽)

List two safety measures that can be taken to avoid inventory losses through theft.

_____

_____

_____

_____

_____

AS-12 (❺)

Describe the reason for applying the principle of lower of cost and net realizable value (LCNRV) to inventory.

_____

_____

_____

_____

AS-13 (❽)

What is the impact on financial statements of inflating inventory? What is the ethical responsibility of management in this regard?

_____

_____

_____

_____

_____

_____

AS-14 (❾)

Describe the differences between the specific identification method under the perpetual and the periodic inventory system.

_____

_____

_____

_____

_____

Application Questions Group A

AP-1A (❶ ❷ ❸)

The following purchases and sales took place at ZZZ Co. during the month of May 2016. The company had no inventory on hand on May 1st. ZZZ Co. uses the perpetual inventory system.

May 5   Purchased 200 units from AAA Co. for $10 per unit.
May 7   Sold 100 units to SSS Co.
May 13   Sold 50 units to TTT Co.
May 15   Purchased 70 units from BBB Co. for $13 per unit.
May 24   Sold 20 units to UUU Co.

Required

a) Fill in the inventory schedule using the weighted-average cost inventory valuation method.

Date	Purchases			Sales			Balance		
	Quantity	Unit Cost	Value	Quantity	Unit Cost	Value	Quantity	Unit Cost	Value
May 1	0						0	$0	$0
May 5	200	10	2000				200	10	2000
May 7				100	10	1000	100	10	1000
May 13				50	10	500	50	10	500
May 15	70	13	910				120	11.75	1410
May 24				20	11.75	235	100	11.75	1175
Ending Inventory									1175

b) If the FIFO method had instead been used, what would the value of COGS have been for the sale to UUU Co.?

_____

_____

_____

_____

_____

c) If the specific identification method had been used, what would the value of COGS have been for the sale to UUU Co.? Assume that 10 of the units sold to UUU Co. were purchased from AAA Co. and the other 10 units were purchased from BBB Co.

_____

_____

_____

d) Complete the following table to compare the inventory and COGS figures for the different inventory valuation methods on the sale to UUU Co.

	Specific Identification	Weighted-Average Cost	FIFO
COGS on sale to UUU			

AP-2A (❸)

Simplex Company has a fiscal year end on December 31. The company has only one product in inventory, and all units of that product are identical (homogenous). Complete the following schedule to calculate the value of ending inventory using the weighted-average cost method under the perpetual inventory system. Then calculate the cost of goods sold for the year of 2016.

Date	Purchases			Sales			Balance		
	Quantity	Unit Cost	Value	Quantity	Unit Cost	Value	Quantity	Unit Cost	Value
Jan 1							15	$10.00	
Feb 13	25	$12							
Mar 26	16	$13							
Apr 17				40					
Jul 25	34	$14							
Sep 28				14					
Nov 3				11					
Ending Inventory									

Cost of goods sold:_____

AP-3A (❸)

An inventory record card for item A–903 shows the following details in 2016.

Mar 1   60 units in opening inventory at a cost of $70 per unit

Mar 9   120 units purchased at a cost of $64 per unit

Mar 18   70 units sold

Mar 24   44 units purchased at a cost of $80 per unit

Mar 29   100 units sold

Required

The company uses the perpetual inventory method. Calculate the value of inventory at each of the above dates and determine the ending inventory at the end of March using the following methods.

(a) FIFO

(b) Weighted-average cost

(a) FIFO

Date	Purchases			Sales			Balance		
	Quantity	Unit Cost	Value	Quantity	Unit Cost	Value	Quantity	Unit Cost	Value
Mar 1									
Mar 9									
Mar 18									
Mar 24									
Mar 29									
Ending Inventory									

(b) Weighted-average cost

Date	Purchases			Sales			Balance		
	Quantity	Unit Cost	Value	Quantity	Unit Cost	Value	Quantity	Unit Cost	Value
Mar 1									
Mar 9									
Mar 18									
Mar 24									
Mar 29									
Ending Inventory									

AP-4A (❸)

GB, a bookseller, had the following transactions during the month of August 2016 and uses the perpetual inventory system.

Aug 1   Bought 10 novels at $30 each

Aug 2   Bought 10 bags at $45 each

Aug 5   Sold 5 novels

Aug 10   Bought 15 pencil cases at $5 each

Aug 21   Sold 3 bags

Required

a) Calculate the value of inventory at each date using the specific identification method. Clearly show August ending inventory.

Date	Purchases			Sales			Balance		
	Quantity	Unit Cost	Value	Quantity	Unit Cost	Value	Quantity	Unit Cost	Value
Aug 1							0	$0	$0
Aug 1									
Aug 2									
Aug 5									
Aug 10									
Aug 21									
Ending Inventory									

b) Calculate the COGS for August.

AP-5A (⑤)

A company has three types of products: gadgets, widgets and gizmos. The cost and market price of each type is listed below. Complete the table by applying the lower of cost and net realizable value.

Description	Category	Cost	NRV	LCNRV Applied to... Individual	Category
Gadget Type 1	Gadgets	$1,000	$900		
Gadget Type 2	Gadgets	5,000	5,200		
Total Gadgets					
Widget A	Widgets	100	100		
Widget B	Widgets	20	200		
Total Widgets					
Gizmo 1	Gizmos	1,500	1,450		
Gizmo 2	Gizmos	1,750	2,000		
Total Gizmos					
Total					

AP-6A (⑤)

Garden Company uses the perpetual inventory system and its inventory consists of four products as at December 31, 2016. Selected information is provided below.

Required

a) Calculate the inventory value that should be reported on December 31, 2016, using the lower of cost or and net realizable value applied on an individual-item basis.

Product	Number of units	Cost (per unit)	Net Realizable Value (per unit)	LCNRV (Individual)
1	15	$80	$120	
2	20	$80	$60	
3	40	$60	$50	
4	5	$120	$180	

Inventory Value:_____

b) Using the results from a), prepare the journal entry to adjust inventory to LCNRV
    (at individual-item level).

JOURNAL			Page 1
Date	Account Title and Explanation	Debit	Credit

AP-7A (❺)

MJ Corporation sells three categories of products: Shirts, Socks and Pants. The following
information was available at the year-end of December 31, 2016.

	Shirts	Socks	Pants
	$ per unit	$ per unit	$ per unit
Original cost	10	13	15
Estimated selling price (net realizable value)	15	12	14
Inventory: number of units held	300	380	240

Required

a) Calculate the value of inventory (apply the LCNRV at the category level).

b) Using the results from a), prepare the journal entry to adjust inventory to LCNRV
   (at category level).

JOURNAL			Page 1
Date	Account Title and Explanation	Debit	Credit

AP-8A (❽)

Tanner Radio Company has an inventory turnover of 4.5, while its competitor, Deej Radio, has
an inventory turnover ratio of 1.0.

Required

a) What do these ratios mean for each company? Which company has the better ratio?

---

b) Calculate the inventory days on hand for each company and interpret their meaning.

AP-9A (8)

The following are relevant inventory numbers from ABC Company for the 2016 fiscal year.

	$ Millions
Inventory—December 31, 2015	$108.5
Inventory—December 31, 2016	169.7
Cost of Goods Sold	$1,452.5

Relevant inventory numbers from XYZ Company for the 2016 fiscal year are shown below.

	$ Millions
Inventory—December 31, 2015	$221.7
Inventory—December 31, 2016	209.6
Cost of Goods Sold	$1,432.0

Handwritten annotations:

$$\frac{365}{\text{Inventory turnover}}$$

$$\frac{\text{Cost of Goods Sold}}{\text{Average Inventory}}$$

$$\frac{1452.5}{\left(\frac{108.5+169.2}{2}\right)} = 10.4$$

$$\frac{365}{10.4} = 34.96 \text{ day} \quad 35 \text{ days} \text{ roun.}$$

Required

a) Calculate the inventory turnover ratio and inventory days on hand for ABC Company.

b) Calculate the inventory turnover ratio and inventory days on hand for XYZ Company.

c) Compare the results between the two companies. What conclusion can we draw about the performance of these two companies comparatively?

AP-10A (❹)

A company reported ending inventory of $100,000 in year 1. It was discovered in year 2 that the correct value of the ending inventory was $90,000 for year 1. Complete the following table, based on this information. Assume the company uses perpetual inventory.

Item	Reported	Correct Amount
Inventory	$100,000	
Current Assets	$150,000	
Total Assets	$500,000	
Owner's Equity year 1	$200,000	
Sales	$1,000,000	
Cost of Goods Sold	$500,000	
Profit (loss) for year 1	$6,000	

AP-11A (❻)

Suppose that you must prepare quarterly financial statements, and the following information is available from the general ledger.

Sales	$200,000
Opening Inventory	$67,000
Purchases	$90,000
Gross Profit Margin (from examination of prior years' statements)	30%

Required

Calculate the estimated closing inventory using the gross profit method.

_____

_____

_____

_____

_____

_____

_____

AP-12A (❼)

Calculate the estimated closing inventory at cost by using the retail method using the following information.

	At Cost	At Retail
Cost of Goods Sold		
Opening Inventory	2,000	4,000
Purchases	42,000	90,000
Cost of Goods Available for Sale	44,000	94,000
Sales at Retail		50,000
Closing Inventory at Retail		44,000

Application Questions Group B

AP-1B (❸)

The following purchases and sales took place at YYY Co. during the month of June 2016. The company had no inventory on hand on June 1st. YYY Co. uses the perpetual inventory system.

June 4	Purchased 260 units from CCC Co. for $12 per unit.
June 8	Sold 160 units to QQQ Co.
June 14	Sold 37 units to III Co.
June 17	Purchased 117 units from LLL Co. for $13 per unit.
June 28	Sold 100 units to VVV Co.

Required

a) Fill in the inventory schedule using the weighted-average cost inventory valuation method.

Date	Purchases			Sales			Balance		
	Quantity	Unit Cost	Value	Quantity	Unit Cost	Value	Quantity	Unit Cost	Value
June 1							0	$0	$0
June 4									
June 8									
June 14									
June 17									
June 28									
Ending Inventory									

b) If the FIFO method had been used, what would the value of COGS have been for the sale to VVV Co.?

_____

_____

_____

_____

_____

_____

c) If the specific identification method had instead been used, what would the value of COGS have been for the sale to VVV Co.? Assume that 32 of the units sold to VVV Co. were purchased from CCC Co. and the other 68 units were purchased from LLL Co.

_____

_____

_____

d) Complete the following table to compare the inventory and COGS figures for the different inventory valuation methods on the sale to VVV Co.

	Specific Identification	Weighted-Average Cost	FIFO
COGS on sale to VVV			

AP-2B (◍)

Simplex Company has a fiscal year end on December 31. The company has only one product in inventory, and all units of that product are identical (homogenous). Complete the following schedule to calculate the value of ending inventory using the weighted-average cost method under the periodic inventory system in 2016.

Date	Purchases			Sales			Balance		
	Quantity	Unit Cost	Value	Quantity	Unit Cost	Value	Quantity	Unit Cost	Value
Jan 1							15		
Feb 13	25	$12							
Mar 26	16	$13							
Jul 25	34	$14							
Average Inventory									
Sales				65					
Ending Inventory									

AP-3B (❷ ❸)

LIME Suppliers is a wholesale company. It focuses primarily on office supplies, furniture and small electronic items. LIME Suppliers uses the perpetual inventory system. For one specific inventory item, it had the following transactions during the month of April 2016.

There were 10 items at the beginning of the month, with a cost of $10 each.

Date	Transaction	Quantity	Price
Apr 5	Purchased items	40	$12
Apr 7	Sold items	20	
Apr 15	Purchased items	50	$14
Apr 19	Purchased items	20	$16
Apr 27	Sold items	50	

Required

a) Calculate the value of COGS for the month of April and the value of ending inventory for April using the FIFO method.

Date	Purchases			Sales			Balance		
	Quantity	Unit Cost	Value	Quantity	Unit Cost	Value	Quantity	Unit Cost	Value
Apr 1									
Apr 5									
Apr 7									
Apr 15									
Apr 19									
Apr 27									

Ending Inventory: _____
Cost of Goods Sold: _____

b) Calculate the value of COGS for the month of April and the value of ending inventory for April using the weighted-average cost method. Round the unit cost to two decimal places.

Date	Purchase			Sale			Balance		
	Quantity	Unit Cost	Value	Quantity	Unit Cost	Value	Quantity	Unit Cost	Value

Ending Inventory: _____
Cost of Goods Sold: _____

Analysis

In a period of rising inventory prices, which of the above methods results in the largest gross profit on the income statement?

_____

_____

_____

AP-4B (⓾ ⓫)

Good Life sells medical support products and records purchases at net amounts. It accounts for its inventory using the periodic system. In 2016, the following information was available from the company's inventory records for ankle support products.

	Units	Unit Cost
January 1, 2016 (beginning inventory)	1,600	$18.00
Purchases		
January 5, 2016	2,600	$20.00
January 25, 2016	2,400	$21.00
February 16, 2016	1,000	$22.00
March 15, 2016	1,400	$23.00

A physical count was taken on March 31, 2016 and showed 2,000 units on hand.

Required

a) Prepare a schedule to calculate the ending inventory at March 31, 2016 under the FIFO valuation method.

b) Prepare a schedule to calculate the ending inventory at March 31, 2016 under the weighted-average cost method.

a) FIFO Valuation Method

Date	Purchases			Sales			Balance		
	Quantity	Unit Cost	Value	Quantity	Unit Cost	Value	Quantity	Unit Cost	Value
Jan 1									
Jan 5									
Jan 25									
Feb 16									
Mar 15									
Sales									
Ending Inventory									

b) Weighted-Average Cost Method

Date	Purchases			Sales			Balance		
	Quantity	Unit Cost	Value	Quantity	Unit Cost	Value	Quantity	Unit Cost	Value
Jan 1									
Jan 5									
Jan 25									
Feb 16									
Mar 15									
Average Inventory									
Sales									
Ending Inventory									

AP-5B (❺)

A company has three types of products: gadgets, widgets and gizmos. The cost and NRV of each type is listed below. Complete the table by applying the lower of cost and net realizable value.

Description	Category	Cost	NRV	LCNRV Applied to	
				Individual	Category
Gadget 1	Gadgets	1,500	1,390		
Gadget 2	Gadgets	4,830	5,430		
Total Gadgets					
Widget A	Widgets	890	470		
Widget B	Widgets	350	300		
Total Widgets					
Gizmo 1	Gizmo	1,350	1,960		
Gizmo 2	Gizmo	2,460	2,320		
Total Gizmos					
Total					

AP-6B (❻)

It is now March 31, 2016 and Garden Company needs to present a set of financial statements showing the performance of the first quarter of 2016 to a local bank for a loan. To prepare the statements in a timely manner, Garden Company decided to estimate the inventory amount instead of doing a physical count. The following information is provided.

Accounts Receivable, January 1, 2015	$1,500
Accounts Receivable, March 31, 2015	2,200
Collections of accounts from January 1 to March 31	5,300
Inventory, January 1, 2015	1,200
Purchases from January 1 to March 31	6,800

Assume all sales are made on account. Garden Company expects its gross margin percentage to be 30%.

Required

Calculate the estimated cost of the inventory on March 31, 2016 using the gross profit method.

Sales Revenue		
Cost of Goods Sold		
Opening Inventory		
Purchases		
Cost of Goods Available for Sale		
Closing Inventory		
Cost of Goods Sold		
Gross Profit		

AP-7B (❷ ❺)

On December 31, 2016 Kranky Bike Shop has three types of bikes: Mountain Bikes, Road Bikes and Hybrid Bikes. The cost and NRV of each type is listed below.

Required

a) Complete the table below by applying the lower of cost and net realizable value.

Description	Category	Cost	NRV	LCNRV Applied to: Individual	LCNRV Applied to: Category
CCM	Mountain	10,000	8,000		
Mikado	Mountain	8,000	5,500		
Oryx	Mountain	2,000	3,100		
Total Mountain Bikes					
Giant	Road	7,000	12,500		
Norco	Road	6,000	8,100		
Total Road Bikes					
Electra	Hybrid	2,800	2,500		
Acquila	Hybrid	2,600	3,000		
Total Hybrid Bikes					
Total					

b) Prepare the adjusting entry, if required, if LCNRV was applied using
   i) individual products
   ii) category

JOURNAL			Page 1
Date	Account Title and Explanation	Debit	Credit

AP-8B (❼)

A list of relevant inventory numbers from SI Company for the year ended December 31, 2016 is provided below.

Average inventory—December 31, 2015	$90,000
Average inventory—December 31, 2016	110,000
Cost of Goods Sold—2015	920,000
Cost of Goods Sold—2016	980,000

Required

a) Calculate the inventory turnover ratio and the inventory days on hand ratio for SI company for the two years.

	2016	2015
Inventory turnover ratio		
Inventory days on hand		

b) Compare the results between two years. What conclusion can be drawn about the performance of the company regarding both years?

AP-9B (⑧)

Delta Corporation reported the following amounts for ending inventory and cost of goods sold in the financial statements.

Ending Inventory	
2016	$799,000
2015	$1,365,000
2014	$3,205,000

Cost of Goods Sold	
2016	$25,927,000
2015	$36,479,000
2014	$47,025,000

Required

a) Calculate the inventory turnover ratio and inventory days on hand for 2016 and 2015.

b) Compare and discuss the results between two years.

c) Delta Corporation is a software company in a rapidly changing industry. Evaluate the results from part a) by using this information and considering the amount of cost of goods sold.

AP-10B (❹)

Trevor and Arkady run Squash Stuff Company The net income earned by their business during the year ended December 31, 2016 is $250,000. However, an inventory clerk realized that the ending inventory for 2016 was overstated by $10,000.

Required

a) If the error is not corrected for, what would be the effect on 2016 net income?

_____

_____

_____

b) If the error is not corrected for, what would be the effect on the 2016 equity balance?

_____

_____

_____

c) Record journal entries to correct the overstatement of inventory assuming that error was discovered on December 31, 2016.

JOURNAL			Page 1
Date	Account Title and Explanation	Debit	Credit

d) If the error is not corrected for, how would the sum of 2016 and 2017 net income be affected?

_____

_____

_____

_____

_____

e) There have been cases where companies applying for bank loans have intentionally overstated their closing inventory. Why would companies overstate their closing inventory and what are some of the methods of overstating closing inventory?

_____

_____

_____

_____

_____

_____

AP-11B (❻)

Fine Grocery Store has been buying and selling grocery items for many years. During the month of January 2016, some inventory was lost due to a fire in the store. The following amounts have been extracted from the accounts of Fine Grocery Store.

Sales		$280,000
Beginning Inventory	$210,000	
Purchases	340,000	
Inventory in good condition after fire	300,000	
Gross Profit Margin		30%

Calculate the amount of inventory lost due to the fire by first calculating the amount of estimated ending inventory before the fire using the gross profit method.

Sales Revenue		$280,000
Cost of Goods Sold		
Opening Inventory	$210,000	
Purchases	340,000	
Cost of Goods Available for Sale		
Closing Inventory Before Fire		
Cost of Goods Sold		
Gross Profit		

_____

_____

_____

_____

AP-12B (6)

The following information has been provided by AS Retailers for the month of August 2016. Calculate the estimated closing inventory at cost using the retail method.

	At Cost	At Retail
Cost of goods sold		
Opening inventory	3,000	6,000
Purchases	32,000	80,000
Cost of goods available for sale	35,000	86,000
Sales at retail		50,000
Closing inventory at retail		36,000

Case Study

CS-1 (❷ ❸ ❺ ❻)

Munder Difflin had the following transactions during the month of November 2016.

Nov 2   Purchased 1,000 widgets for $20 per unit on credit.

Nov 5   Sold 900 widgets for $55 each for cash.

Nov 10   Purchased 500 widgets for $25 per unit on credit.

Nov 18   Sold 100 widgets for $60 each on credit.

Nov 29   Sold 300 widgets for $50 each for cash.

Munder Difflin uses a perpetual inventory system and the FIFO inventory valuation method. There were no widgets in the company's opening inventory for November.

Required

a) Record the above transactions in the general journal.

b) Prepare the schedule to calculate ending inventory after the above transactions.

c) Calculate the value of inventory using the lower of cost and net realizable value (LCNRV).

d) Record the journal entry to adjust the value of inventory to the lower of cost and net realizable value based on individual items using the results from c).

e) Prepare an excerpt of the multistep income statement for the month showing sales revenue, cost of goods sold, and gross profit.

f) Sales for December are $100,000 and purchases were $68,500. Calculate the gross profit margin.

g) Use the gross profit method to estimate the balance of inventory.

a) Journal Entries

JOURNAL			Page 1
Date	**Account Title and Explanation**	**Debit**	**Credit**

b) Ending Inventory Calculation

Date	Purchases			Sales			Balance		
	Quantity	Unit Cost	Value	Quantity	Unit Cost	Value	Quantity	Unit Cost	Value
Nov 1									
Nov 2									
Nov 5									
Nov 10									
Nov 18									
Nov 29									
Ending Inventory									

c) Valuing Inventory Using LCNRV

Description	Category	Cost	NRV	LCNRV Applied to...	
				Individual	Category
Widget A	Widgets	3,000	2,300		
Widget B	Widgets	2,000	3,300		
Total Widgets					
Total					

d) LCNRV Based on Individual Items

JOURNAL			Page 1
Date	Account Title and Explanation	Debit	Credit

e) An Excerpt of the Multistep Income Statement

f) Gross Profit Margin

Sales Revenue		$100,000
Cost of Goods Sold		
Opening Inventory		
Purchases	<u>68,500</u>	
Cost of Goods Available for Sale		
Closing Inventory		
Cost of Goods Sold		
Gross Profit		

g) Gross Profit Method

_____

_____

_____

_____

_____

Notes

Chapter 9

ACCOUNTING INFORMATION SYSTEMS

LEARNING OUTCOMES

❶ Explain the flow of accounting information through the accounting paper trail

❷ Describe and record transactions in special journals

❸ Describe and record transactions in subsidiary ledgers

❹ Identify features of a computerized accounting system

Appendix

❺ Prepare special journals under a periodic inventory system

AMEENGAGE™ *Access **ameengage.com** for integrated resources including tutorials, practice exercises, the digital textbook and more.*

Assessment Questions

AS-1 (❶)

What are the features of an effective accounting information system?

_____

_____

_____

_____

_____

_____

AS-2 (❶)

Describe the paper trail in a manual accounting system.

_____

_____

_____

_____

_____

_____

_____

_____

_____

_____

AS-3 (❹)

How do the elements in a computerized system differ from those in a manual system?

_____

_____

_____

_____

_____

_____

_____

_____

_____

_____

AS-4 (❷)

What are special journals used for?

_____

_____

_____

AS-5 (❷)

What type of information would be found in the sales journal?

_____

_____

_____

AS-6 (❷)

What are general journals used for?

_____

_____

AS-7 (❸)

Why are subsidiary ledgers used?

_____

_____

_____

AS-8 (❸)

What is the relationship between a control account and its corresponding subledgers?

_____

_____

_____

AS-9 (❸)

What type of information can be found in an accounts payable subsidiary ledger?

_____

_____

_____

_____

AS-10 (❸)

At the end of the accounting period what is done with the totals in the purchases special journal?

_____

_____

_____

_____

AS-11 (❸)

When preparing a sales return in the general journal, what accounts are updated? How is the post reference column updated to indicate the accounts are updated?

_____

_____

_____

_____

Application Questions Group A

AP-1A (❷)

For each transaction, indicate in which journal it should be recorded.

- Sales Journal (SJ)
- Cash Receipts Journal (CR)
- Purchases Journal (PJ)
- Cash Payments Journal (CP)
- General Journal (GJ)

_____ Sold products for cash.

_____ Received a loan from the bank.

_____ Owner invested cash into the business.

_____ Owner withdrew cash from the business.

_____ Paid amount owing to a supplier.

_____ Received a utility bill, which will be paid later.

_____ Returned products to a supplier.

_____ Recorded adjustment for depreciation.

AP-2A (❷)

Hidson Inc. is a small retailer. The following is a list of sales transactions for the month of April.

Apr 2   Made a sale on account (Invoice #5703) to B. Fager for $450 (cost $300).

Apr 5   Made a sale on account (Invoice #5704) to J. Dryer for $1,150 (cost $900).

Apr 10   Made a sale on account (Invoice #5705) to T. Burton for $550 (cost $450).

Apr 12   Made a sale on account (Invoice #5706) to JB Inc. for $670 (cost $500).

Required

Record these transactions in the sales journal.

					Sales Journal				Page 1
Date		Account		Invoice #	PR	Accounts Receivable/ Sales (DR/CR)		COGS/ Inventory (DR/CR)	

AP-3A (❷)

F. Benjuman owns a small clothing store. The following is the list of prices he charges for different types of products.

Product	Price	Cost
Blue cotton	$6 per sheet	$4 per sheet
Black silk	$20 per metre	$15 per metre
White tape	$10 per roll	$6 per roll
Green felt	$4 per metre	$2 per metre

During the month of July, the company made the following sales.

Jul 1   Sold 3 rolls of white tape, 5 sheets of blue cotton, and 1 metre of black silk to F. Grey, on account (Invoice #5739).

Jul 5   Sold 6 rolls of white tape and 30 metres of green felt to A. Gray, on account (Invoice #5740).

Jul 9   Sold 1 metre of black silk to E. Hines, on account (Invoice #5741).

Jul 11   Sold 10 rolls of white tape, 6 sheets of blue cotton, 3 metres of black silk and 11 metres of green felt to M. Allen, on account (Invoice #5742).

Jul 14   Made a sale on account (Invoice #5743) to B. Cooper: 12 rolls of white tape, 14. sheets of blue cotton and 9 metres of green felt.

Required

Record these transactions in the sales journal.

Sales Journal				Accounts Receivable/ Sales (DR/CR)	Page 1
Date	**Account**	**Invoice #**	**PR**	**Accounts Receivable/ Sales (DR/CR)**	**COGS/ Inventory (DR/CR)**

AP-4A (❷)

Riya Cosmetics has provided you with the following information about the transactions the company incurred during the month of June.

Jun 2   Received $2,000 from a cash sale to Faces Inc. (cost $1,500).

Jun 6   Received $840 from Beauty Breeze regarding outstanding accounts receivable.

Jun 10   Received $650 for the cash sale of 5 facial scrubs (cost $540) to Seizers Salon.

Jun 13   Received $325 in interest earned from the TD Bank.

Jun 25   Took out a loan of $3,000 from a bank.

Required

Record these transactions in the cash receipts journal.

Cash Receipts Journal								Page 1
Date	**Account**	**PR**	**Cash (DR)**	**Accounts Receivable (CR)**	**Sales (CR)**	**Interest Revenue (CR)**	**Other (CR)**	**COGS/ Inventory (DR/CR)**

AP-5A (❷)

Lin Z is an owner-operated sporting goods retailer. The following is a list of the company's transactions for the month of June.

Jun 2   The owner, Lin Zarra, invested $16,500 into the business.

Jun 6   Received a loan of $1,000 from the bank.

Jun 10   Received $150 of interest earned on the savings account with Bank of Montreal (BMO).

Jun 13   Received $2,000 from cash sales to Dawn Sports (sold sports items costing $1,500).

Jun 25   Received $800 from AD Sports regarding outstanding accounts receivable.

Required

Record these transactions in the cash receipts journal.

Cash Receipts Journal								Page 1
Date	Account	PR	Cash (DR)	Accounts Receivable (CR)	Sales (CR)	Interest Revenue (CR)	Other (CR)	COGS/ Inventory (DR/CR)

AP-6A (❷ ❸)

Peter's Pewter sells figurines. During the month of August 2016, the following transactions occurred.

Aug 3   Peter invested $4,000 into his business.

Aug 7   Sold inventory to Joyce Fontane for $500 cash. The inventory had a cost of $240.

Aug 16 Sold inventory to Carol Balsdon for $750 on account. The inventory had a cost of $310.

Aug 17 Sold inventory to James Stewart for $820 on account. The inventory had a cost of $420.

Aug 24 Received full payment from Carol Balsdon from the Aug 16 transaction.

Required

a) Record the above transactions in the sales journal and the cash receipts journal.

b) Post the appropriate transactions from the journals to the subledger accounts.

c) At the end of the month, total the journals and update the accounts receivable control account.

Assume zero opening balances for the subledger and general ledger accounts. Assume no entries were made directly to the A/R general ledger from the general journal.

Use the following selected accounts to complete the posting references.

Account Description	Account #	Account Description	Account #
Cash	101	Pewter, Drawings	310
Accounts Receivable	110	Sales Revenue	400
Inventory	120	Sales Discount	405
Office Supplies	130	Interest Revenue	410
Accounts Payable	200	Cost of Goods Sold	500
Bank Loan	220	Salaries Expense	520
Pewter, Capital	300	Telephone Expense	525

Sales Journal						Page 1
Date	Account	Invoice #	PR	Accounts Receivable/ Sales (DR/CR)	COGS/ Inventory (DR/CR)	

Cash Receipts Journal								Page 3
Date	Account	PR	Cash (DR)	Accounts Receivable (CR)	Sales (CR)	Bank Loan (CR)	Other (CR)	COGS/ Inventory (DR/CR)

Account: Accounts Receivable   **110**

Date	Description	PR	DR	CR	Balance

Account: Carol Balsdon

Date	PR	DR	CR	Balance

Account: James Stewart

Date	PR	DR	CR	Balance

AP-7A (❷ ❸)

Ryan Manufacturing sells flat-pack bookcases to retailers. The following transactions occurred during the month of September 2016. All sales on account come with terms of 2/10, net 30.

Sep 1   Received a loan from the bank for $15,000.

Sep 5   Sold products for cash to Brock Retailer for $8,400. The products had a cost of $4,620.

Sep 8   Sold products on account to Furniture Outlet for $10,600. The products had a cost of $6,360.

Sep 12   Furniture Outlet paid the amount owing from Sep 8.

Sep 21   Sold products on account to Brock Retailer for $6,200. The products had a cost of $3,410.

Required

a) Record the transactions in the appropriate journal.

b) Where appropriate, update the accounts receivable subledgers.

c) At the end of the month, calculate the totals of the columns in the journals and update the control account.

Sales Journal					Page 1
Date	Account	PR	Invoice #	Accounts Receivable/Sales (DR/CR)	COGS/ Inventory (DR/CR)

Cash Receipts Journal								Page 1
Date	Account	PR	Cash (DR)	Sales Discount (DR)	Accounts Receivable (CR)	Sales (CR)	Other (CR)	COGS/ Inventory (DR/CR)

Account:	Accounts Receivable				GL. No.	110
Date	Description	PR	DR	CR	Balance	

Account:	Furniture Outlet			
Date	PR	DR	CR	Balance

Account:	Brock Retailer			
Date	PR	DR	CR	Balance

Chapter 9 Checkheading
buying on account
paying anything
usually
cash payments
Journal

if balance 0
Put credit

AP-8A (❷)

J. Glen, a sports retailer, made the following purchases during the month of May.

May 2   Received a bill (Invoice #125) from F. Day for the purchase of 2 basketballs worth $100 each and 6 footballs worth $45 each.

May 4   Received a bill (Invoice #135) from G. Smith for the purchase of 7 cricket bats worth $65 each, 5 pairs of ice skates worth $32 each and 4 rugby balls worth $32 each.

May 10   Received a bill (Invoice #145) from L. Todd for the purchase of 6 cricket bats worth $55 each.

May 12   Received a bill (Invoice #222) from M. Moore for the purchase of 9 packages of golf balls at $45 each.

Required

Record these transactions in the purchases journal.

	Purchases Journal				Page 1
Date	Account	Invoice #	PR	Inventory (DR)	Accounts Payable (CR)

AP-9A (❷)

Vina Duckworth has provided the following information relating to her activities in the month of June 2016.

Jun 2   Paid amount owing $650 (Invoice #780) to SK Depot (Cheque #195).

Jun 6   Paid back loan of $800 to Crystal Inc. (Cheque #196).

Jun 10   Handed over cheque #197 to Nektel Inc. for $3,000 worth of inventory.

Jun 13   Received the telephone bill for $350 and paid the amount owing to CasTech Inc. for telephone services (Cheque #198).

Jun 25   Paid $205 to SFC Inc. for general expenses (Cheque #199). ·

Required

Record these transactions in the cash payments journal.

| | | | | | | Accounts | |
| | Cash Payments Journal | | | | | | Page 1 |
Date	Account	Cheque #	PR	Other (DR)	Inventory (DR)	Payable (DR)	Cash (CR)

AP-10A (❷)

Medicines World, a medical store, makes all transactions in cash only. It has provided you with the following information about the transactions for the month of May.

May 2   Paid $1,000 rent for the month of May to Mrs. Elizabeth (Cheque #23).

May 4   Paid $800 salary to James Jones for the month of April (Cheque #24).

May 6   Paid repair and maintenance charges amounting $300 to Building Services Inc. (Cheque #25).

May 10   Paid $200 of internet charges to Castech (Cheque #26).

May 12   Bought medicine costing $8,000 from Medicines Inc. (Cheque #27).

Required

Record these transactions in the cash payments journal.

| | | | | | | Accounts | |
| | Cash Payments Journal | | | | | | Page 1 |
Date	Account	Cheque #	PR	Other (DR)	Inventory (DR)	Payable (DR)	Cash (CR)

AP-11A (❷ ❸)

Blossoming Gardens sells landscaping materials. During the month of May 2016, the following transactions occurred.

May 3   Purchased office supplies for $800 on account from Office Supply Shop.

May 7   Purchased inventory for $1,200 cash from Rock Bottom with cheque #456.

May 10   Paid telephone bill for $350 cash with cheque #457.

May 17   Paid the amount owing to Office Supply Shop with cheque #458.

May 24   Purchased inventory for $3,500 from Paving Stones on account.

Required

a)   Record the above transactions in the purchases journal and the cash payments journal.

b)   Post the appropriate transactions from the journals to the subledger accounts.

c)   At the end of the month, total the journals and update the accounts payable control account.

Assume zero opening balances for the subledger and general ledger accounts. Assume no entries were made directly to the A/P general ledger from the general journal.

Use the following selected accounts to complete the posting references.

Account Description	Account #	Account Description	Account #
Cash	101	Owner's Drawings	310
Accounts Receivable	110	Sales Revenue	400
Inventory	120	Sales Discount	405
Office Supplies	130	Interest Revenue	410
Accounts Payable	200	Cost of Goods Sold	500
Bank Loan	220	Salaries Expense	520
Owner's Capital	300	Telephone Expense	525

Purchases Journal							Page 6
Date	Account	Invoice	PR	Inventory (DR)	Office Supplies (DR)	Other (DR)	Accounts Payable (CR)
May 3	office supplies	x x x			800		800
May 24	Pavingstone	xxx		3500			3500
				3500	800	—	4,300

Cash Payments Journal							Page 4
Date	Account	Cheque #	PR	Accounts Payable (DR)	Other (DR)	Inventory (DR)	Cash (CR)

Account:	Accounts Payable				GL. No	200
Date	Description	PR	DR	CR	Balance	

Account:	Office Supply Shop			
Date	PR	DR	CR	Balance

Account:	Paving Stones			
Date	PR	DR	CR	Balance

AP-12A (❷ ❸)

Cap It sells a variety of hats. The following is a list of transactions for the month of November 2016.

Nov 5   Received invoice #2563 for $4,000 worth of office supplies from Office Depot.

Nov 9   Received invoice #8475 from Aqua for $180 for water.

Nov 12   Paid amount owing to Office Depot with cheque #153.

Nov 21   Purchased inventory from Fedora Company for $4,000 with cheque 154.

Nov 22   Paid amount owing to Aqua with cheque #155.

Nov 25   Paid $260 to John Walker for repair expenses with cheque #155.

Nov 26   Received invoice #563 from Lids for $3,700 worth of inventory.

Accounts payable
other
control account

Required

a) Record the above entries in the appropriate journal.

b) Post the entries in the subledger accounts.

c) At the end of the month, total the special journals and update the control account.

Purchases Journal							Page 1
Date	Account	Invoice #	PR	Water Expense (DR)	Office Supplies (DR)	Inventory (DR)	Accounts Payable (CR)

Cash Payments Journal							Page 1
Date	Account	Chq #	PR	Other (DR)	Inventory (DR)	Accounts Payable (DR)	Cash (CR)

Opening Balances

Office Depot:	$400 (CR)
Aqua:	$40 (CR)
Lids:	$1,300 (CR)

Note that Cap It's accounts payable records consist of only these three subledgers. Assume no entries were made directly to accounts payable through the general journal. Update the PR columns in both the subledgers and special journals.

General Ledger Accounts Payable				
Date	PR	DR	CR	Balance

Accounts Payable Subsidiary Ledger					
Office Depot					
Date	PR	DR	CR	Balance	

Accounts Payable Subsidiary Ledger					
Aqua					
Date	PR	DR	CR	Balance	

Accounts Payable Subsidiary Ledger					
Lids					
Date	PR	DR	CR	Balance	

AP-13A (❷ ❸)

Gherry is a small shoe retailer. The following is a list of transactions for the month of May.

May 4   Received $6,000 from a cash sale to Teamster Inc. (sold sport shoes costing $700).

May 5   Received a bill (Invoice #5780) for $800 worth of supplies from BZDepot Inc.

May 6   Received $840 from Jo-Ann regarding her outstanding accounts receivable.

May 9   Received $650 for the cash sale of 5 pairs of shoes (costing a total of $85) to Sgt. Pepper.

May 9   Received a bill from ComTech Inc. (Invoice #167) for $150 for telephone services.

May 10   Received $325 in interest from loan to Lance Livestrong.

May 12   Paid amount owing (Invoice #5780) to BZDepot Inc. (Cheque #201).

May 15   The company received a loan of $1,000 from TD Bank.

May 18   Made a sale on account (Invoice #2341) to Keith Ricardo, for $250 (with inventory costing $200).

May 21   Handed over cheque #202 to Nikel Inc for $2,000 worth of inventory.

May 22   Paid amount owing (Invoice #167) to ComTech Inc. for telephone services with cheque #203.

May 25   Paid $205 to BFG Inc., for maintenance expenses (Cheque #204).

May 26   Received bill from Adibas Inc. (Invoice #113) for $5,500 worth of inventory

May 28   Made a sale, on account (Invoice #2342), to Gary Lineker for $2,000 worth of shoes (shoes cost $1,700).

Required

a) Record these transactions in the Cash Receipts, Sales, Purchases and Cash Payments Journal.

b) Post from the special journals to the accounts receivable subledger and then to the general ledger control account at the end of the month. Assume the following opening subledger balances.

- Jo-Ann: $940 (DR)
- Keith Ricardo: $600 (DR)
- Gary Lineker: $800 (DR)

Note that Gherry's accounts receivable records consist of only these three subledgers. Assume no entries were made directly to accounts receivable through the general journal. Update the PR columns in the subledgers and special journals.

c) Post from the special journals to the accounts payable subledger and then to the general ledger control account at the end of the month. Assume the following opening subledger balances.

- BZDepot Inc.: $1,000 (CR)
- ComTech Inc.: $1,200 (CR)
- Adibas Inc.: $1,400 (CR)

Note that Gherry's accounts payable records consist of only these three subledgers. Assume no entries were made directly to accounts payable through the general journal. Update the PR columns in both the subledgers and special journals.

a)   Record the transactions in the special journals.

Cash Receipts Journal								**Page 1**
Date	Account	PR	Cash (DR)	Accounts Receivable (CR)	Sales (CR)	Interest Revenue (CR)	Loans Payable (CR)	Other (CR)	COGS/ Inventory (DR/CR)

Sales Journal					**Page 1**
Date	Account	Invoice #	PR	Accounts Receivable/ Sales (DR/CR)	COGS/Inventory (DR/CR)

Purchases Journal							**Page 1**
Date	Account	Invoice #	PR	Telephone Expense (DR)	Office Supplies (DR)	Inventory (DR)	Accounts Payable (CR)

Cash Payments Journal							**Page 1**
Date	Account	Cheque #	PR	Other (DR)	Inventory (DR)	Accounts Payable (DR)	Cash (CR)

b) Post to updated the accounts receivable subledger and general ledger.

Accounts Receivable Subsidiary Ledger Jo-Ann					
Date	PR	DR	CR	Balance	

Accounts Receivable Subsidiary Ledger Keith Ricardo					
Date	PR	DR	CR	Balance	

Accounts Receivable Subsidiary Ledger Gary Lineker					
Date	PR	DR	CR	Balance	

Post to general ledger.

General Ledger Accounts Receivable					
Date	PR	DR	CR	Balance	

c) Post to update the accounts payable subledger and general ledger.

Accounts Payable Subsidiary Ledger BZDepot Inc.					
Date	PR	DR	CR	Balance	

Accounts Payable Subsidiary Ledger ComTech Inc.					
Date	PR	DR	CR	Balance	

Accounts Payable Subsidiary Ledger Adibas Inc.					
Date	PR	DR	CR	Balance	

Post to general ledger.

General Ledger Accounts Payable					
Date	PR	DR	CR	Balance	

AP-14A (⑤)

Blossoming Gardens sells landscaping materials. During the month of May 2016, the following transactions occurred. Blossoming Gardens uses the periodic inventory system.

May 3   Purchased office supplies for $800 on account from Office Supply Shop.

May 7   Purchased inventory for $1,200 cash from Rock Bottom with cheque #456.

May 10   Paid telephone bill for $350 cash with cheque #457.

May 17   Paid the amount owing to Office Supply Shop with cheque #458.

May 24   Purchased inventory for $3,500 from Paving Stones on account.

Required

a)   Record the above transactions in the purchases journal and the cash payments journal.

b)   Post the appropriate transactions from the journals to the subledger accounts.

c)   At the end of the month, total the journals and update the accounts payable control account.

Assume zero opening balances for the subledger and general ledger accounts. Assume no entries were made directly to the A/P general ledger from the general journal.

Use the following selected accounts to complete the posting references.

Account Description	Account #	Account Description	Account #
Cash	101	Owner's Drawings	310
Accounts Receivable	110	Sales Revenue	400
Inventory	120	Sales Discount	405
Office Supplies	130	Interest Revenue	410
Accounts Payable	200	Cost of Goods Sold	500
Bank Loan	220	Salaries Expense	520
Owner's Capital	300	Telephone Expense	525

Purchases Journal							Page 6
Date	Account	Invoice	PR	Purchases (DR)	Office Supplies (DR)	Other (DR)	Accounts Payable (CR)

Cash Payments Journal							Page 4
Date	Account	Cheque #	PR	Accounts Payable (DR)	Other (DR)	Purchases (DR)	Cash (CR)

Account:	Accounts Payable				GL. No	200
Date	Description	PR	DR	CR	Balance	

Account:	Office Supply Shop			
Date	PR	DR	CR	Balance

Account:	Paving Stones			
Date	PR	DR	CR	Balance

Application Questions Group B

AP-1B (❷)

For each transaction, indicate in which journal it should be recorded.

- Sales Journal (SJ)
- Cash Receipts Journal (CR)
- Purchases Journal (PJ)
- Cash Payments Journal (CP)
- General Journal (GJ)

_____ Received payment from a customer.

_____ Paid salaries to employees.

_____ Sold products on accounts.

_____ A customer returned unused product.

_____ Purchased inventory on account.

_____ Recorded adjustment for unearned revenue.

_____ Paid interest on a bank loan.

_____ Purchased office supplies on account.

AP-2B (❷)

Smart has provided you with the following information about its sales transactions during the month of September.

Sep 1   Made a sale on account (Invoice #1122) to Fat Inc. for $1,450 (cost $1,200).

Sep 5   Made a sale on account (Invoice #1123) to Charisma Ltd. for $2,150 (cost $1,900).

Sep 9   Made a sale on account (Invoice #1124) to Hidendsa Inc. for $750 (cost $600).

Sep 11   Made a sale on account (Invoice #1125) to Henry Inc. for $1,270 (cost $1,080).

Sep 14   Made a sale on account (Invoice #1126) to Snoob Inc. for $970 (cost $800).

Sep 20   Made a sale on account (Invoice #1127) to Lime&Lemon for $ 1,150 (cost $1,020).

Required

Record these transactions in the sales journal.

	Sales Journal					Page 1
Date	Account	Invoice #	PR	Accounts Receivable/ Sales (DR/CR)	COGS/ Inventory (DR/CR)	

AP-3B (❷)

Jane Fisher is selling the following items at the prices listed below.

Product	Price	Cost
Plastic tubing	$1 per metre	$0.5 per metre
Polythene sheeting	$2 per metre	$1 per metre
Vinyl Padding	$5 per box	$3 per box
Foam rubber	$3 per sheet	$2 per sheet

She has provided you the following data about sales transactions incurred during the month of August.

Aug 2   Sold 22 metres of plastic tubing, 6 sheets of foam rubber and 4 boxes of vinyl padding to A. Portsmouth, on account (Invoice #1240).

Aug 4   Sold 50 metres of polythene sheeting, 6 sheets of foam rubber and 4 boxes of vinyl padding to B. Butler, on account (Invoice #1241).

Aug 6   Sold 4 metres of plastic tubing to A. Gate, on account (Invoice #1242).

Aug 10   Sold 29 metres of plastic tubing to L. Makeson, on account (Invoice #1243).

Aug 12   Made a sale on account (Invoice #1244) to M. Alison: 32 metres of plastic tubing, 24 metres of polythene sheets and 20 boxes of vinyl padding.

Required

Record these transactions in the sales journal.

Sales Journal					Page 1
Date	Account	Invoice #	PR	Accounts Receivable/ Sales (DR/CR)	COGS/ Inventory (DR/CR)

AP-4B (❷)

Book World is a dealer for stationery items. The company has provided you the following information about the transactions incurred in the month of March.

Mar 2   Received $3,500 from cash sale to Books n Books (cost $3,000).

Mar 9   Received $300 in interest earned from TD Bank.

Mar 14   Received bank loan of $500 from TD Bank.

Mar 19   Received $700 from cash sale to Book Ocean (cost $500).

Mar 21   Received $900 from cash sale to Beacon Books (cost $700).

Required

Record these transactions in the cash receipts journal.

Cash Receipts Journal								Page 1
Date	Account	PR	Cash (DR)	Sales (CR)	Accounts Receivable (CR)	Interest Revenue (CR)	Other (CR)	COGS/ Inventory (DR/CR)

AP-5B (❷ ❸)

Highway Interchange sells clothing to retailers. During the month of July 2016, the following transactions occurred.

Jul 7	Sold inventory to Fashion House for $5,600 cash. The inventory had a cost of $2,400. The invoice number was #526.
Jul 10	Received a loan from the Royal Bank for $5,000.
Jul 15	Sold inventory to Stella Lanes on account for $8,500. The inventory had a cost of $3,400. The invoice number was #527.
Jul 17	Sold inventory to Cover Me for $7,500 on account. The inventory had a cost of $3,100. The invoice number was #528.
Jul 24	Received full payment from Stella Lanes for the sale on July 15.
Jul 31	Received $50 of interest earned on a savings account.

Required

a) Record the above transactions in the sales journal and the cash receipts journal.

b) Post the appropriate transactions from the journals to the subledger accounts.

c) At the end of the month, total the journals and update the accounts receivable control account.

Assume zero opening balances for the subledger and general ledger accounts. Assume no entries were made directly to the A/R general ledger from the general journal.

Use the following selected accounts to complete the posting references.

Account Description	Account #	Account Description	Account #
Cash	101	Owner's Drawings	310
Accounts Receivable	110	Sales Revenue	400
Inventory	120	Sales Discount	405
Office Supplies	130	Interest Revenue	410
Accounts Payable	200	Cost of Goods Sold	500
Bank Loan	220	Salaries Expense	520
Owner's Capital	300	Telephone Expense	525

Sales Journal					Page 1
Date	Account	Invoice #	PR	Accounts Receivable/ Sales (DR/CR)	COGS/ Inventory (DR/CR)

Cash Receipts Journal							Page 1
Date	Account	PR	Cash (DR)	Accounts Receivable (CR)	Sales (CR)	Bank Loan (CR)	Other (CR)	COGS/ Inventory (DR/CR)

Account:	Accounts Receivable				Gl. No.	110
Date	Description	PR	DR	CR	Balance	

Account:	Stella Lanes			
Date	PR	DR	CR	Balance

Account:	Cover Me			
Date	PR	DR	CR	Balance

AP-6B (❷ ❸)

Blip Wholesalers provides wholesale pastries to supermarkets. Since most customers are large retailers, Blip Wholesalers sells a lot of products on account and will provide discounts for early payment. The following transactions occurred during the month of July 2016. All sales on account come with terms of 2/10, net 30.

Jul 3   Sold products on account to Farmer's Market for $5,200. The products had a cost of $3,120.

Jul 7   Sold products for cash to Renfrew for $4,200. The products had a cost of $2,310.

Jul 8   Received a loan from the Bank of Montreal (BMO) for $3,000.

Jul 10   Farmer's Market paid the amount owing from July 3.

Jul 15   Sold products on account to Renfrew for $3,200. The products had a cost of $1,760.

Required

a) Record the transactions in the appropriate journal.

b) Where appropriate, update the accounts receivable subledgers.

c) At the end of the month, calculate the totals of the columns in the journals and update the control account.

Sales Journal					Page 1
Date	Account	PR	Invoice #	Accounts Receivable/Sales (DR/CR)	COGS/ Inventory (DR/CR)

Cash Receipts Journal								Page 1
Date	Account	PR	Cash (DR)	Sales Discount (DR)	Accounts Receivable (CR)	Sales (CR)	Other (CR)	COGS/ Inventory (DR/CR)

Account:	Accounts Receivable				GL. No.	110
Date	Description	PR	DR	CR	Balance	

Account: Farmer's Market				
Date	PR	DR	CR	Balance

Account: Renfrew				
Date	PR	DR	CR	Balance

AP-7B (❷)

Bob123, a household items retailer, made the following purchases during the month of March.

Mar 2   Received a bill (Invoice #305) from D. Pope for the purchase of 4 DVDs, worth $240 each.

Mar 4   Received a bill (Invoice #426) from F. Lolyd for the purchase of 2 washing machines worth $560 each and 5 vacuum cleaners worth $400 each.

Mar 6   Received a bill (Invoice #765) from B. Sankey for the purchase of 1 internet modem worth $600 and 2 washing machines worth $320 each.

Mar 10   Received a bill (Invoice #2132) from J. Wilson for the purchase of 6 CD/Radios worth $45 each.

Mar 12   Received a bill (Invoice #1234) from R. Freer for the purchase of 4 dishwashers worth $240 each.

Required

Record these transactions in the purchases journal.

Purchases Journal					Page 1
Date	Account	Invoice #	PR	Inventory (DR)	Accounts Payable (CR)

AP-8B (❷)

Philips, a clothing store, has the following purchases for the month of September.

Sep 2   Received a bill (Invoice #723) from Smith Inc. for the purchase of $80 worth of silk, and $100 worth of cotton.

Sep 7   Received a bill (Invoice #657) from Grantley Store for the purchase of Lycra goods worth $38 and woolen items worth $64.

Sep 12   Received a bill (Invoice #498) from Henry Inc. for the purchase of silk worth $45, cotton worth $130 and lycra worth $135.

Sep 17   Received a bill (Invoice #342) from Kelly Inc. for the purchase of $98 worth of cotton and $56 worth of Lycra goods.

Sep 22   Received a bill (Invoice #290) of $380 from Hamilton Inc. for the purchase of Lycra goods.

Required

Record these transactions in the purchases journal.

Purchases Journal					Page 1
Date	Account	Invoice #	PR	Inventory (DR)	Accounts Payable (CR)

AP-9B (❷)

Ambassador uses a cash payments journal to record all the payments made by the company. Ambassador has provided you with the following information about the transactions incurred in the month of August.

Aug 2   Paid salary to Amanda Black, $1,600 cash (Cheque #241).

Aug 12   Paid $2,400 owing (Invoice #543) to Hargrave Inc. (Cheque #242).

Aug 14   Paid insurance premium of $300 (Cheque #243).

Aug 20   Paid newspaper bill of $150 to News & Paper (Cheque #244).

Aug 26   Handed over cheque #245 to JKL Company for $2,000 worth of inventory.

Required

Record these transactions in the cash payments journal.

Cash Payments Journal							Page 1
Date	Account	Cheque #	PR	Other (DR)	Inventory (DR)	Accounts Payable (DR)	Cash (CR)

AP-10B (❷ ❸)

Put-A-Wrench-In-It sells hand tools. During the month of October 2016, the following transactions occurred.

Oct 3   Purchased inventory for $6,300 on account from Block and Deck.

Oct 7   Paid salaries for $2,100 with cheque #256.

Oct 10   Purchased inventory for $4,100 cash from Malida Inc. with cheque #257.

Oct 17   Paid the full amount owing to Block and Deck from the Oct 3 transaction.

Oct 24   Purchased inventory for $7,700 on account from Debolt Inc.

Required

a)   Record the above transactions in the purchases journal and the cash payments journal.

b)   Post the appropriate transactions from the journals to the subledger accounts.

c)   At the end of the month, total the journals and update the accounts payable control account.

Assume zero opening balances for the subledger and general ledger accounts. Assume no entries were made directly to the A/P general ledger from the general journal.

Use the following selected accounts to complete the posting references.

Account Description	Account #	Account Description	Account #
Cash	101	Owner's Drawings	310
Accounts Receivable	110	Sales Revenue	400
Inventory	120	Sales Discount	405
Office Supplies	130	Interest Revenue	410
Accounts Payable	200	Cost of Goods Sold	500
Bank Loan	220	Salaries Expense	520
Owner's Capital	300	Telephone Expense	525

Purchases Journal							Page 6
Date	Account	Invoice	PR	Inventory (DR)	Office Supplies (DR)	Other (DR)	Accounts Payable (CR)

Cash Payments Journal							Page 4
Date	Account	Cheque #	PR	Accounts Payable (DR)	Other (DR)	Inventory (DR)	Cash (CR)

Account: Accounts Payable   **GL. No**   200

Date	Description	PR	DR	CR	Balance	

Account: Block and Deck

Date	PR	DR	CR	Balance	

Account: Debolt Inc.

Date	PR	DR	CR	Balance	

AP-11B (❷ ❸)

Step On It is a small shoe retailer. The following is a list of transactions for the month of June 2016.

June 5   Received a bill (Invoice #5780) for $4,000 worth of office supplies from Runner.

June 9   Received a bill from Telly (Invoice #167) for $200 for telephone services.

June 12   Paid amount owing (Invoice #5780) to Runner (Cheque #201).

June 21   Handed over cheque #202 to Jumper for $3,500 worth of inventory.

June 22   Paid amount owing (Invoice #167) to Telly for telephone services with cheque #203.

June 25   Paid $300 to Daley Company for maintenance expenses (Cheque #204).

June 26   Received bill from The Walker (Invoice #113) for $4,200 worth of inventory.

Required

a) Record the above entries in the appropriate journal.

b) Post the entries in the subledger accounts.

c) At the end of the month, total the special journals and update the control account.

Purchases Journal							Page 1
Date	Account	Invoice #	PR	Telephone Expense (DR)	Office Supplies (DR)	Inventory (DR)	Accounts Payable (CR)

Cash Payments Journal							Page 1
Date	Account	Chq #	PR	Other (DR)	Inventory (DR)	Accounts Payable (DR)	Cash (CR)

Opening Balances

Runner:	$1,000 (CR)
Telly:	$1,200 (CR)
The Walker:	$1,400 (CR)

Note that Step On It's accounts payable records consist of only these three subledgers. Assume no entries were made directly to accounts payable through the general journal. Update the PR columns in both the subledgers and special journals.

General Ledger Accounts Payable					
Date	PR	DR	CR	Balance	

Accounts Payable Subsidiary Ledger Runner					
Date	PR	DR	CR	Balance	

Accounts Payable Subsidiary Ledger Telly					
Date	PR	DR	CR	Balance	

Accounts Payable Subsidiary Ledger The Walker					
Date	PR	DR	CR	Balance	

AP-12B (❷ ❸)

Horizon Company had the following transactions for the month of November 2016. They are recorded in the journals and posted to the ledger accounts.

Nov 1   Purchased inventory from Diagonal Company for $8,600 with cheque #153.

Nov 5   Received invoice #2563 for $1,500 worth of office supplies from Office Depot.

Nov 9   Received invoice #8475 from Vertical for $250 for water.

Nov 10   Paid $320 to John Walker for repair expenses with cheque #154.

Nov 18   Paid amount owing to Vertical with cheque #155.

Nov 19   Paid amount owing to Office Depot with cheque #156.

Nov 26   Received invoice #563 from Lids for $4,600 worth of inventory.

Required

Identify the errors made when the transactions were posted to the journals or when they were posted to the ledgers. What impact would these errors have on account balances?

Purchases Journal							Page 1
Date	Account	Invoice #	PR	Water Expense (DR)	Office Supplies (DR)	Inventory (DR)	Accounts Payable (CR)
Nov 1	Diagonal Company	153				8,600	8,600
Nov 5	Office Depot	2563	√			1,500	1,500
Nov 9	Vertical	8475	√	250			250
Nov 26	Lids	563	√			4,600	4,600
	TOTAL			250	-	14,700	14,950

Cash Payments Journal							Page 1
Date	Account	Chq #	PR	Other (DR)	Inventory (DR)	Accounts Payable (DR)	Cash (CR)
Nov 10	Repair Expense	154		320			320
Nov 18	Vertical	155	√			250	250
Nov 19	Office Depot	156	√	1,500			1,500
	TOTAL			1,820	-	250	2,070

Opening Balances

Office Depot:	$200 (CR)
Vertical:	$60 (CR)
Lids:	$1,400 (CR)

General Ledger					
Accounts Payable					
Date	**PR**	**DR**	**CR**	**Balance**	
Opening				1,660	CR
Nov 30	PJ1		14,950	16,610	CR
Nov 30	CP1	250		16,360	CR

Accounts Payable Subsidiary Ledger					
Office Depot					
Date	**PR**	**DR**	**CR**	**Balance**	
Opening				200	CR
Nov 5	PJ1	1,500		1,300	DR
Nov 19	CP1		1,500	200	CR

Accounts Payable Subsidiary Ledger					
Vertical					
Date	**PR**	**DR**	**CR**	**Balance**	
Opening				60	CR
Nov 9	PJ1		250	310	CR
Nov 18	CP1	250		60	CR

Accounts Payable Subsidiary Ledger					
Lids					
Date	**PR**	**DR**	**CR**	**Balance**	
Opening				1,200	CR
Nov 26	PJ1		4,600	5,800	CR

_____

_____

_____

_____

_____

_____

_____

_____

_____

_____

_____

_____

_____

_____

AP-13B (❶)

TR Retailer has the following unadjusted trial balance at its year end, December 31, 2016.

Account Titles	DR	CR
TR Retailer		
Adjusted Trial Balance		
December 31, 2016		
Cash	$12,800	
Accounts Receivable	32,400	
Inventory	41,500	
Prepaid Insurance	2,400	
Equipment	65,000	
Accumulated Depreciation		$3,000
Accounts Payable		39,500
Interest Payable		0
Unearned Revenue		7,600
Bank Loan		20,000
Rogers, Capital		32,660
Rogers, Drawings	8,500	
Sales Revenue		164,800
Cost of Goods Sold	74,160	
Depreciation Expense	0	
Insurance Expense	0	
Interest Expense	0	
Rent Expense	26,000	
Telephone Expense	4,800	
Total	**$267,560**	**$267,560**

Regarding the bank loan, $10,000 will be paid by December 31, 2017.

TR Retailer also had the following adjusting entries that had to be entered into the books.

1. Interest accrued on the bank loan was $80.

2. Insurance used as of December 31, 2016 was $400.

3. TR Retailer had earned $1,000 of unearned revenue. Assume no accompanying COGS entry.

4. Depreciation for the year was $600.

Required

a) Complete the worksheet for TR Retailer for December 31, 2016.

Account Titles	Unadjusted Trial Balance		Adjustments		Adjusted Trial Balance	
	DR	CR	DR	CR	DR	CR

b) Based on the values from the adjusted trial balance from part a), complete a multistep
income statement and a classified balance sheet.

b. Based on the values from the adjusted trial balance section of the work sheet, determine the revenue, expenses, and net income for ABC Corporation.

AP-14B (❷ ❸)

Highway Interchange sells clothing to retailers. During the month of July 2016, the following transactions occurred. Highway Interchange uses the periodic inventory system.

Jul 7   Sold inventory to Fashion House for $5,600 cash. The inventory had a cost of $2,400. The invoice number was #526.

Jul 10   Received a loan from the TD Bank for $5,000.

Jul 15   Sold inventory to Stella Lanes on account for $8,500. The inventory had a cost of $3,400. The invoice number was #527.

Jul 17   Sold inventory to Cover Me for $7,500 on account. The inventory had a cost of $3,100. The invoice number was #528.

Jul 24   Received full payment from Stella Lanes for the sale on July 15.

Jul 31   Received $50 of interest earned on a savings account.

Required

a) Record the above transactions in the sales journal and the cash receipts journal.

b) Post the appropriate transactions from the journals to the subledger accounts.

c) At the end of the month, total the journals and update the accounts receivable control account.

Assume zero opening balances for the subledger and general ledger accounts. Assume no entries were made directly to the A/R general ledger from the general journal.

Sales Journal				Page 1
Date	Account	Invoice #	PR	Accounts Receivable/ Sales (DR/CR)

Cash Receipts Journal						Page 1
Date	Account	PR	Cash (DR)	Accounts Receivable (CR)	Sales (CR)	Bank Loan (CR)	Other (CR)

Account: Accounts Receivable					**Gl. No.** 110
Date	**Description**	**PR**	**DR**	**CR**	**Balance**

Account: Stella Lanes				
Date	**PR**	**DR**	**CR**	**Balance**

Account: Cover Me				
Date	**PR**	**DR**	**CR**	**Balance**

Case Study

CS-1 (❸ ❹)

Easy Riser sells pre-fabricated staircases to builders for new homes and renovations. Lately, the owner has been receiving calls from suppliers regarding late payments. The owner is aware of the late payments because he has been holding back payments due to a shortage of cash. The company is having excellent sales, and earning a very good profit even though it has a cash shortfall.

After asking the bookkeeper about the cash shortage problem, the bookkeeper informed the owner about the accounting process. All transactions are entered into the general journal and posted to the general ledger. The supplier invoices were stored in one folder and the sales invoices in another folder in the bookkeeper's desk. When the owner asked to see a sales invoice from last month (to see if the amount had been collected), the bookkeeper had trouble finding it. When it was finally found, it was determined that it had not been collected yet.

a)   What ethical and control issues does this company have?

_____

_____

_____

_____

_____

_____

b)   What would you suggest to improve the bookkeeping for this company?

_____

_____

_____

_____

_____

_____

_____

_____

Notes

Chapter 10

CASH CONTROLS

LEARNING OUTCOMES

❶ Apply cash controls

❷ Prepare journal entries for cash rounding, debit and credit transactions

❸ Prepare a bank reconciliation and related journal entries

❹ Prepare a petty cash fund and record related journal entries

❺ Apply general business controls

AMEENGAGE Access **ameengage.com** for integrated resources including tutorials, practice exercises, the digital textbook and more.

Assessment Questions ---

AS-1 (❸)

What is a bank reconciliation?

_____

_____

_____

AS-2 (❸)

List three typical reasons for the bank making additional deductions from the company's cash account.

_____

_____

_____

AS-3 (❸)

What are two typical reasons for the bank making additional deposits to the company's cash account?

_____

_____

_____

AS-4 (❸)

In a typical bank reconciliation, what are the titles of the two column headers?

_____

_____

_____

AS-5 (❸)

What are non-sufficient funds (NSF) cheques?

_____

_____

_____

AS-6 (❸)

What is an outstanding deposit?

_____

_____

_____

AS-7 (❸)

When is a journal entry required during a bank reconciliation?

_____

_____

_____

AS-8 (❸)

How are outstanding cheques recorded on the bank reconciliation?

_____

_____

_____

AS-9 (❹)

What is an imprest system (in the context of petty cash)?

_____

_____

_____

AS-10 (❹)

Briefly describe the responsibilities of the petty cash custodian.

_____

_____

_____

AS-11 (❹)

What does an employee that requires petty cash need to present to the petty cash custodian?

_____

_____

_____

AS-12 (❹)

What is a petty cash summary sheet?

_____

_____

_____

AS-13 (❷ ❹)

Why do petty cash overages or shortages occur?

_____

_____

_____

AS-14 (❷ ❹)

When does the cash over and short account behave like an expense account?

_____

_____

_____

AS-15 (❹)

What are the only two times that the petty cash account in the ledger is debited or credited?

_____

_____

_____

AS-16 (❶ ❺)

List two general controls that can be used for petty cash.

_____

_____

_____

AS-17 (❶)

List two controls that can be used to prevent the misuse of cash?

_____

_____

_____

AS-18 (❶)

Define cash equivalents.

_____

_____

AS-19 (❶)

Briefly describe what it means to be in bank overdraft.

_____

_____

AS-20 (❶)

Describe the position of cash equivalents on the balance sheet.

_____

_____

AS-21 (❶)

List two reasons why cash equivalents are entered with cash on the balance sheet.

_____

_____

AS-22 (❶)

List three examples of cash equivalent items.

_____

_____

_____

_____

_____

AS-23 (❶)

Why would a business invest in cash equivalents?

_____

_____

AS-24 (❶)

Name three systems to record cash immediately when it is received.

_____

_____

_____

_____

AS-25 (❶)

When receiving a cash sale, why is it important for the customer to participate in the transaction?

_____

_____

_____

AS-26 (❶)

Describe how the business can protect cash when it is on the premises.

_____

_____

_____

_____

_____

AS-27 (❶)

What is the overall goal of the business in managing its cash?

_____

_____

_____

Application Questions Group A

AP-1A (❸)

Quality Electronic is preparing a bank reconciliation and has identified the following potential reconciling items. For each item, indicate if it is (i) added to the balance of the ledger, (ii) deducted from the balance of the ledger, (iii) added to the balance of the bank statement, or (iv) deducted from the balance of the bank statement.

a) Deposits that are not shown on the bank statement *Add to bank statemets*

b) Interest deposited to the company's account *Add to ledger*

c) Bank service charges *deduct it off ledger*

d) Outstanding cheques *deduct from bank statement*

e) NSF cheques returned *deduct cash*

Same balance under both the ledger and the bank statment

AP-2A (❸)

The following data represents information necessary to assist in preparing the June 30, 2016 bank reconciliation for Trimore Company.

- The June 30 bank balance was $5,300.

- The bank statement indicated a deduction of $30 for bank service charges.

- A customer deposited $1,200 directly into the bank account to settle an outstanding accounts receivable bill.

- Cheque number 850 for $600 and cheque number 857 for $420 have been recorded in the company ledger but did not appear on the bank statement.

- A customer paid an amount of $4,534 to Trimore on June 30 but the deposit did not appear on the bank statement.

- The accounting clerk made an error and recorded a $200 cheque as $2,000. The cheque was written to pay outstanding accounts payable account.

- Cheque number 9574 for $100 was deducted from Trimore's account by the bank. This cheque was not written by Trimore and needs to be reversed by the bank.

- The bank included an NSF cheque in the amount of $820 relating to a customer's payment.
- The general ledger cash account showed a balance of $6,764 on June 30.

Required

a) Complete the bank reconciliation for Trimore Company
b) Write the necessary journal entries to correct Trimore's records

Explanation	Ledger	Bank
Balance	$6764	$5300
Bank charges	⟨30⟩	
Customer Paid	1200	
Check #850		⟨600⟩
#857		⟨420⟩
Deposit		4534
Error	1800	
NSF		100
	8914	8914

JOURNAL			Page 1
Date	Account Title and Explanation	Debit	Credit

AP-3A (❸)

Mike's Cleaning Service received its monthly bank statement for its business bank account, with a balance of $55,062 for the month of July 2016. The total for the ledger account as at July 31, 2016 was $59,461.

After a comparison of the cheques written by the company and those deducted from the bank account, Mike's accountant determined that three cheques, totalling $2,806 (cheque #256 for $606, cheque #261 for $1,200, and cheque #262 for $1,000), were outstanding on July 31. A review of the deposits showed that a deposit on July 1 for $12,610 was actually recorded in the company's ledger on June 30 and a July 31 deposit of $9,760 was recorded in the company's ledger on the date but had not been recorded by the bank yet. The July bank statement showed a service fee of $18, a customer's cheque in the amount of $70 that had been returned NSF, a loan payment of $857 that was deducted automatically by the bank, and a customer automatically made a $3,500 payment which was deposited into Mike's Cleaning bank account.

Required

a) Prepare bank reconciliation as at July 31, 2016.

b) How much cash does Mike's Cleaning Service actually have in its cash account on July 31?

c) Prepare journal entries to record all necessary adjustments to bring the cash account to its adjusted balance.

a)

Explanation	Ledger	Bank

b)

c)

JOURNAL			Page 1
Date	Account Title and Explanation	Debit	Credit

AP-4A (❸)

The following data represents information necessary to assist in preparing the January 31, 2016 bank reconciliation for Sellmore Company.

- The January 31 bank balance was $4,598.

- A customer deposited $900 directly into the bank account to settle an outstanding accounts receivable bill.

- The bank statement indicated a deduction of $33 for bank service charges.

- Cheque #821 for $360 and cheque #865 for $252 have been recorded in the company ledger but did not appear on the bank statement.

- A customer paid an amount of $4,589 to Sellmore on January 31 but the deposit did not appear on the bank statement.

- The accounting clerk made an error and recorded a $180 cheque as $1,800. The cheque was written to pay outstanding accounts payable account.

- The bank included an NSF cheque in the amount of $710 relating to a customer's payment.

- Cheque #9504 for $153 was deducted from Sellmore's account by the bank. This cheque was not written by Sellmore and needs to be reversed by the bank.

- The general ledger cash account showed a balance of $6,951 on January 31.

Required

a) Complete the bank reconciliation for Sellmore Company.

b) Write the necessary journal entries to correct Sellmore's records.

	Explanation	Ledger	Bank

JOURNAL			Page 1
Date	Account Title and Explanation	Debit	Credit

AP-5A (③)

Use the following information to prepare the bank reconciliation for Jeremiah Motors.

- The bank balance on March 31 was $13,500.

- The general ledger cash account showed a balance of $14,950 on March 31.

- Received cheque #80 from a customer for $950 but it has not been deposited yet.

- The bank statement shows a charge of $110 for service fees.

- A customer transferred $800 directly into the company's bank account to pay their account.

- Recorded cheque #94 to pay for supplies in the journal for $480 instead of $840.

- The bank statement showed an NSF cheque from a customer for $830.

Complete the bank reconciliation for Jeremiah Motors and prepare any necessary journal entries to update the company's records for March 2016.

	Explanation	Ledger	Bank

JOURNAL			Page 1
Date	Account Title and Explanation	Debit	Credit

AP-6A (❸)

The following cash ledger contains information about RJ Cosmetics' cash account.

GENERAL LEDGER

Account: Cash				GL. No. 101	
Date	Description	DR	CR	Balance	
Feb 1	Opening balance			4,000	DR
Feb 3	Cheque #1		800	3,200	DR
Feb 12	Deposit	2500		5,700	DR
Feb 21	Cheque #2		1200	4,500	DR
Feb 26	Cheque #3		950	3,550	DR
Feb 27	Cheque #4		600	2,950	DR
Feb 29	Deposit	1300		4,250	DR

RJ Cosmetics' bank statement for the month of February is shown below.

	BANK STATEMENT			
Date	**Explanation**	**Withdrawal**	**Deposit**	**Balance**
Feb 01	Opening balance			4,000
Feb 03	Cheque # 1	800		3,200
Feb 12	Deposit		2,500	5,700
Feb 14	NSF Cheque	500		5,200
Feb 14	NSF Charge	15		5,185
Feb 21	Cheque # 2	1,200		3,985
Feb 25	EFT—Monthly rent expense	1,000		2,985
Feb 29	Service charges	25		2,960
Feb 29	Interest on bank account		20	2,980

Required

a) Prepare a bank reconciliation for RJ Cosmetics as at February 29, 2016.

Explanation	**Ledger**	**Bank**

b) Prepare the required journal entries for the corrections made in the bank reconciliation.

JOURNAL			Page 1
Date	Account Title and Explanation	Debit	Credit

c) Prepare the full reconciled cash ledger account for the month of February.

GENERAL LEDGER

Account: Cash				GL. No. 101	
Date	Description	DR	CR	Balance	

d) Using last month's data along with the bank statement and the general ledger provided, prepare a bank reconciliation for RJ Cosmetics for March 31, 2016.

GENERAL LEDGER

Account: Cash				GL. No. 101	
Date	Description	DR	CR	Balance	
Mar 1	Opening balance			2,730	DR
Mar 7	Cheque #5		920	1,810	DR
Mar 13	Deposit	850		2,660	DR
Mar 18	Cheque #6		450	2,210	DR
Mar 28	Deposit	2,135		4,345	DR
Mar 29	Cheque #7		1,100	3,245	DR

BANK STATEMENT				
Date	Explanation	Withdrawal	Deposit	Balance
Mar 1	Opening balance			2,980
Mar 2	Deposit		1,300	4,280
Mar 3	Cheque #4	600		3,680
Mar 7	Cheque #5	920		2,760
Mar 13	Deposit		850	3,610
Mar 18	Cheque #6	450		3,160
Mar 25	EFT—Monthly rent expense	1,000		2,160
Mar 28	Deposit		2,135	4,295
Mar 31	Service charges	25		4,270
Mar 31	Interest on bank account		13.65	4,283.65

Please note that the deposit from March 28, contains a cheque from the customer who provided an NSF cheque from the month before. The customer paid for the original amount of $500, plus the $15 charge.

Explanation	Ledger	Bank

AP-7A (❸)

Consider the following general ledger and bank statement for Meena Salon.

GENERAL LEDGER

Account: Cash					GL. No. 101	
Date	Explanation	Debit	Credit	Balance		
Apr 1	Opening balance			8,000	DR
Apr 6	Jimmy Supplies—cheque #101		500	7,500	DR
Apr 10	HitHit Supplies—cheque #102		1,000	6,500	DR
Apr 11	Mary Malony	250		6,750	DR
Apr 14	Inner Beauty Inc.—cheque #103		757	5,993	DR
Apr 19	Shona Care Ltd.—cheque #104		840	5,153	DR
Apr 29	Deposit	2,500		7,653	DR

BANK STATEMENT				
Date	Explanation	Withdrawal	Deposit	Balance
Apr 1	Opening balance			8,000
Apr 6	Cheque #101	500		7,500
Apr 10	Cheque #102	1,000		6,500
Apr 10	EFT—Monthly rent	800		5,700
Apr 11	Mary Malony		250	5,950
Apr 11	NSF cheque	250		5,700
Apr 11	NSF charge	5		5,695
Apr 14	Cheque #103	575		5,120
Apr 21	Cheque #1520	3,000		2,120
Apr 30	Service charges	25		2,095
Apr 30	Interest on bank account		20	2,115

Additional Information

1. On April 14, Meena Salon purchased $575 worth of salon supplies from Inner Beauty Inc.

2. The salon's cheque numbers are always three digits in length.

Required

a) Prepare a bank reconciliation for Meena Salon on April 30, 2016.

	Explanation	Ledger	Bank

b) Prepare the necessary journal entries.

JOURNAL			Page 1
Date	**Account Title and Explanation**	**Debit**	**Credit**

AP-8A (❸)

Shine Laundry's bank reconciliation is provided for the month of September 2016. However, due to some errors on the bank reconciliation, the reconciled balance for the ledger and the bank are different from each other.

Shine Laundry Bank Reconciliation September 30, 2016		
	Ledger	Bank
Opening balance	$5,100	$3,820
Add: Outstanding deposit—Sep 29	400	
Outstanding deposit—Sep 30	1,220	
Less: Outstanding cheque #3—Sep 8		(1,000)
Outstanding cheque #4—Sep 10	(600)	
EFT—Insurance—Sep 15		(400)
EFT—Monthly rent—Sep 18		(600)
NSF Cheque—Sep 19		(250)
Charges for NSF cheque—Sep 19		(5)
Service charges—Sep 30	(15)	
Interest on bank account—Sep 30	(10)	
Reconciled balance	$6,095	$1,565

Required

a) Prepare a reconciled bank reconciliation. Assume the dollar amounts of the individual items on the bank reconciliation are correct.

Explanation	**Ledger**	**Bank**

b) Prepare all journal entries required by Shine Laundry.

JOURNAL			Page 1
Date	**Account Title and Explanation**	**Debit**	**Credit**

AP-9A (❸)

The bookkeeper for Brose Industrial Supply has prepared a bank reconciliation for the month but, although it balances, it is not correct. Prepare a corrected bank reconciliation for Brose Industrial Supply. Assume that all figures show the correct dollar amounts, and that the opening balances are both correct.

Brose Industrial Supply Bank Reconciliation July 31, 2016		
	Ledger	**Bank**
Opening Balance	$14,630	$16,070
Add:		
Bank service charges		80
Interest earned	100	
Less:		
Outstanding cheques		(1,600)
Outstanding deposits	(730)	
Unrecorded deposit		(550)
Reconciled Balance	$14,000	$14,000

	Ledger	**Bank**

Analysis

After preparing a bank reconciliation, journal entries must be prepared to record adjustments to cash. Name three items that require an adjusting entry. Why don't all items on the reconciliation require adjusting entries?

AP-10A (④)

On June 7, 2016, Mary decided to use a petty cash fund for her small business. A cheque of $125 was issued and cashed. The $125 cash was given to the store supervisor who was to act as petty cashier. The petty cashier was told to obtain authorized vouchers for all payments. Petty cash was to be replenished when the balance in the cash box reached $23.

Required

a) Record the establishment of the fund on June 7.

JOURNAL			Page 1
Date	Account Title and Explanation	Debit	Credit

b) On June 19, the following summary was prepared.

Delivery Expense	$50.90
Miscellaneous Expense	20.40
Office Expense	24.10
Postage Expense	6.60
Total	$102

Prepare the entry to replenish the petty cash.

JOURNAL			Page 1
Date	Account Title and Explanation	Debit	Credit

c) On June 23, it was decided to increase the amount of the petty cash fund from $125 to $175. A cheque of $50 was issued. Record the transaction.

JOURNAL			Page 1
Date	Account Title and Explanation	Debit	Credit

AP-11A (❷ ❹)

The petty cash fund was established on August 12, 2016 in the amount of $250.00. Expenditures from the fund by the custodian as of August 31, 2016, were evidenced by approved receipts for the following.

Postage expense	$30.00
Supplies expense	65.00
Maintenance expense	42.00
Delivery expense	58.20
Newspaper advertising	21.95
Miscellaneous expense	15.75

On August 31, 2016, the petty cash fund was replenished and increased to $300.00; currency and coin in the fund at that time totalled $15.60.

Required

Prepare the journal entries to record the transactions related to the petty cash fund for the month of August.

JOURNAL			Page 1
Date	**Account Title and Explanation**	**Debit**	**Credit**

AP-12A (❷ ❹)

On June 29, 2016, Fire It Up Grill decided to establish a petty cash fund for the office. The frequency of small item purchases and payments became unnecessary for the accounting system to update each time. A cheque of $250 was issued and cashed. The $250 cash was given to the office manager who was to act as the petty cashier. He decided that the petty cash fund should be replenished when the balance in the cash box reached $70.

Required

a) Record the establishment of the petty cash fund on June 29.

JOURNAL				Page 1
Date	Account Title and Explanation		Debit	Credit

b) On July 31, the balance in the petty cash account was $70. A summary of the expenses was prepared.

Delivery Expense	$68
Office Supplies Expense	96
Miscellaneous Expense	10
Postage Expense	7
Total	$181

c) Determine the balance of the petty cash fund after all transactions have occurred for the month of July.

d) Prepare the journal entry to replenish the petty cash fund.

JOURNAL			Page 1	
Date	Account Title and Explanation		Debit	Credit

e) Based on your response from part d), determine if the cash amount is over or short.

f) On July 31, with input from the petty cashier, management decided to increase the amount of the petty cash fund from $250 to $350. This was based on the fact that more items were approved to be paid by petty cash. A cheque for $100 was issued and cashed. Record the transaction.

JOURNAL			Page 1	
Date	Account Title and Explanation		Debit	Credit

AP-13A (❷ ❹)

On January 1, 2016, Hit Design set up a petty cash fund for $250. At the end of the first week, the petty cash fund contains the following items.

Cash on hand	$50
Receipt for the purchase of office supplies	40
Receipt for delivery charges	10
Receipt for the purchase of stamps	20
Receipt for travel to a client meeting	50
Receipt for the payment of newspaper advertising	75

Required

a) Calculate any cash overage or shortage.

_____

_____

_____

b) Prepare the journal entries for setting up and replenishing the petty cash fund.

JOURNAL			Page 1
Date	**Account Title and Explanation**	**Debit**	**Credit**

AP-14A (❷ ❹)

Eric Dravin Enterprises decided to establish a petty cash fund for the office on January 11, 2016. Management decided to set up the fund, and appointed the office administrator as the petty cashier as his role is to processing shipping orders, as well as doing multiple tasks as needed. A cheque was issued for the petty cash fund for $175, and was cashed. Management decided that the petty cash fund should be replenished when the balance in the cash box reaches $75.

Required

a) Record the establishment of the petty cash fund on January 11.

JOURNAL			Page 1
Date	Account Title and Explanation	Debit	Credit

b) On January 31, the balance in the petty cash account was $30. The totalled receipts showed the following information.

Delivery Expense	$89
Postage Expense	22
Office Supplies	13
Travel Expense	25
Total	$149

c) Determine the balance of the petty cash fund based on the totalled receipts provided.

_____

_____

d) Prepare the journal entry to replenish the petty cash fund at the end of the month.

JOURNAL			Page 1
Date	Account Title and Explanation	Debit	Credit

e) Based on your response from part d), determine if the cash amount is over or short.

_____

_____

f) On February 4, 2016, management determined that the petty cash fund's balance ran too low for the month of January and it should not happen again. They suggested doubling the petty cash fund balance. A cheque for $175 was issued and cashed. Record the transaction.

JOURNAL			Page 1
Date	Account Title and Explanation	Debit	Credit

AP-15A (❷ ❹)

Sky Auctions set up a petty cash fund of $250 on January 1, 2016. The custodian found the following receipts in the cash box for the month.

$35 for food for the office employees
$63 for fuel for the company vehicle
$50 to pay a specialist to update the computer system
$46 to purchase supplies for the office

Required

The custodian counted $81 cash remaining in the cash box. Prepare journal entries to establish the petty cash fund and replenish the petty cash fund on January 31, 2016.

JOURNAL				Page 1
Date	Account Title and Explanation		Debit	Credit

Analysis

What is the purpose of a petty cash system?

_____

_____

_____

AP-16A (❷)

Shirley's Wraps operates as a sandwich and wrap shop. Their customers can pay by cash, debit or credit card. For each debit transaction, Shirley pays $0.20. For the credit card, she pays 2% of the total of credit card transactions. On May 13, 2016, Shirley had compiled the following summary for the work day.

Transaction Type	Total	Number of Transactions
Cash	$425	52
Debit Card	327	43
Credit Card	0	0

Required

a) Calculate the total debit/credit card expense for May 13.

_____

_____

b) Record the journal entry for the day's sales.

Date	Account Title and Explanation	Debit	Credit

AP-17A (❷)

Tommy's Bistro operates as a restaurant. Its customers can pay by cash, debit or credit card. For each debit transaction, Tom pays $0.15. For the credit card, he pays 3% of the total of credit card transactions. On March 22, 2016, Tom had compiled the following summary for the work day.

Transaction Type	Total	Number of Transactions
Cash	$2,203	49
Debit Card	0	0
Credit Card	3,731	83

Required

a) Calculate the total debit/credit card expense for March 22.

_____

_____

b) Record the journal entry for the day's sales.

Date	Account Title and Explanation	Debit	Credit

AP-18A (❷)

Leslie and Ben run a dry cleaners together, called Pawny Cleaners. Their customers can pay by cash, debit or credit card. For each debit transaction, they pay $0.35. For the credit card, they pay 1.5% of the total of credit card transactions. On August 20, 2016, Ben had compiled the following summary for the work day.

Transaction Type	Total	Number of Transactions
Cash	$741	35
Debit Card	4,376	120
Credit Card	2,883	68

Required

a) Calculate the total debit/credit card expense for August 20.

\
\
\
\

b) Record the journal entry for the day's sales.

Date	Account Title and Explanation	Debit	Credit

Application Questions Group B

AP-1B (❸)

For the month of September 2016, Jared Anitco has noticed that the bank has processed a cheque that he was not aware of. As a result, he calls the bank and determines that the cheque belongs to another account. The following is the general ledger report for cash in the bank and bank statement for Jared Anitco for the month of September.

GENERAL LEDGER

Account: Cash					GL. No. 101	
Date	Explanation	Debit	Credit	Balance		
Sep 1	Opening balance			7,000	DR
Sep 6	CandyMan—cheque #200		500	6,500	DR
Sep 6	Supply Store—cheque #201		754	5,746	DR
Sep 10	Jordan Lo—cheque #1000	800		6,546	DR
Sep 25	Book Store—cheque #202		200	6,346	DR

BANK STATEMENT

Date	Explanation	Withdrawal	Deposit	Balance
Sep 1	Opening balance			7,000
Sep 10	CandyMan—cheque #200	500		6,500
Sep 10	Supply Store—cheque #201	754		5,746
Sep 14	Jordan Lo—cheque #1000		800	6,546
Sep 20	Mooris Mo—cheque #1107	820		5,726
Sep 30	Book Store—cheque #202	200		5,526

Required

Identify the cheque that does not belong to Jared. If necessary, prepare the required journal entries.

JOURNAL				Page 1
Date	Account Title and Explanation		Debit	Credit

AP-2B (❸)

Required

a) Prepare the July 2016 bank reconciliation statement for World's Computer using the following information.

- Cash balance per general ledger is $2,219.
- Bank statement balance is $2,478.80.
- These cheques were recorded in the ledger but did not appear on the bank statement. They are: Cheque #186 for $100; Cheque #193 for $57; Cheque #199 for $143.
- A deposit for $368 dated July 31 was recorded in the ledger but did not appear on the bank statement.
- Service charges of $18 are shown on the bank statement.
- A cheque for $37.50 has been cashed (correctly) by the bank but was incorrectly recorded in the company's ledger as $375.50. The cheque was issued for the purchase of office supplies.
- The bank automatically deposited interest of $7.80 at the end of the month.

b) Record any journal entries required to bring the company records up to date.

a)

	Explanation	Ledger	Bank

b)

JOURNAL			Page 1
Date	Account Title and Explanation	Debit	Credit

AP-3B (❸)

The bank statement for Fashion Fly had an ending cash balance of $1,500 on December 31, 2016. On this date the cash balance in their general ledger was $2,000. After comparing the bank statement with the company records, the following information was determined.

- The bank returned an NSF cheque in the amount of $320 that Fashion Fly deposited on December 20.
- Direct deposit received from a customer on December 30 in payment of their accounts totalling $3,850. This has not yet been recorded by the company.
- On December 30 the bank deposited $10 for interest earned.
- The bank withdrew $20 for bank service charges.
- Deposits in transit on December 31 totalled $4,020.

Required

Reconcile the ledger and bank statement and prepare the required journal entries.

	Explanation	Ledger	Bank

JOURNAL			Page 1
Date	Account Title and Explanation	Debit	Credit

AP-4B (❸)

The bank statement for Flying Fashion had an ending cash balance of $1,640 on March 31, 2016. On this date the cash balance in the general ledger was $1,921. After comparing the bank statement with the company records, the following information was determined.

- The bank returned an NSF cheque in the amount of $264 that Flying Fashion deposited on March 20.

- Direct deposit received from a customer on March 30 in payment of their accounts totalling $3,900. This has not yet been recorded by the company.

- The bank withdrew $41 for bank service charges.

- On March 30 the bank deposited $14 for interest earned.

- Deposits in transit on March 31 totalled $3,890.

Required

Reconcile the ledger and bank statement and create the required journal entries.

Explanation	Ledger	Bank

JOURNAL			Page 1
Date	**Account Title and Explanation**	**Debit**	**Credit**

AP-5B (❸)

Lux Transportation Services has just received its bank statement for the month and has compared it to the general ledger cash account.

GENERAL LEDGER					
Account: Cash					**GL. No. 101**
Date	**Description**	**DR**	**CR**	**Balance**	
Oct 1	Opening Balance			13,100	DR
Oct 2	Cheque #401		750	12,350	DR
Oct 5	Cheque #220	900		13,250	DR
Oct 8	Cheque #403		750	12,500	DR
Oct 16	Cheque #404		200	12,300	DR

BANK STATEMENT				
Date	Description	Withdrawal	Deposit	Balance
Oct 1	Opening Balance			13,100
Oct 2	Cheque #401	750		12,350
Oct 6	Cheque #220		900	13,250
Oct 6	Cheque #402	750		12,500
Oct 10	Cheque #403	750		11,750
Oct 16	Cheque #88		445	12,195
Oct 30	Interest		50	12,245
Oct 31	Service Charge	110		12,135

Prepare the bank reconciliation for Lux Transportation as at October 31, 2016.

Explanation	**Ledger**	**Bank**

Analysis

After some investigation, it is discovered that Cheque #88 is not from a customer and should not have been deposited into the company's bank account by the bank. How does this discovery change the bank reconciliation and any necessary journal entries?

_____

_____

_____

_____

AP-6B (❸)

Shelley Company had completed October's bank reconciliation with an exact reconciled balance on the last day of the month. Consider the bank reconciliation for October.

Shelley Company Bank Reconciliation October 31, 2016		
Explanation	**Ledger**	**Bank**
Opening balance	$6,500	$4,725.63
Add: Outstanding deposit 1		700
Error on cheque #366	189	
Outstanding deposit 2		950
Bank error cheque #45928		1,000
Interest on bank account	23.63	
Less: Outstanding cheque #354		(300)
Outstanding cheque #367		(2,265)
Direct Insurance billing	(1,100)	
EFT—Monthly rent	(1,325)	
NSF cheque	(875)	
NSF charges	(25)	
Outstanding cheque #368		(1,463)
Service charges	(40)	
Reconciled balance	$3,347.63	$3,347.63

The following items were discovered in November.

- An NSF cheque was entered by the bank for $570, it charged the bank account for $25.
- There are three deposits outstanding by the bank for $450, $200, and $1,465 respectively.
- Insurance is a preauthorized payment taken out every month for the same amount each month.
- Shelley Company paid its monthly rent via an EFT.
- Cheques #354 and #367 are still outstanding.
- Cheque #378 is outstanding for $675.
- Cheque #379 is outstanding for $1,110.96.
- Interest earned on the bank account $27.85.
- Service charges for the bank account are $40.
- The balance of the ledger on November 30 is $6,289.17.
- The bank balance provided from the bank statement dated November 30 is $5,488.76.

Required

a)   Complete the bank reconciliation for Shelley Company for the month of November.

Explanation	Ledger	Bank

b) Prepare the necessary journal entries.

JOURNAL			Page 1
Date	**Account Title and Explanation**	**Debit**	**Credit**

AP-7B (❸)

Consider the following general ledger and bank statement for Saleen Salon.

GENERAL LEDGER

Account: Cash				GL. No. 101	
Date	**Explanation**	**DR**	**CR**	**Balance**	
Dec 1	Opening balance			8,100	DR
Dec 6	Jonny Supplies—cheque #120		660	7,440	DR
Dec 10	WalkWalk Supplies—cheque #121		1,180	6,260	DR
Dec 11	Bethany Balony	230		6,490	DR
Dec 14	Salon Beauty Inc.—cheque #122		686	5,804	DR
Dec 19	Shona Care Ltd.—cheque #123		930	4,874	DR
Dec 29	Deposit	2,200		7,074	DR

BANK STATEMENT				
Date	Explanation	Withdrawal	Deposit	Balance
Dec 1	Opening balance			8,100
Dec 6	Cheque #120	660		7,440
Dec 10	Cheque #121	1,180		6,260
Dec 10	EFT—Monthly rent	680		5,580
Dec 11	Bethany Balony		230	5,810
Dec 11	NSF cheque	230		5,580
Dec 11	NSF charge	19		5,561
Dec 14	Cheque #122	866		4,695
Dec 21	Cheque #1470	3,700		995
Dec 31	Service charges	32		963
Dec 31	Interest on bank account		17	980

Additional Information

1. On Dec 14, Saleen Salon purchased $866 worth of salon supplies from Salon Beauty Inc.

2. The salon's cheque numbers are always three digits in length.

Required

a) Prepare a bank reconciliation for Saleen Salon on December 31, 2016.

b) Prepare the necessary journal entries.

	Explanation	Ledger	Bank

JOURNAL			Page 1
Date	Account Title and Explanation	Debit	Credit

AP-8B (3)

The owner of Lucy Learning has attempted to prepare the month-end bank reconciliation. However, she has noticed that the ending balances do not match.

Required

a) Prepare a corrected bank reconciliation for Lucy Learning, assuming all figures show the correct dollar amounts.

Lucy Learning		
Bank Reconciliation		
November 30, 2016		
Explanation	Ledger	Bank
Opening balance	$3,400	$200
Add:		
Outstanding deposits	1,600	
EFT—monthly bank loan payment		1,500
Interest earned	250	
Less:		
NSF cheque	(800)	
NSF charge		(40)
Bank service charge		(60)
Direct customer deposit for balance owed	(550)	
Reconciled balance	$3,900	$1,600

Explanation	Ledger	Bank

b) Record any journal entries necessary to update the cash account.

JOURNAL			Page 1
Date	Account Title and Explanation	Debit	Credit

AP-9B (③)

Tobias has been given the general ledger and bank statement for Eaton Company. Help him prepare the bank reconciliation based on the two documents on September 30, 2016.

GENERAL LEDGER					
Account: Cash				**GL No:**	**101**
Date	**Description**	**Debit**	**Credit**	**Balance**	
Sep 1	Opening balance			8,400	DR
Sep 7	Cheque #412	500		8,900	DR
Sep 9	Cheque #900—Equipment		4,800	4,100	DR
Sep 16	Cheque #901—Inventory		405	3,695	DR
Sep 19	Cheque #81	2,300		5,995	DR
Sep 27	Cheque #902—Office Supplies		180	5,815	DR

BANK STATEMENT				
Date	**Description**	**Withdawal**	**Deposit**	**Balance**
Sep 1	Opening balance			8,400
Sep 7	EFT—rent payment	1,300		7,100
Sep 9	Cheque #900	4,800		2,300
Sep 16	Cheque #901	450		1,850
Sep 19	Cheque #81		2,300	4,150
Sep 19	NSF—Cheque #81	2,300		1,850
Sep 19	NSF Charge	40		1,810
Sep 30	Interest		80	1,890

Note: In case of any discrepency between dollar amounts, assume the bank statement is correct.

Explanation	Ledger	Bank
Balances	5815	1890
EFT - Rent	-1300	
Dep 2412		500
ERROR	-45	
Interest Revenue	80	
Cheque 902		-180
NSF Cheque	-40	
	2210	2210

AP-10B (❶ ❹ ❺)

Last year, Holtzman Company established a petty cash fund of $100. The custodian complained that she had to reimburse the fund on a weekly basis, and suggested that the fund be increased to $400. That way, she would only have to summarize payouts and get a cheque from the cashier once per month.

Management agreed with the custodian, and on April 1, 2016, advised the cashier to increase the fund to $400.

Required

a) Write the journal entry to increase the fund to $400.

b) List five internal controls that should be established around the use of petty cash.

a)

JOURNAL				Page 1
Date	Account Title and Explanation		Debit	Credit

b) _____

_____

_____

_____

_____

_____

_____

_____

_____

_____

_____

_____

_____

_____

_____

_____

_____

_____

AP-11B (❷ ❹)

On April 1, 2016, Clayton Company established a petty cash fund of $200.

During the month the custodian paid out the following amounts:

Apr 6   Purchased stamps for $40.
Apr 8   Paid a $20 delivery charge on an outgoing package.
Apr 10   Paid $25 for public transit fares for employees on company business.
Apr 14   Purchased coffee and donuts for $8 for clients during a meeting.
Apr 15   Bought a package of paper for $7 for the copy machine.

The custodian counted the fund on April 16 and found $105 in the petty cash box.

Required

a) Prepare the journal entry to record the establishment of the fund.

JOURNAL			Page 1
Date	Account Title and Explanation	Debit	Credit
2016			
Apr 16	Petty cashense.	200	
	Cash		200
	To set up the petty cash fund		

b) Prepare the journal entry to record the reimbursement of the fund on April 16, 2016.

JOURNAL			Page 1
Date	Account Title and Explanation	Debit	Credit
2016			
Apr 16	Postage Expense	40	
	Delivery Expense	20	
	Travel Expense	25	
	Food Expense	8	
	Office Supplies	7	
	Cash over and Short		5
	Cash		95
	To Replenish petty cash fund		

AP-12B (❷ ❹)

On March 20, 2016, Skyline Enterprises established a $300 petty cash fund.

Required

a) Prepare the entry to record the establishment of the fund.

b) At the end of the month, the petty cash custodian analyzed all the monthly transactions. She opened the petty cash box and counted $100 cash remaining. There were also two receipts in the petty cash box: receipt #1: $100—Entertainment and receipt #2: $98—Travel. Record the journal entries for this month's expenses and replenish the fund.

c) At the end of the month, Skyline Enterprises wanted to increase the petty cash fund by $100. Prepare the journal entry to record the increase in petty cash fund.

JOURNAL			Page 1
Date	Account Title and Explanation	Debit	Credit

AP-13B (❷ ❹)

The following information was taken from the records of the JoJo Store.

Apr 14   Paid $25 for public transit.

Apr 16   Paid $20 for food.

Apr 17   Purchased stamps for $5.

Apr 17   Paid $50 for window washing.

Apr 19   Paid $15 for the delivery of packages.

Apr 20   Purchased office supplies for $30.

JoJo is the owner of the store and he established a petty cash fund of $200 on April 12, 2016. All the transactions listed above were paid using petty cash. Petty cash needs to be replenished when $50 is left in the petty cash box. On April 21, there was $50 left in the petty cash box.

Required

Prepare the journal entries for setting up and replenishing the petty cash fund.

JOURNAL			Page 1
Date	Account Title and Explanation	Debit	Credit

AP-14B (❶ ❹ ❺)

On September 24, 2016, Charlie decided to set up a petty cash fund for his small business. Charlie transferred $150 to a cash box and informed his employees that they could use the money for small expenses for the business. He told them to leave a short note with the reason for each withdrawal. Charlie decided to replenish the cash box when its balance reached $30.

Required

a) Established the petty cash fund on September 24.
b) On October 10, the following notes and cash were found inside the cash box.

Notes	
Travel	$94
Postage	4
Miscellaneous	17
Office Supplies	9
Total Notes	124
Cash Remaining	15
Total	$139

c) On November 3, Charlie decided to increase the amount of the petty cash fund to $200.

Record the transactions for the above three events.

JOURNAL			Page 1
Date	Account Title and Explanation	Debit	Credit

Analysis

Charlie has noticed quite a few significant shortages in the cash box since the fund was established. What are two controls that Charlie could implement around the use of petty cash to protect against shortages?

_____

_____

_____

_____

AP-15B (❹)

On March 20, 2016, Michaelangelo's decided to establish a petty cash fund for the restaurant. A cheque of $350 was issued and cashed. The $350 cash was given to the manager, April, who was to act as the petty cashier, and the petty cash box could be locked in her office. With the suggestion from management, it was decided that the petty cash fund should be replenished when the balance in the cash box reached $85.

Required

a) Record the establishment of the petty cash fund on March 20.

JOURNAL			Page 1
Date	Account Title and Explanation	Debit	Credit

b) On March 31 the balance in the petty cash account was $84. A summary of the expenses was prepared.

Advertising Expense	$155
Delivery Expense	76
Miscellaneous Expense	18
Postage Expense	23
Total	**$272**

c) Determine the balance of the petty cash fund after all transactions have occurred for the month of April.

_____

_____

d) Prepare the journal entry to replenish the petty cash fund.

JOURNAL			Page 1
Date	Account Title and Explanation	Debit	Credit

e) Based on your response from part d), determine if the cash amount is over or short.

_____

_____

AP-16B (❷)

Brad Chang runs his own restaurant. Customers can pay by cash, debit or credit card. For each debit transaction, Brad pays $0.25. For the credit card, he pays 2% of the total of credit card transactions. On May 9, 2016, Brad had compiled the following summary for the work day.

Transaction Type	Total	Number of Transactions
Cash	$1,459	23
Debit Card	4,632	72
Credit Card	0	0

Required

a) Calculate the total debit/credit card expense for May 9.

_____

_____

b) Record the journal entry for the day's sales.

Date	Account Title and Explanation	Debit	Credit

AP-17B (❷)

Burt Mecklin operates a large pet store. Its customers can pay by cash, debit or credit card. For each debit transaction, Burt pays $0.15. For the credit card, he pays 2% of the total of credit card transactions. On November 15, 2016, Burt had compiled the following summary for the work day.

Transaction Type	Total	Number of Transactions
Cash	$2,640	33
Debit Card	0	0
Credit Card	5,440	68

Required

a) Calculate the total debit/credit card expense for November 15.

_____

_____

b) Record the journal entry for the day's sales.

Date	Account Title and Explanation	Debit	Credit

AP-18B (❷)

Ron runs his own butcher shop. His customers can pay by cash, debit or credit card. For each debit transaction, Ron pays $0.25. For the credit card, Ron pays 3% of the total of credit card transactions. On April 3, 2016, Ron had compiled the following summary for the work day.

Transaction Type	Total	Number of Transactions
Cash	$836	27
Debit Card	1,298	40
Credit Card	1,366	32

Required

a) Calculate the total debit/credit card expense for April 3.

_____

_____

_____

_____

b) Record the journal entry for the day's sales.

Date	Account Title and Explanation	Debit	Credit

Case Study

CS-1 (❶ ❺)

M & G Block (M & G) is an incorporated tax preparation company. Most of its clients pay for the completion of their tax returns with either a debit or a credit card. The rest pay with cash.

At the office in Toronto, Ontario, M & G has employed 20 tax preparers, two supervisors and a manager. The office collects thousands of dollars in cash every day. After a tax return is prepared by one of the 20 tax preparers, a supervisor is responsible for recording information (i.e. customer name, amount charged, payment method) related to the return in a log.

The receipt of cash is recorded immediately when it is received. Receipts are issued immediately, in numerical order. Copies of the receipts are also kept with the logs. The cash is kept in the drawer of the employee who prepared the tax return. At the end of the day, the cash being kept by the various employees is pooled together and then passed on to the supervisor, who will keep it in his drawer. The cash is deposited into the bank at the end of each work week.

Over the past few weeks, the manager has noted that the amount of cash on hand in the office has consistently been less than the amount recorded in the logs. In fact, the difference between the actual cash on hand and the recorded amount is increasing little by little over time.

Required

a) Is M & G exhibiting any positive aspects in its system of cash controls? Explain.

b)   What are the negatives in M & G's cash control system? Explain. (You can refer to
      controls that do not exist, or controls that exist but are ineffective).

_____

_____

_____

_____

_____

_____

_____

_____

_____

_____

_____

_____

_____

_____

_____

Chapter 11

PAYROLL

LEARNING OUTCOMES

❶ Describe payroll accounting

❷ Calculate gross pay and net pay

❸ Describe payroll liabilities, employer's contributions and payroll payments

❹ Record payroll liabilities, employer's contributions and payroll payments

❺ Prepare payroll registers

❻ Describe payroll controls

Appendix

❼ Calculate statutory deductions

AMEENGAGE *Access **ameengage.com** for integrated resources including tutorials, practice exercises, the digital textbook and more.*

———— Assessment Questions ————

AS-1 (❶)

Define gross pay.

_____

_____

AS-2 (❶)

What is net pay?

_____

_____

AS-3 (❸)

Define statutory deductions, and identify three statutory deductions in Canada.

_____

_____

_____

AS-4 (❸)

Define voluntary deductions, and provide three examples of voluntary deductions.

_____

_____

_____

_____

AS-5 (❸)

True or False: There is no maximum amount for the Canada Pension Plan (CPP) deductions, so employees will contribute to the CPP no matter how much they earn in a year.

_____

_____

AS-6 (❼)

How much is the annual CPP exemption amount, and what does it mean for employees?

_____

_____

_____

AS-7 (❸)

How much must an employer contribute to CPP on behalf of its employees?

_____

_____

AS-8 (❸)

Is there any limitation to the amount of Employment Insurance (EI) that will be deducted from an employee's pay (i.e. age, exemption amounts or maximum deductions)?

_____

_____

_____

AS-9 (❸)

How much must the employer contribute to EI on behalf of its employees?

_____

_____

AS-10 (❸ ❼)

Is there any limitation to the amount of income tax that will be deducted from an employee's pay (i.e. age, exemption amounts or maximum amounts)?

_____

_____

_____

AS-11 (❸)

True or False: The total cost of paying an employee is equal to the amount of gross pay the employee earns.

_____

_____

_____

AS-12 (❺)

What type of information is recorded in a payroll record and what is the information used for?

_____

_____

_____

AS-13 (❺)

When would a company use a payroll register?

_____

_____

AS-14 (⑥)

Identify two payroll controls and briefly explain them.

_____

_____

_____

_____

_____

_____

_____

AS-15 (⑥)

How does an imprest bank account help control payroll?

_____

_____

_____

_____

Application Questions Group A

AP-1A (❸)

1. Identify the following payroll deductions and expenses as statutory or voluntary,
    based on legislation.

Description	Statutory	Voluntary
Income taxes	✓	
Dental benefits		✓
Union dues		✓
Savings bond purchase		✓
Uniform allowance		✓
Tuition		✓
Canada Pension Plan	✓	
Prescription coverage		✓
Retirement deduction		✓
Employment Insurance	✓	✓
Long-term disability		✓
Professional dues		✓
Charitable donations		✓
Tools and safety apparel		✓

AP-2A (❷)

The records of Dipsum Soft Drinks show the following figures.

Employee Earnings	
Salaries for the month	?
Overtime Pay	2,200
Total Gross Pay	?
Deductions and Net Pay	
Withheld Statutory Deductions	3,000
Charitable Contributions	?
Medical Insurance	150
Total Deductions	3,250
Net Pay	5,650

Required

Calculate the missing amounts.

_____

_____

_____

AP-3A (❷)

Phineas Company has two employees who are paid on an hourly basis every week. Payroll information for the week ending June 26, 2015 is listed below. Overtime is paid on hours over 48 hours per week.

Employee	Hours	Hourly Rate	Income Tax	CPP	EI
H. Farnsworth	37	$16.25	$120.25	$26.43	$11.30
P. Fry	42	19.00	155.80	35.23	14.65

Calculate the gross pay and net pay for each employee.

Employee	Gross Pay	Net Pay
H. Farnsworth		
P. Fry		

AP-4A (❷ ❸ ❹)

An employer has calculated the following amounts for an employee during the last week of January 2015.

Gross wages	$1,500
Income taxes	331
Canada Pension Plan	71
Employment Insurance	28

Required

a) Calculate the employee's net pay.

_____

_____

b) Assuming the employer's contribution is 100% for Canada Pension Plan and 140% for Employment Insurance, what is the employer's total expense?

_____

_____

c) Prepare the journal entries to record payroll for the employee and record the employer's contribution.

JOURNAL			Page 1
Date	Account Title and Explanation	Debit	Credit

AP-5A (❷ ❸ ❹ ❺)

The payroll records of Russon Corporation's district office provided the following information for the weekly pay period ended December 31, 2015.

Employee	Hours worked	Hourly Rate	Income Tax	Canada Pension Plan	Employment Insurance	Dues
Clay York	43 hrs	$12	$61	$23	$10	$10
Karen Cooper	46 hrs	15	101	33	14	10
Stephen James	48 hrs	17	134	40	17	10
Jessie Moore	40 hrs	14	66	24	11	10

Note

All employees are paid 1.5 times their hourly wage for hours worked in excess of 40 hours per week. The company contributes 100% for its share of pension plan and 140% of employment insurance.

Required

a) Calculate gross and net pay for each employee. Round all answers to the nearest whole number.

Employee	Gross Pay	Income Tax	Canada Pension Plan	Employment Insurance	Dues	Net Pay	Employer's Cost: Canada Pension Plan	Employer's Cost: Employment Insurance
Clay York								
Karen Cooper								
Stephen James								
Jessie Moore								
Total								

b) Prepare the payroll journal entries for December 31, 2015.

JOURNAL			Page 1
Date	Account Title and Explanation	Debit	Credit

c) Prepare a journal entry to record cash payment of the payroll liabilities due to the CRA on January 15, 2016.

JOURNAL			Page 1
Date	Account Title and Explanation	Debit	Credit

AP-6A (❷ ❸ ❹)

An employee has the following information for her pay for the week ending September 25, 2015. Her employer contributes 100% towards the pension plan and 140% towards employment insurance. Vacation pay is accrued at 4% of gross pay. Workers' Compensation is 1% of gross pay.

Hours	38
Hourly Rate	$16.50
Income Tax	$100.32
Canada Pension Plan	$27.70
Employment Insurance	$11.79
Union Dues	$20.00
Charity Donations	$5.00

Required

a) Prepare the journal entry to record the payroll entry for the employee. The employee will be paid immediately.

JOURNAL			Page 1
Date	**Account Title and Explanation**	**Debit**	**Credit**

b) Prepare the journal entry to record accrued vacation pay.

JOURNAL			Page 1
Date	**Account Title and Explanation**	**Debit**	**Credit**

c) Prepare the journal entry to record the employer's payroll expense.

JOURNAL			Page 1
Date	Account Title and Explanation	Debit	Credit

d) Prepare the journal entry on October 10, 2015 to record the cash payment for statutory amounts owed to the CRA.

JOURNAL			Page 1
Date	Account Title and Explanation	Debit	Credit

e) Prepare the journal entry on October 20, 2015 to record the cash payment to Workers' Compensation.

JOURNAL			Page 1
Date	Account Title and Explanation	Debit	Credit

AP-7A (❷ ❸ ❹)

Sampson Company has three employees who are paid on an hourly basis, plus time and one half for hours in excess of 44 hours per week. Payroll information for the week ending August 14, 2015 is listed below.

Employee	Hours	Hourly Rate	Income Tax	CPP	EI	Union Dues
A. Knopf	41	$14.25	$116.85	$25.59	$10.98	$10
B. Penguin	48	16.00	160.00	36.27	15.04	10
D. House	38	15.75	119.70	26.29	11.25	10

Required

a) Calculate the gross pay for each employee and the amount the employer will have to pay for CPP and EI.

Employee	Gross Pay	Employer CPP	Employer EI
A. Knopf			
B. Penguin			
D. House			
Total			

b) Prepare the journal entries for the August 14 payroll and the employer's portion of payroll. Employees will not be paid until the next week.

JOURNAL			Page 1
Date	Account Title and Explanation	Debit	Credit

c) Record the payment of the statutory deductions to the CRA on August 31, 2015.

JOURNAL			Page 1
Date	Account Title and Explanation	Debit	Credit

AP-8A (❸ ❹)

Bertrand Company has calculated the gross pay of one of its employees to be $2,500 semi-monthly. The company must pay 4% of the gross pay as vacation pay and 0.5% for Workers' Compensation. The pay date is August 15, 2015.

Required

a) Calculate and prepare the journal entry for accrued vacation pay.

JOURNAL				Page 1
Date	Account Title and Explanation		Debit	Credit

b) Calculate and prepare the journal entry for Workers' Compensation.

JOURNAL				Page 1
Date	Account Title and Explanation		Debit	Credit

AP-9A (❷ ❼)

Beverly earns a salary of $48,000 per year and is paid semi-monthly. Assuming her income tax rate is 21%, calculate her net pay for each semi-monthly pay period.

_____

_____

_____

_____

_____

AP-10A (❷ ❸ ❹ ❺ ❼)

Tremolo Manufacturing has three employees who work on an hourly basis and are paid bi-weekly. The current CPP rate is 4.95%, the current EI rate is 1.88%, and the appropriate income tax rate is 18%. Each employee contributes a portion of their pay to the United Way. The employer pays the entire amount of the health care premium for the employees. Assume the employer contributes 100% toward CPP and 140% toward EI. Payroll information for the week ending August 20, 2015 is listed below.

Employee	Total Hours	Hourly Rate	United Way	Health Care
Sing Ing	80	$12.50	$5.00	$14.00
Roc N. Role	78	14.00	7.00	20.00
Hip Hopp	75	13.50	4.00	17.00

Required

a) Calculate gross and net pay for each employee.

			Payroll Register				
		Deductions					
Employee	Gross	Income Tax	CPP*	EI	United Way	Total Deductions	Net Pay
Sing Ing							
Roc N. Role							
Hip Hopp							
Total							

*Remember to properly account for the $3,500 exemption

b) Calculate the employer contributions.

Employer Contributions	
CPP	
EI	
Health Care	

c) Prepare the payroll journal entries for August 20, 2015 to record the salaries payable to the employees and accrue the employer contributions.

| JOURNAL | | | Page 1 |
Date	Account Title and Explanation	Debit	Credit

d) Prepare the entry to pay the employees on August 23, 2015.

| JOURNAL | | | Page 1 |
Date	Account Title and Explanation	Debit	Credit

e) Prepare the entries to pay the liabilities to the United Way and the health insurance company on August 31, 2015.

| JOURNAL | | | Page 1 |
Date	Account Title and Explanation	Debit	Credit

f) Prepare the entry to pay the liabilities to the government on September 15, 2015.

JOURNAL			Page 1
Date	Account Title and Explanation	Debit	Credit

Application Questions Group B

AP-1B (❷ ❸)

ABC Company showed the following information relating to employees' salaries for the month.

Gross wages	$4,300
Income taxes	739
Canada Pension Plan contributions	198
Employment Insurance contributions	81

Note: the company matches 100% of employees' pension and 140% of employees' employment insurance.

Required

a) Calculate the company's total expense.

_____

_____

_____

_____

b) Calculate the employee's net pay.

_____

_____

_____

_____

_____

AP-2B (❷)

Hurley Johnson works as a janitor in a hospital and earns $11.00 per hour. Johnson's payroll deductions include withheld income tax of 7% of total earnings, Canada Pension Plan of $77, Employment Insurance amounting to $35, and a monthly deduction of $40 for a charitable contribution.

Required

Calculate Hurley Johnson's gross pay and net pay assuming he worked 168 hours during the month. Round to the nearest whole dollar.

_____

_____

_____

_____

_____

_____

_____

AP-3B (❷)

Sigma Five Consulting has two employees who are paid on an hourly basis every week. Payroll information for the week ending July 31, 2015 is listed below. Overtime is paid on hours over 48 hours per week.

Employee	Hours	Hourly Rate	Income Tax	CPP	EI
K. Bill	39	$22.50	$175.50	$40.10	$16.50
Q. Tarantino	43	24.00	204.00	47.16	19.18

Calculate the gross pay and net pay for each employee.

Employee	Gross Pay	Net Pay
K. Bill	877.50	645.40
Q. Tarantino	1032.00	761.66

AP-4B (❷ ❸ ❹)

An employer has calculated the following amounts for an employee during the last week of February 2015.

Gross wages	$1,800 =
Income taxes	445 ⌐
Canada Pension Plan	86 ⌐
Employment Insurance	34 ⌐
Workers' Compensation	20

Required

a) Calculate the employee's net pay.

Net Pay = 1800 - 445 - 86 - 34 = 1235.00

b) Assuming the employer's contribution is 100% for Pension Plan and 140% for Employment Insurance, what is the employer's total expense?

CPP = 86   EI = 34 x 1.4 = 47.60

Total Expenses = 1,800 + 86 + 47.60 + 20 = 1953.60

c) Prepare the journal entries to record payroll for the employee and record the employer's contribution.

JOURNAL			Page 1
Date	Account Title and Explanation	Debit	Credit
2015			
Jan 31	Salaries Expense	1,800	
	income Tax payable		495
	Canada Pension Plan Payable		86
	Cash		34
	Record payroll		1,235
Jan 31	Employee benefits Expense	153.60	
	Canada Pension Plan payable		86.00
	Employment insurance Payable		47.60
	workers' compensation Payable		20.00
	Record additional employer expenses		

AP-5B (❷ ❸ ❹ ❺)

Learn Company has four employees who are paid on an hourly basis, plus time and one half for hours in excess of 40 hours per week. Payroll information for the week ending June 15, 2015 is listed below.

Employee	Total Hours	Hourly Rate	Income Tax	CPP	EI	Union Dues
A. Bee	40	$9.50	$26.00	$15.48	$7.14	$25.00
E. Fields	47	11.00	64.85	24.17	10.44	0.00
L. Parsons	42	11.75	55.15	21.68	9.50	15.00
I. Jay	44	10.50	51.45	20.58	9.08	15.00

Required

a) Assume the employer contributes 100% towards the pension plan and 140% towards employment insurance. Calculate gross and net pay for each employee.

Payroll Register							
		Deductions					
Employee	Gross*	Income Tax	CPP	EI	Union Dues	Total Deductions	Net Pay
A. Bee							
E. Fields							
L. Parsons							
I. Jay							
Total							

*Remember to calculate time and one half for overtime hours.

b) Prepare the payroll journal entries for June 15 to pay the employees and accrue the employer contributions.

JOURNAL			Page 1
Date	Account Title and Explanation	Debit	Credit

c) Prepare the journal entry to record the cash payment on June 30 for the employer's liability to the government.

JOURNAL			Page 1
Date	Account Title and Explanation	Debit	Credit

AP-6B (❷ ❸ ❹)

An employee has the following information for his pay for the week ending April 24, 2015. His employer contributes 100% towards the pension plan and 140% towards employment insurance. Vacation pay is accrued at 4% of gross pay. Workers' Compensation is 0.8% of gross pay. Any hours worked over 40 per week is paid overtime at 1.5 times the hourly rate.

Hours	44
Hourly Rate	$18.00
Income Tax	$126.72
Canada Pension Plan	$35.87
Employment Insurance	$14.89

Required

a) Prepare the journal entry to record the payroll entry for the employee. The employee will be paid immediately.

JOURNAL			Page 1
Date	Account Title and Explanation	Debit	Credit

b) Prepare the journal entry to record accrued vacation pay.

JOURNAL			Page 1	
Date	Account Title and Explanation	Debit	Credit	

c) Prepare the journal entry to record the employer's payroll expense.

JOURNAL			Page 1	
Date	Account Title and Explanation	Debit	Credit	

d) Prepare the journal entry on May 9, 2015 to record the cash payment for statutory amounts owed to the CRA.

JOURNAL			Page 1	
Date	Account Title and Explanation	Debit	Credit	

e) Prepare the journal entry on May 15, 2015 to record the cash payment to Workers' Compensation.

JOURNAL			Page 1	
Date	Account Title and Explanation	Debit	Credit	

AP-7B (❷ ❸ ❹)

Ridell Company has two employees who are paid on an hourly basis, plus time and one half for hours in excess of 44 hours per week. Payroll information for the week ending May 29, 2015 is listed below.

Employee	Hours	Hourly Rate	Income Tax	CPP	EI
D. Troi	38	$15.25	$115.90	$25.35	$10.89
W. Crusher	50	18.00	190.80	43.89	17.94

Required

a) Calculate the gross pay for each employee and the amount the employer will have to pay for CPP and EI.

Employee	Gross Pay	Employer CPP	Employer EI
D. Troi			
W. Crusher			
Total			

b) Prepare the journal entries for the May 29 payroll and the employer's portion of payroll. Employees will not be paid until the next week.

JOURNAL			Page 1
Date	Account Title and Explanation	Debit	Credit

c) Record the payment of the statutory deductions to the CRA on June 15, 2015.

JOURNAL			Page 1
Date	Account Title and Explanation	Debit	Credit

AP-8B (❸ ❹)

Sigmund Accounting has calculated the gross pay of all its employees for the month of August 2015 to be $43,000. The company must pay 4% of the gross pay as vacation pay and 1.5% for Workers' Compensation. The pay date is August 31, 2015.

Required

a) Calculate and prepare the journal entry for accrued vacation pay.

JOURNAL			Page 1
Date	Account Title and Explanation	Debit	Credit

b) Calculate and prepare the journal entry for Workers' Compensation.

JOURNAL			Page 1
Date	Account Title and Explanation	Debit	Credit

AP-9B (❷ ❼)

Katrina earns a salary of $43,000 per year and is paid bi-weekly. Assuming her income tax rate is 19%, calculate her net pay for each bi-weekly pay period.

_____

_____

_____

_____

_____

AP-10B (❷ ❸ ❹ ❺ ❼)

Rippling Waters rents canoes and other watercraft to campers and hikers. On May 15, 2015, Rippling Waters prepared its semi-monthly payroll for employees. The current CPP rate is 4.95%, the current EI rate is 1.88%, and the appropriate income tax rate is 20%. The employer pays half of the health care premium, and the employees pay the other half. Assume the employer contributes 100% toward the pension plan and 140% toward employment insurance. Payroll information for May 15, 2015 is listed below.

Employee	Total Hours	Hourly Rate	Health Care
M. Swift	87.5	$14.50	$18.00
S. Current	85.5	15.00	20.00
B. Wavey	73.5	13.50	14.00

Required

a) Calculate gross and net pay for each employee.

Payroll Register							
		Deductions					
Employee	Gross	Income Tax	CPP*	EI	Health Care	Total Deductions	Net Pay
M. Swift							
S. Current							
B. Wavey							
Total							

*Remember to properly account for the $3,500 exemption

b) Calculate the employer contributions.

Employer Contributions	
CPP	
EI	
Health Care	

c) Prepare the payroll journal entries for May 15, 2015 to record the salaries payable to the employees and accrue the employer contributions.

JOURNAL			Page 1
Date	Account Title and Explanation	Debit	Credit

d) Prepare the entry to pay the employees on May 17, 2015.

JOURNAL			Page 1
Date	Account Title and Explanation	Debit	Credit

e) Prepare the entry to pay the liability to the health insurance company on May 31, 2015.

JOURNAL			Page 1
Date	Account Title and Explanation	Debit	Credit

f) Prepare the entry to pay the liabilities to the government on June 15, 2015.

JOURNAL			Page 1
Date	Account Title and Explanation	Debit	Credit

——————————— **Case Study** ———————————

CS-1 (⑥)

Tarantula Publishing prints advertising flyers, booklets and magazines for customers. The company has 12 employees who work the small printing presses and binding machines. Susan is the bookkeeper and deals with all items relating to the financial recordkeeping of the business. Among her many duties, she prepares all the paperwork for new hires, collects the punch cards from the employees at the end of each pay period and completes and signs the paycheques.

When a new employee is hired, the general manager sends the individual to Susan to complete the appropriate paperwork for payroll. Susan is responsible for properly completing the paperwork regarding the employee's SIN, gross pay and other details.

Susan sometimes has to track down employees to get their time cards so she can pay them. Employees manually fill out the time cards and sometimes take them home in their uniforms.

The general manager does not review the paycheques that Susan writes. He is often too busy dealing with customers and planning the production runs to have time to do much of the paperwork that Susan presents him. Since Susan is allowed to sign cheques, she prepares the cheques and hands them out to the employees.

Susan prepares the paycheques manually and is currently using the 2014 payroll tables to calculate income tax, CPP and EI deductions. The 2015 year has just started, and Susan is unaware that the rates for income tax, CPP and EI change each year. She is still using the 2014 payroll tables for 2015 paycheques.

Required

a) What are the consequences of using older payroll tables to calculate payroll deductions?

_____

_____

_____

_____

_____

_____

_____

_____

b) Discuss the control issues with this company and what can be done to implement better controls.

_____

_____

_____

_____

_____

_____

_____

_____

_____

_____

_____

_____

_____

_____

_____

_____

_____

_____

_____

_____

_____

_____

_____

Notes

Chapter 12

USING ACCOUNTING INFORMATION

Assessment Questions

AS-1 (❶)

For the equity section of a balance sheet, describe the differences between how a corporation and a sole proprietorship would present the information.

_____

_____

_____

_____

AS-2 (❶)

Describe the three primary differences between common shares and preferred shares.

_____

_____

_____

_____

AS-3 (❷)

On an income statement, what is a gain and how does a gain occur?

_____

_____

AS-4 (❸)

Describe horizontal analysis.

_____

_____

_____

_____

AS-5 (❸)

Describe vertical analysis.

_____

_____

AS-6 (❹)

What is the formula for gross profit margin?

_____

_____

AS-7 (❹)

What does gross profit margin tell us?

_____

_____

_____

_____

AS-8 (④)

What is the formula for net profit margin?

_____

_____

AS-9(④)

What is the formula for return on equity?

_____

_____

AS-10 (④)

For a particular company, if net income increased significantly from one year to the next, does this guarantee that the return on equity will also increase? Explain.

_____

_____

_____

AS-11 (④)

What is the formula for working capital?

_____

_____

AS-12 (④)

What does working capital indicate?

_____

_____

_____

AS-13 (❹)

If current assets decrease from one period to the next, but current liabilities remain constant, what will happen to working capital?

_____

_____

AS-14 (❹)

What is the formula for the current ratio?

_____

_____

AS-15 (❹)

What does the current ratio indicate?

_____

_____

_____

AS-16 (❹)

If current assets stay constant from one period to the next, but current liabilities increases, what will happen to the current ratio?

_____

_____

AS-17 (❹)

What is the formula for the quick ratio?

_____

_____

AS-18 (❹)

How do you calculate the debt-to-equity ratio?

_____

_____

AS-19 (❹)

If liabilities increase from one period to the next, but equity remains constant, what will happen to the debt-to-equity ratio?

_____

_____

AS-20 (❹)

Consider the following changes that occurred from one accounting period to the next. Current liabilities decreased, while cash, short term investments, and accounts receivable have all increased. What will happen to the quick ratio?

_____

_____

_____

AS-21 (❹)

What does the inventory turnover ratio tell you?

_____

_____

AS-22 (❹)

How is inventory days on hand calculated?

_____

_____

AS-23 (❹)

What is the formula for the inventory turnover ratio?

_____

_____

AS-24 (❹)

If the inventory turnover ratio increases, what will happen to the inventory days on hand ratio?

_____

_____

_____

AS-25 (❺)

Is the cash flow statement an optional statement? Explain.

_____

_____

AS-26 (❺)

Identify the three ways a business can generate and use cash.

_____

_____

AS-27 (❺)

What does cash flow from operations represent?

_____

_____

AS-28 (❺)

What does cash flow from investments represent?

_____

_____

AS-29 (❺)

What does cash flow from financing represent?

_____

_____

AS-30 (❺)

What does the cash flow statement show?

_____

_____

Application Questions Group A

AP-1A (⑤)

Indicate the section of the cash flow statement where each item would be located (operations, investing or financing).

Item	Section
Net Income	
Increase in Accounts Payable	
Decrease in Accounts Receivable	
Purchase of Equipment	
Payment of Bank Loan	
Increase in Inventory	
Pay Dividends	
Increase in Prepaid Insurance	

AP-2A (⑤)

Bonus Company had the following amounts in its cash flow statement for the year ended December 31, 2016.

Net decrease in cash from operations	$100,000
Net decrease in cash from investment	400,000
Net increase in cash from financing	350,000
Cash balance, January 1, 2016	600,000

Required

Calculate the cash balance at December 31, 2016

AP-3A (❺)

Mark Mortton Company had the following totals in its cash flow statement for the year ended October 31, 2016.

Net increase from investment	$250,000
Net decrease from operations	120,000
Net increase from financing	330,000
Cash balance, November 1, 2015	65,000

Required

Calculate the net increase (decrease) in the cash balance at October 31, 2016.

_____

_____

_____

_____

_____

AP-4A (❹)

A company reports current assets of $6,572 and current liabilities of $2,786. Calculate the current ratio.

_____

_____

AP-5A (❹)

Selected financial data from Crew Company is provided below.

	As at December 31, 2016
Cash	$75,000
Accounts Receivable	225,000
Merchandise Inventory	270,000
Short-Term Investments	40,000
Land and Building	500,000
Current Portion of Long-Term Debt	30,000
Accounts Payable	120,000

Required

a) Calculate the quick ratio.

_____

_____

_____

_____

b) What does Crew Company's quick ratio suggest about the company's performance?

_____

_____

AP-6A (❹)

A company had a debt to equity ratio last year of 1.46. This year liabilities totalled $452,000 while shareholders' equity amounted to $226,000 for the year.

Required

a) Calculate the debt-to-equity ratio.

_____

_____

b) Between the two years, are things getting better or worse? Explain your answer.

_____

_____

_____

AP-7A (④)

A company reported the following

- Sales: $1 million
- Cost of Goods Sold: $0.7 million
- Operating Expenses: $0.2 million

Calculate the gross profit margin. Differentiate between gross profit margin and gross profit.

_____

_____

_____

_____

_____

_____

_____

_____

AP-8A (④)

Components of the income statement of Raphael Inc. for 2016 and 2015 shows the following information.

	2016	2015
Service Revenue	$856,000	$813,000
Cost of Goods Sold	545,000	529,000
Operating Expenses	208,000	203,000

Required

a) Calculate the gross profit and the net income for both years.

	2016	2015
Sales Revenue	$856,000	$813,000
Cost of Goods Sold	545,000	529,000
Operating Expenses	208,000	203,000

(handwritten notes in right margin:) Gross Profit − Operating expenses

$\frac{\text{Gross Profit}}{\text{Cost of sales}} \times \frac{100}{1}$

$\frac{103,000}{856,000}$

b) Calculate the net profit margin for both years.

_____

_____

c) In which year does Raphael Inc. have a better net profit margin? Explain.

_____

_____

AP-9A (④)

At the beginning of 2016, Acatela Corp. had inventory of $350,000. They ended the year with inventory of $70,000 after purchasing $220,000 worth of inventory. The cost of goods sold totalled $500,000.

Required

a) Calculate the inventory turnover ratio.

_____

_____

_____

b) Calculate the inventory days on hand ratio.

_____

_____

_____

c) What does the inventory turnover ratio mean in terms of Acatela Corp?

_____

_____

d)   What does the inventory days on hand ratio mean in terms of Acatela Corp?

_____

_____

AP-10A (❸)

Perform horizontal analysis for Groff Inc. Use 2014 as the base-year and comment on the results. A table has been provided to conduct the analysis.

Groff Inc. Income Statement (in Thousands) For Years Ended December 31, 2014 - 2016	2016	2015	2014
Revenue	500	400	300
Expenses	334	242	156
Net Income	166	158	144

Groff Inc.
Income Statement (in Thousands)
For Years Ended December 31, 2014 - 2016

	2016			2015			2014		
	Value	% Of 2014	% Ch	Value	% Of 2014	% Ch	Value	% Of 2014	% Ch
Revenue	500			400			300		
Expenses	334			242			156		
Net Income	166			158			144		

_____

_____

_____

AP-11A (❸)

Perform a vertical analysis for Hiltonia Inc, using sales as the base-figure for both years. The comparative income statement has already been done for you. Calculate the percentages to two decimal places. Comment on the results of significant changes.

Hiltonia Inc. Income Statement (in Millions) For Years Ended June 30, 2016 and 2015		
	2016	**2015**
Sales	210	250
COGS	150	200
Gross Profit	60	50
Expenses		
Advertising Expense	12	8
Insurance Expense	2	1.8
Rent Expense	4	3
Salaries Expense	20	19
Selling Expenses	3	2
Total Expenses	41	33.8
Net Income	19	16.2

Required

Use the modified income statement below to perform a vertical analysis.

Hiltonia Inc. Income Statement (in Millions) and Vertical Analysis For Years Ended June 30, 2016 and 2015				
	2016	**% of Base-Figure**	**2015**	**% of Base-Figure**
Sales	210		250	
COGS	150		200	
Gross Profit	60		50	
Expenses				
Advertising Expense	12		8	
Insurance Expense	2		1.8	
Rent Expense	4		3	
Salaries Expense	20		19	
Selling Expenses	3		2	
Total Expenses	41		33.8	
Net Income	19		16.2	

_____

_____

_____

_____

AP-12A (❸)

The following financial statements are taken from the records of Abaya Inc.

Abaya Inc. Balance Sheet As at December 31, 2016 and 2015		
	2016	**2015**
Assets		
Current Assets		
Cash	$315,000	$325,000
Accounts Receivable	140,000	198,000
Inventory	411,000	397,000
Short-Term Investments	115,000	100,000
Total Current Assets	**981,000**	**1,020,000**
Other Assets	356,000	250,000
Total Assets	**$1,337,000**	**$1,270,000**
Liabilities and Equity		
Current Liabilities	214,000	265,000
Long-Term Debt	22,000	150,000
Total Liabilities	**236,000**	**415,000**
Shareholders' Equity	1,101,000	855,000
Total Liabilities and Equity	**$1,337,000**	**$1,270,000**

Abaya Inc. Income Statement For the Years Ended December 31, 2016 and 2015		
	2016	**2015**
Sales	**$701,000**	**$689,000**
COGS	379,000	396,000
Gross Profit	**322,000**	**293,000**
Operating Expenses		
Advertising	4,200	3,100
Bank Charges	2,400	1,600
Communication	5,600	3,700
Depreciation	2,500	2,500
Professional Fees	11,800	5,400
Rent	5,000	5,000
Repairs and Maintenance	3,000	3,000
Salaries and Wages	41,000	11,500
Transportation	8,950	6,400
Utilities	8,600	7,580
Total Operating Expenses	**93,050**	**49,780**
Net Income	**$228,950**	**$243,220**

Required

a) Use horizontal analysis tools to compare the changes between 2015 and 2016 line items for the balance sheet. The comparative balance sheet has already been done for you. For all percentages, calculate to two decimal places. Comment on the results of significant changes.

Abaya Inc. Balance Sheet and Horizontal Analysis As at December 31, 2016 and 2015				
	2016	**2015**	**% of 2015**	**% Change**
Assets				
Current Assets				
Cash	$315,000	$325,000		
Accounts Receivable	140,000	198,000		
Inventory	411,000	397,000		
Short-Term Investments	115,000	100,000		
Total Current Assets	**981,000**	**1,020,000**		
Other Assets	356,000	250,000		
Total Assets	**$1,337,000**	**$1,270,000**		
Liabilities and Equity				
Current Liabilities	214,000	265,000		
Long-Term Debt	22,000	150,000		
Total Liabilities	**236,000**	**415,000**		
Shareholders' Equity	1,101,000	855,000		
Total Liabilities and Equity	**$1,337,000**	**$1,270,000**		

_____

_____

_____

_____

_____

_____

_____

b) Use horizontal analysis tools to compare the changes between 2015 and 2016 line items for the income statement. The comparative income statement has already been done for you. For all percentages, calculate to two decimal places. Comment on the results of significant changes.

Abaya Inc. Income Statement and Horizontal Analysis For the Years Ended December 31, 2016 and 2015				
	2016	**2015**	**% of 2015**	**% Change**
Sales	**$701,000**	**$689,000**		
COGS	379,000	396,000		
Gross Profit	**322,000**	**293,000**		
Operating Expenses				
Advertising	4,200	3,100		
Bank Charges	2,400	1,600		
Communication	5,600	3,700		
Depreciation	2,500	2,500		
Professional Fees	11,800	5,400		
Rent	5,000	5,000		
Repairs and Maintenance	3,000	3,000		
Salaries and Wages	41,000	11,500		
Transportation	8,950	6,400		
Utilities	8,600	7,580		
Total Operating Expenses	**93,050**	**49,780**		
Net Income	**$228,950**	**$243,220**		

_____

_____

_____

_____

_____

_____

c) Use vertical analysis tools to compare line items to the total assets base-figure. For all percentages, calculate to two decimal places. Comment on the results.

	2016	Vertical	2015	Vertical
Abaya Inc. **Balance Sheet and Vertical Analysis** **As at December 31, 2016 and 2015**				
Assets				
Current Assets				
Cash	$315,000		$325,000	
Accounts Receivable	140,000		198,000	
Inventory	411,000		397,000	
Short-Term Investments	115,000		100,000	
Total Current Assets	**981,000**		**1,020,000**	
Other Assets	356,000		250,000	
Total Assets	**$1,337,000**		**$1,270,000**	
Liabilities and Equity				
Current Liabilities	214,000		265,000	
Long-Term Debt	22,000		150,000	
Total Liabilities	**236,000**		**415,000**	
Shareholders' Equity	1,101,000		855,000	
Total Liabilities and Equity	**$1,337,000**		**$1,270,000**	

_____

_____

_____

_____

_____

_____

_____

d) Use vertical analysis tools to compare line items to the sales base-figure. For all percentages, calculate to two decimal places. Comment on the results.

Abaya Inc. Income Statement and Vertical Analysis For the Years Ended December 31, 2016 and 2015				
	2016	**Vertical**	**2015**	**Vertical**
Sales	**$701,000**		**$689,000**	
COGS	379,000		396,000	
Gross Profit	**322,000**		**293,000**	
Operating Expenses				
Advertising	4,200		3,100	
Bank Charges	2,400		1,600	
Communication	5,600		3,700	
Depreciation	2,500		2,500	
Professional Fees	11,800		5,400	
Rent	5,000		5,000	
Repairs and Maintenance	3,000		3,000	
Salaries and Wages	41,000		11,500	
Transportation	8,950		6,400	
Utilities	8,600		7,580	
Total Operating Expenses	**93,050**		**49,780**	
Net Income	**$228,950**		**$243,220**	

_____

_____

_____

_____

_____

AP-13A (❹)

The income statements and balance sheets for Hathaway Inc. are shown below for the last three fiscal years. All sales are on credit.

Hathaway Inc. Income Statement For the Years Ended December 31, 2014 - 2016			
	2016	**2015**	**2014**
Sales	$800,000	$720,000	$760,000
Cost of Goods Sold	260,000	288,000	266,000
Gross Profit	540,000	432,000	494,000
Expenses			
Operating expense	320,000	216,000	342,000
Depreciation expense	64,000	72,000	76,000
Advertising expense	80,000	72,000	114,000
Interest expense	10,000	10,000	10,000
Total expenses	474,000	370,000	542,000
Net income (loss) before taxes	66,000	62,000	(48,000)
Income tax expense (return)	29,700	27,900	(21,600)
Net income (loss) after taxes	$36,300	$34,100	($26,400)

Hathaway Inc. Balance Sheet As at the Years Ended December 31, 2014 - 2016			
	2016	**2015**	**2014**
Cash	234,400	149,600	80,000
Accounts Receivable	84,000	70,000	56,000
Inventory	136,000	102,000	61,200
Equipment	110,000	174,000	246,000
Total Assets	**564,400**	**495,600**	**443,200**
Accounts Payable	54,600	45,500	36,400
Unearned Revenue	21,000	23,100	18,900
Long-Term Debt	50,000	50,000	50,000
Common Shares	85,500	60,000	55,000
Retained Earnings	353,300	317,000	282,900
Total Liabilities and Shareholders' Equity	**564,400**	**495,600**	**443,200**

Required

a) Calculate the following ratios for Hathaway Inc. for 2015 and 2016, and state whether the ratios improved or weakened in 2016.

	2016	2015	Improved or Weakened
Gross Profit Margin			
Net Profit Margin			
Return on Equity (ROE)			
Current Ratio			
Quick Ratio			
Debt-to-Equity Ratio			
Inventory Turnover			
Inventory Days on Hand			

b) The owner of Hathaway Inc. is pleased to see that the company has started generating profits again and assumes that profitability must be improving. Perform a ratio analysis to determine if the owner's assumption is correct or not. Explain.

_____

_____

_____

_____

_____

_____

c) What does the company's Inventory Turnover ratio indicate/suggest?

_____

_____

_____

Application Questions Group B

AP-1B (❺)

Indicate the section of the cash flow statement where each item would be located (operations, investing or financing).

Item	Section
Change in Accounts Payable	
Change in Inventory	
Change in Equipment	
Change in Long-term portion of Bank Loan	
Change in Short-term portion of Bank Loan	
Change in Prepaid Rent	
Change in Accounts Receivable	
Change in Common Shares	

AP-2B (❺)

The Grading Company's cash account decreased by $14,000 and its short-term investment account increased by $18,000. Cash increase from operations was $21,000. Net cash decrease from investments was $22,000.

Required

Based on the above information, calculate the cash increase (or decrease) from financing.

_____

_____

_____

_____

AP-3B (❺)

Brothers Christoph and Wilson Adler are the owners of Adler Bros Company. They had the following totals in their cash flow statement for the year ended February 29, 2016.

Net increase from financing	$560,000
Net increase from operations	112,000
Net decrease from investment	400,000
Cash balance, March 1, 2015	88,000

Required

Calculate the net increase (decrease) in the cash balance at February 29, 2016.

_____

_____

_____

_____

AP-4B (❹)

Total current liabilities for a company are $2,786. If cash is $2,000, short-term investments are $3,000, long-term investments are $1,000 and accounts receivable is $1,200, calculate the quick ratio.

_____

_____

AP-5B (❹)

Information from Silky Company's year-end financial statements is as follows.

	2016	2015
Current Assets	$200,000	$210,000
Current Liabilities	100,000	90,000
Shareholders' Equity	250,000	270,000
Net Sales	830,000	880,000
Cost of Goods Sold	620,000	640,000
Operating Income	50,000	55,000

Required

a) Calculate the current ratio for both years.

_____

_____

_____

_____

b) In which year does Silky Company have a better current ratio? Explain.

_____

_____

_____

AP-6B (❹)

Gross profit increased from $0.3 million in 2015, to $0.4 million in 2016. Gross profit margin decreased from 30% in 2009, to 28% in 2016. Comment on whether or not the company's profitability improved or deteriorated.

_____

_____

_____

AP-7B (❹)

The income statement of Ellen Corporation for the years 2016 and 2015 showed the following gross profit calculation.

	2016	2015
Sales Revenue	$97,200	$80,000
Cost of Goods Sold	72,000	50,000
Gross Profit	$25,200	$30,000

Required

a) Calculate the gross profit margin for both years.

_____

_____

_____

_____

b) In which year does Ellen Corporation have a better gross profit margin? Explain.

_____

_____

_____

_____

_____

AP-8B (❹)

Selected information for the Universal Company is as follows.

	December 31		
	2016	**2015**	**2014**
Common Shares	$840,000	$648,000	$550,000
Retained Earnings	370,000	248,000	150,000
Net income for the year	240,000	122,000	98,000

Required

a) Calculate the return on equity ratio for 2016 and 2015.

_____

_____

_____

_____

b) Has the Universal Company's performance improved in 2016? Explain using the return on equity ratio.

_____

_____

_____

AP-9B (④)

Components of the balance sheet of Leonardo Corporation for 2016 and 2015 shows the following information.

	2016	2015
Current Assets	$7,000	$13,000
Current Liabilities	$10,000	$9,000

Required

a) Calculate the working capital for both years.

b) In which year does Leonardo Corporation have a better working capital? Explain.

c) What are some implications regarding the working capital for 2016?

AP-10B (❸)

Perform a horizontal analysis for Gob Blooth Inc. Use 2014 as the base-year and comment on the results.

Gob Blooth Inc. Income Statement (in Thousands) For Years Ended October 31, 2014 - 2016			
	2016	**2015**	**2014**
Revenue	1,234	1,100	988
Expenses	907	1,009	678
Net Income	327	91	310

Required

A table has been provided to conduct the analysis.

Gob Blooth Inc. Horizontal Analysis For Years Ended October 31, 2014 - 2016									
	2016			**2015**			**2014**		
	Value	**% Of**	**% Ch**	**Value**	**% Of**	**% Ch**	**Value**	**% Of**	**% Ch**
Revenue	1,234			1,100			988		
Expenses	907			1,009			678		
Net Income	327			91			310		

_____

_____

_____

_____

_____

AP-11B (❸)

Perform a vertical analysis for G Michael Inc., using sales as the base-figure for both years. The comparative income statement has already been done for you. For all percentages, calculate to two decimal places. Comment on the results of significant changes.

G Michael Inc. Income Statement (in Millions) For Years Ended August 31, 2016 and 2015		
	2016	**2015**
Sales	**456**	**386**
COGS	222	201
Gross Profit	**234**	**185**
Expenses		
Advertising Expense	15	12
Insurance Expense	3	2
Rent Expense	21	19
Salaries Expense	55	50
Selling Expenses	34	31
Total Expenses	**128**	**114**
Net Income	**106**	**71**

Required

Use the modified income statement below to perform your vertical analysis.

G Michael Inc. Income Statement (in Millions) and Vertical Analysis For Years Ended August 31, 2016 and 2015				
	2016	**% of Base-Figure**	**2015**	**% of Base-Figure**
Sales	**456**		**386**	
COGS	222		201	
Gross Profit	**234**		**185**	
Expenses				
Advertising Expense	15		12	
Insurance Expense	3		2	
Rent Expense	21		19	
Salaries Expense	55		50	
Selling Expenses	34		31	
Total Expenses	**128**		**114**	
Net Income	**106**		**71**	

_____

_____

_____

_____

AP-12B (❸)

The following financial statements are taken from the records of Pop-Pop Products Inc.

Pop-Pop Products Inc. Balance Sheet (in Thousands) As at April 30, 2016 and 2015	2016	2015
Assets		
Current Assets		
Cash	$35	$12
Accounts Receivable	147	188
Inventory	249	267
Short-Term Investments	98	34
Total Current Assets	**529**	**501**
Other Assets	521	487
Total Assets	**$1,050**	**$988**
Liabilities and Equity		
Current Liabilities	298	379
Long-Term Debt	101	321
Total Liabilities	**399**	**700**
Shareholders' Equity	651	288
Total Liabilities and Equity	**$1,050**	**$988**

Pop-Pop Products Inc. Income Statement (in Thousands) For the Years Ended April 30, 2016 and 2015	2016	2015
Sales	**$2,139**	**$2,395**
COGS	1,098	1,230
Gross Profit	**1,041**	**1,165**
Operating Expenses		
Advertising	10	14
Bank Charges	5	6
Communication	13	11
Depreciation	112	98
Professional Fees	0	30
Rent	103	307
Repairs and Maintenance	62	86
Salaries and Wages	212	178
Transportation	52	50
Utilities	24	22
Total Operating Expenses	**593**	**802**
Net Income	**$448**	**$363**

Required

a) Use horizontal analysis tools to compare the changes between 2015 and 2016 line items for the balance sheet. The comparative balance sheet has already been done for you. For all percentages, calculate to two decimal places. Comment on the results of significant changes.

Pop-Pop Products Inc. Balance Sheet (in Thousands) and Horizontal Analysis As at April 30, 2016 and 2015				
	2016	**2015**	**% of 2015**	**% Change**
Assets				
Current Assets				
Cash	$35	$12		
Accounts Receivable	147	188		
Inventory	249	267		
Short-Term Investments	98	34		
Total Current Assets	**529**	**501**		
Other Assets	521	487		
Total Assets	**$1,050**	**$988**		
Liabilities and Equity				
Current Liabilities	298	379		
Long-Term Debt	101	321		
Total Liabilities	**399**	**700**		
Shareholders' Equity	651	288		
Total Liabilities and Equity	**$1,050**	**$988**		

b) Use horizontal analysis tools to compare the changes between 2015 and 2016 line items for the income statement. The comparative income statement has already been done for you. For all percentages, calculate to two decimal places. Comment on the results of significant changes.

Pop-Pop Products Inc. Income Statement (in Thousands) and Horizontal Analysis For the Years Ended April 30, 2016 and 2015				
	2016	**2015**	**% of 2015**	**% Change**
Sales	**$2,139**	**$2,395**		
COGS	1,098	1,230		
Gross Profit	**1,041**	**1,165**		
Operating Expenses				
Advertising	10	14		
Bank Charges	5	6		
Communication	13	11		
Depreciation	112	98		
Professional Fees	0	30		
Rent	103	307		
Repairs and Maintenance	62	86		
Salaries and Wages	212	178		
Transportation	52	50		
Utilities	24	22		
Total Operating Expenses	**593**	**802**		
Net Income	**$448**	**$363**		

c) Use vertical analysis tools to compare line items to the total assets base-figure. For all percentages, calculate to two decimal places. Comment on the results.

	2016	Vertical	2015	Vertical
Pop-Pop Products Inc.				
Balance Sheet (in Thousands) and Vertical Analysis				
As at April 30, 2016 and 2015				
Assets				
Current Assets				
Cash	$35		$12	
Accounts Receivable	147		188	
Inventory	249		267	
Short-Term Investments	98		34	
Total Current Assets	**529**		**501**	
Other Assets	521		487	
Total Assets	**$1,050**		**$988**	
Liabilities and Equity				
Current Liabilities	298		379	
Long-Term Debt	101		321	
Total Liabilities	**399**		**700**	
Shareholders' Equity	651		288	
Total Liabilities and Equity	**$1,050**		**$988**	

_____

_____

_____

_____

_____

_____

_____

d) Use vertical analysis tools to compare line items to the Sales base-figure. For all percentages, calculate to two decimal places. Comment on the results.

Pop-Pop Products Inc. Income Statement (in Thousands) and Vertical Analysis For the Years Ended April 30, 2016 and 2015				
	2016	**Vertical**	**2015**	**Vertical**
Sales	$2,139		$2,395	
COGS	1,098		1,230	
Gross Profit	**1,041**		**1,165**	
Operating Expenses				
Advertising	10		14	
Bank Charges	5		6	
Communication	13		11	
Depreciation	112		98	
Professional Fees	0		30	
Rent	103		307	
Repairs and Maintenance	62		86	
Salaries and Wages	212		178	
Transportation	52		50	
Utilities	24		22	
Total Operating Expenses	**593**		**802**	
Net Income	**$448**		**$363**	

_____

_____

_____

_____

AP-13B (❹)

Chicken Inc. and Egg Inc. are both in the toy retail business. All sales are on credit. Below is select financial information for the current year.

	Chicken Inc.	Egg Inc.
Income Statement:		
Sales	$150,000	$135,000
Cost of Goods Sold	48,750	41,850
Gross Profit	101,250	93,150
Expenses:		
Salaries Expense	22,500	27,000
Depreciation Expense	15,000	13,500
Advertising Expense	7,500	6,750
Interest Expense	6,750	5,130
Total Expenses	51,750	52,380
Net Income Before Taxes	49,500	40,770
Income Tax Expense	26,250	24,300
Net Income after taxes	**$23,250**	**$16,470**
Balance Sheet:		
Cash	$40,850	$24,510
Accounts Receivable	15,000	9,000
Inventory	34,500	20,125
Equipment	85,800	51,480
Total Assets	**$176,150**	**$105,115**
Accounts Payable	21,000	32,000
Unearned Revenue	27,800	18,670
Long-term Debt	39,350	15,635
Shareholders' Equity	88,000	38,810
Total Liabilities and Shareholders' Equity	**$176,150**	**$105,115**

a) Calculate each ratio listed below for each company and indicate which company is stronger for each one.

	Chicken Inc.	Egg Inc.	Which company is stronger?
Gross Profit Margin			
Net Profit Margin			
Return on Equity (ROE)			
Current Ratio			
Quick Ratio			
Debt-to-Equity Ratio			
Inventory Turnover			
Inventory Days on Hand			

a) Examining all of the ratios, explain which company has a stronger financial position with respect to

    i. Profitability

_____

_____

_____

_____

_____

    ii. Liquidity

_____

_____

_____

_____

_____

    iii. Operations mangement

_____

_____

_____

Case Study

CS-1 (❶ ❸ ❹)

After learning that you're taking an accounting course, Kim, your close friend, has come to ask you for investment advice. She went skiing at Whistler Blackcomb last winter and was so impressed by the resort that she has been thinking about investing in it. Because she doesn't know how to read financial statements, she asked you to analyze Whistler Blackcomb's financial statements and comment on the company's liquidity, profitability and leverage. The statements are presented below.

Whistler Blackcomb Consolidated Balance Sheet (in thousands) As at September 30, 2014 and 2013		
	2014	**2013**
Assets		
Cash	$ 8,410	$ 41,353
Short-term Investments	145	311
Accounts receivable	4,496	3,323
Inventory	18,633	15,856
Prepaid expenses	3,985	2,727
Total Current Assets	**35,669**	**63,570**
Notes receivable	777	2,636
Property, buildings and equipment	319,897	322,316
Property held for development	9,244	9,244
Intangible assets	300,778	311,428
Goodwill	137,354	137,259
Total Assets	**$ 803,719**	**$ 846,453**
Liabilities		
Accounts payable and accrued liabilities	25,715	24,927
Income taxes payable	2,403	1,645
Provisions	2,139	2,858
Deferred revenue	27,610	22,347
Total Current Liabilities	**57,867**	**51,777**
Long-term debt	229,855	258,042
Deferred income tax liability	21,974	20,690
Limited partner's interest	72,796	72,796
Total Liabilities	**382,492**	**403,305**
Shareholders' Equity		
Common shares	495,176	497,929
Retained earnings (deficit)	(73,949)	(54,781)
Shareholders' Equity	**421,227**	**443,148**
Liabilities and Shareholders' Equity	**$ 803,719**	**$ 846,453**

Whistler Blackcomb Consolidated Income Statement (in thousands) For the Years Ended September 30, 2014 and 2013		
	2014	2013
Resort revenue	$ 254,517	$ 240,780
Operating expenses	134,081	126,673
Depreciation and amortization	41,254	40,249
Selling, general and administrative	27,761	27,673
Total Expenses	203,096	194,595
Operating Income Before Tax	**51,421**	**46,185**
Other income	3,068	0
Other expense	(30,712)	(25,607)
Income Before Income Tax	23,777	20,578
Income tax expense	5,737	7,248
Net Income	**$ 18,040**	**$ 13,330**

Whistler Blackcomb Summary of the Cash Flow Statement (in thousands) For the Years Ended September 30, 2014 and 2013		
	2014	2013
Net cash provided by operations	$ 67,848	$ 64,725
Net cash used by investing	(28,398)	(24,345)
Net cash used by financing	(72,393)	(42,661)
Net increase (decrease) in cash	$ (32,943)	$ (2,281)

For the calculation that requires average shareholders' equity, the Whistler Blackcomb's shareholders' equity balance at the end of 2012 is $544,479

Required

a) Explain to Kim what a retained earnings deficit in Whistler Blackcomb's balance sheet means.

_____

_____

b) Perform horizontal and vertical analyses on Whistler Blackcomb's balance sheet and income statement. Interpret the figures for Kim.

	Horizontal Analysis			Vertical Analysis	
Whistler Blackcomb **Horizontal and Vertical Analysis on the Balance Sheet** **As at September 30, 2014 and 2013**	**2014**	**2013**	**% change**	**2014**	**2013**

	Horizontal analysis			Vertical analysis	
Whistler Blackcomb **Horizontal and Vertical Analysis on the Income Statement** **For the Years Ended September 30, 2014 and 2013**					
	2014	**2013**	**% change**	**2014**	**2013**

_____

_____

_____

_____

_____

_____

_____

c) Assess Whistler Blackcomb's liquidity using relevant ratios and provide explanation.

_____

_____

_____

_____

_____

_____

_____

_____

_____

_____

_____

_____

_____

d) Assess Whistler Blackcomb's profitability using relevant ratios and provide explanation.

_____

_____

_____

_____

_____

_____

_____

_____

_____

_____

_____

e) Assess Whistler Blackcomb's leverage using relevant ratio and provide explanation.

_____

_____

_____

_____

_____

_____

_____

f) Based on all of the above analyses, would you advise Kim to invest in Whistler Blackcomb?

_____

_____

_____

_____

_____

_____

_____

_____

_____

_____

_____